FOCUS ON EPILEPSY RESEARCH

FOCUS ON EPILEPSY RESEARCH

SHAWN M. BENJAMIN
EDITOR

Nova Biomedical Books
New York

Editorial Production Manager: Donna Dennis
Senior Production Editor: Susan Boriotti
Production Editors: Marius Andronie, Rusudan Razmadze and Keti Datunashvili
Office Manager: Annette Hellinger
Graphics: Magdalena Nuñez
Editorial Production: Maya Columbus, Vladimir Klestov, and Lorna Loperfido
Circulation: Ave Maria Gonzalez, Vera Popovic, Luis Aviles, Alexandra Columbus, Raymond Davis, Cathy DeGregory, Melissa Diaz, Marlene Nuñez and Jeannie Pappas

Library of Congress Cataloging-in-Publication Data
Focus on epilepsy research / Shawn M. Benjamin, editor
p. cm.
Includes bibliographical references and index.
ISBN 1-59454-087-X (hardcover)
1. Epilepsy.
[DNLM: 1. Epilepsy. WL 385 F652 2004] I. Benjamin, Shawn M.
RC372.F638 2004
616.8'53'0072--dc22 2004014068

An imprint of Nova Science Publishers, Inc.
400 Oser Ave, Suite 1600
Hauppauge, New York 11788-3619
Tele. 631-231-7269 Fax 631-231-8175
e-mail: Novascience@earthlink.net
Web Site: http://www.novapublishers.com

Printed in the United States of America

CONTENTS

Preface

Epilepsy, also called seizure disorder, is a condition of the brain marked by a susceptibility to recurrent seizures. Epilepsy affects 1% to 2% of the population. In about half the cases of epilepsy, the cause is unknown. However, some possible causes of epilepsy include: birth trauma, perinatal infection, anoxia, infectious diseases, ingestion of toxins, tumors of the brain, inherited disorders or degenerative disease, head injury or trauma, metabolic disorders, cerebrovascular accident and alcohol withdrawal. This volume presents international research on the prevention, pathogenesis, diagnosis and treatment of epilepsy.

The objective of chapter I is to review the preventive and prophylactic aspects of epilepsy. It describes the prevention of the causes of epilepsy, and the methods to prevent epilepsy and epileptic seizures. The concept of antiepileptogenesis is discussed according to the available information about the role that both, the classic and new antiepileptic drugs (AEDs) play in this process. Neuroprotection is discussed in the context of the mechanisms of action of AEDs and of the pathogenesis of neuronal lesion produced by the causes of epilepsy or by the seizures themselves. Among the new therapeutic modalities, the current knowledge on the vagus nerve stimulator and the surgical treatment is summarized. Future potential therapeutic approaches include alternative pharmacologic compounds, direct AED administration into the epileptogenic focus, genetic treatments and immunization. The first step in preventing epilepsy is to avoid the causes or the risk factors. Some classic AEDs have demonstrated to be effective in the prophylaxis of provoked seizures (acute symptomatic) but not of unprovoked seizures (epileptic). Better knowledge of the pathogenesis and the molecular and biological basis of epileptogenesis secondary to lesional causes, suggest that antioxidant and neuroprotective agents, including the new AEDs, may prevent epilepsy. There is a need to design studies with the goal of demonstrating their antiepileptogenic and/or neuroprotective activity at different ages in life. New and future therapeutic modalities may offer additional preventive options.

Mesial temporal lobe epilepsy (MTLE) is the commonest form of epilepsy. Seizures usually start during childhood, remit for a period of time, and then reappear and become more frequent and harder to control during adulthood. Although mesial temporal sclerosis (MTS) is the characteristic pathological finding in adults with intractable MTLE, it is rarely present in children. Both clinical and experimental evidence support that the immature brain is more resistant to the development of seizure-induced hippocampal pathology akin to MTS compared with the mature brain, although functional changes may occur. A variety of factors may alter the susceptibility of the brain to seizures and their consequences. These include genetic predisposition, prior neurological abnormalities, sex, etiology and severity of seizures. The impact of these factors changes through development. Aristea S. Galanopoulo et al. will summarize the current knowledge on the pathological and functional consequences of seizures on the immature and mature brain, the age-specific role of the known modifying factors and will discuss how this knowledge may be implemented in the design of age-appropriate preventative or therapeutic interventions.

Animal models help us to define the development of temporal lobe epilepsy after an early event. Some models exhibit a latent period in which many changes appear: neuronal loss, inflammatory reaction, dispersion of granular layer, neurogenesis, sprouting leading to hyperexcitability and hypersynchronism. Some of these alterations can be observed in surgically removed specimens of temporal lobe epilepsy from patients with early events such as febrile seizures. After general considerations, chapter III focuses on the author's interest in glial cells observed in human temporal epilepsies. Indeed, glial cells are represented in the epileptic hippocampus by activated microglia and reactive astrocytes in damaged areas, where inflammatory markers are overexpressed. Moreover, associated with the dispersion of the dentate gyrus, characteristic glial cells have been described, which constitute a kind of scaffold evoking the developmental radial glia. The presence of radial glia in a neurogenic region such as the granular and subgranular layers is particularly interesting. Therefore, Arielle Crespel et al. attempt to describe the possible participation of glial inflammatory reactions and of immature astrocytes in the development of epilepsy, taking into account the current opinions on the role of glia in controlling cell death, excitability, neurogenesis and neuronal circuitry.

The brainstem is closely involved in the generation of rapid-eye-movement (REM) sleep, and a reduction of the amount of REM sleep is a commonly reported sleep character of West syndrome (WS). Function of the brainstem might closely be correlated with the pathophysiology of WS. Chapter IV tried to verify this possibility. A reduction of REM sleep is a too nonspecific finding seen in various types of brain impairment. In addition, this finding did not correlate with clinical features of WS. In 1976, Fukuyama's group reported the prolongation of the period of muscle atonia during the slow wave sleep stage in WS. In 1996, the weakness of rapid eye movement-related phasic loss of muscle activity in REM sleep of WS was reported by our group. The degree of this weakness reflected a patient's prognosis as to convulsions. These findings are both implicated in muscle tone activity during sleep. Then, basic studies involved in the muscle tone control during sleep were reviewed. The following tentative conclusions were obtained; 1) dorsolateral pontine tegmentum is a key site to produce rapid eye movement-related phasic muscle activity loss, 2) prolongation of the period of muscle atonia during non-REM sleep is produced by the decrease of monoaminergic activity and/or the increase of cholinergic activity in the brainstem. The period of muscle atonia during non-REM sleep was examined in the series of WS patients, and found to show no significance difference from the controls. Based on the weakness of rapid eye movement-related phasic loss of muscle activity in REM sleep of WS, instability of the rostral pontine tegmentum is assumed to be indispensable for the development of WS. This instability could lead to the occurrence of WS by itself, but a cortical influence on this region might also promote WS. ACTH is hypothesized to suppress the spasms in WS patients not only through corticosteroids, but also through a direct action on the pontine tegmentum. Since phasic inhibition index has been reported to be elevated in patients with an autistic tendency, the appearance of an autistic tendency is also hypothesized to be involved in the functional disturbance of the pontine tegmentum.

Hannah R Cock reviews mitochondrial dysfunction and oxidative stress in epilepsy. Mitochondria, in addition to a primary role in energy production, are of increasingly recognized importance in intracellular calcium homeostasis, signalling and ROS (reactive oxygen species or free radicals) production. The role of mitochondria in excitotoxic cell death in many disease states has been extensively studied, and in recent years this has extended to studies of mitochondrial function in seizure related cell death. The process of mitochondrial permeability transition, releasing chemicals into the cytoplasm that initiate cell death pathways, is central in this context. Numerous triggers to permeability transition have now been identified. Many, if not all may act specifically through effects on the redox state of the cell and oxidative stress. There is accumulating evidence that seizures disrupt normal redox homeostasis in the cell. This may be important for seizure related cell death, and have significant functional consequences in surviving neurons. However, which of these changes are compensatory following seizures, and which might be involved both in epileptogenesis and/or neurological damage as a result of seizures requires further study. In addition, many factors including genetic background, seizure type and duration may influence to what extent the biochemical consequences of seizures are detrimental. Reliable markers of pathological, as opposed to physiological, changes are required, which then need to be validated in a clinical setting. This is particularly so given the emerging evidence supporting a role for Reactive oxygen species (ROS or free radicals) in physiological intracellular signalling. At present a range of antioxidant and other neuroprotective strategies appear promising in principle, but detailed studies across a range of in vivo seizure models, in clinically relevant paradigms, are needed before human trials should be considered.

In EL mice, ictogenesis has been established at around 10 weeks of age, whereas epileptogenesis will be established through experience of repetitive seizures during development. It is suggested that an "abnormal neural plasticity" may play a crucial role in the establishment of ictogenesis and epileptogenesis, and therefore, can be a potential target for the development of a new pharmacotherapy to the epilepsy. Chapter VI investigates the the role of antiapoptotic, proapoptotic factors and neurotrophic factors in the ictogenesis and epileptogenesis in EL mice brain, developmental changes of these factors are determined. Continuous IEG expression and abnormal GABAergic function may be involved in epileptogenesis in EL mice. It is likely that transiently expressed IEG is involved in the ictogenesis. iNOS is more conspicuous than eNOS, it is conceivable that excess iNOS (and subsequent increase in antimicrobial NO) and relatively lower concentration eNOS (and subsequent decrease in NO identified as endothelium derived relaxing factor (EDRF) may work together to contribute to a focus complex and ictogenesis. the DNA fragmentation may be associated with the formation of epileptogenesis. And drugs which can suppress free radicals generation and protect brain - such as allopurinol (ALP) - may be promising in new antiepileptic agents. DNA fragmentation without cell loss in EL mice, the susceptibility of hippocampal neurons to DNA fragmentation increases after experiencing repetitive seizures during development probably due to a change in the balance between protective mechanism and proapoptotic pathway's inactivation. Neurotrophic factors may also play a role in ictogenesis and epileptogenesis through the developmental stages by promoting abnormal synaptic plasticity.

Therapy with traditional antiepileptic drugs (AEDs) is associated with a wide range of pharmacokinetic drug-drug interactions; in particular enzyme induction and enzyme inhibition can result in considerable changes in plasma concentrations of concomitantly administered drugs. In the design and development of new AEDs, emphasis has been put on the importance that these agents be poorly metabolized and that they be as much as possible devoid of the enzyme inducing and/or inhibitory properties of the older drugs. In contrast, the role of the uptake and efflux transporters on the disposition of the AEDs and the consequences of these compounds being substrates, inhibitors and/or inducers of such transporters as far as drug interactions are concerned have been poorly taken into account. Even in very recent review papers, the involvement of transporters in drug interactions in epilepsy therapy is not discussed. Indeed some antiepileptic drug interactions at the level of absorption, distribution and/or excretion that are currently ascribed to other mechanisms could be due, at least partially, to interactions with transporters. There is now an increasing appreciation of transport processes as determinants of drug disposition. The main purpose of this paper is to review the role of the efflux transporter P-glycoprotein (P-gp) on the disposition of the AEDs (including brain penetration) as well as the impact of the AEDs which are substrates, inhibitors or inducers of this transport protein on the pharmacokinetics of concomitantly administered drugs. Moreover, the possible impact of AEDs on the overexpression of this efflux protein in pharmacoresistant epilepsy will also be examined in chapter VII.

In: Focus on Epilepsy Research
Editor: Shawn M. Benjamin, pp. 1-21

ISBN 1-59454-087-X

Chapter I

PREVENTION OF EPILEPSY[*]

Ignacio Valencia and Agustín Legido[†]
Section of Neurology, Department of Pediatrics,
St. Christopher's Hospital for Children,
Drexel University College of Medicine
Philadelphia, PA 19134

ABSTRACT

The objective of this manuscript is to review the preventive and prophylactic aspects of epilepsy. It describes the prevention of the causes of epilepsy, and the methods to prevent epilepsy and epileptic seizures. The concept of antiepileptogenesis is discussed according to the available information about the role that both, the classic and new antiepileptic drugs (AEDs) play in this process. Neuroprotection is discussed in the context of the mechanisms of action of AEDs and of the pathogenesis of neuronal lesion produced by the causes of epilepsy or by the seizures themselves. Among the new therapeutic modalities, the current knowledge on the vagus nerve stimulator and the surgical treatment is summarized. Future potential therapeutic approaches include alternative pharmacologic compounds, direct AED administration into the epileptogenic focus, genetic treatments and immunization. The first step in preventing epilepsy is to avoid the causes or the risk factors. Some classic AEDs have demonstrated to be effective in the prophylaxis of provoked seizures (acute symptomatic) but not of unprovoked seizures (epileptic). Better knowledge of the pathogenesis and the molecular and biological basis of epileptogenesis secondary to lesional causes, suggest that antioxidant and neuroprotective agents, including the new AEDs, may prevent epilepsy. There is a need to design studies with the goal of demonstrating their antiepileptogenic and/or neuroprotective activity at different ages in life. New and future therapeutic modalities may offer additional preventive options.

---

[*] Modified and published with permission from Revista de Neurologia (*Rev Neurol* 34:181-186,2002)

[†] Correspondence: Section of Neurology, St. Christopher's Hospital for Children, Erie Avenue at Front Street, Philadelphia, PA 19134-1095 - USA, Tel.: 215-427 5452, Fax: 215-427 4393, Email: Agustin.Legido@drexel.edu

Key words. Epilepsy - Seizures - Prophylaxis - Prevention - Anticonvulsants -Antiepileptic drugs - Antiepileptogenesis - Neuroprotection

INTRODUCTION

Prophylaxis is a process that protects from the development of a specific disease through a treatment that affects its pathogenesis. Prevention on the other hand refers to a process that avoids the development of a disease by applying measures before it occurs. Prevention can non-specifically modify some disease component without affecting its pathogenesis [1].

In this chapter we will review the prophylactic aspects of seizures and epilepsy. *A seizure* is the consequence of a cerebral dysfunction, secondary to the disorganized and paroxystic depolarization of neurons with propagation of the resulting electric discharges through the brain. The first unprovoked seizure and the febrile seizures are not considered epilepsy by definition. *Epilepsy* is a chronic, recurrent disorder with 2 or more nonfebrile, unprovoked seizures [2].

The importance of prevention is emphasized by the frequency of epilepsy and its drastic consequences. Most of the studies have reported a prevalence of 5 to 9 cases for 1,000 people, an incidence of 30-50 cases for 100,000 person-years and one cumulative incidence of 3% up to 75 years. Epilepsy is more frequent in children. Up to 5% of children and adolescents have a seizure before the age 20 years, and 75% of patients with epilepsy start having seizures before the 18 years [3, 4]. Mortality, mainly sudden death, is increased in patients with epilepsy [5-7]. Morbidity is severe, mainly when the epilepsy is refractory to treatment or when the patient has status epilepticus. There is an increased a risk of accidents, intellectual deterioration, psychological problems and social difficulties. In addition, epilepsy has been associated with lower educational level, decrease marriage rate, reproductive dysfunction, greater incidence of unemployment and lower quality of life [6-7]. Epilepsy is also a social disease, as its treatment represents an important economical burden [8-9].

During the last few decades there has been a better understanding of epilepsy, including the importance of the psychosocial aspects and risk factors, as well as the advances in the pharmacotherapy and the concept of antiepileptogenesis. Therefore, prevention of epilepsy is a current topic. The fundamental, ideal objective of the treatment of seizures is their complete control [10, 11]. The objective of prophylaxis and prevention of epilepsy is also the absence of seizures. In fact, both go further in the etiopathogenic mechanisms and try to look for the cure of the disease.

PREVENTION OF THE CAUSES OF EPILEPSY

Epidemiological studies have demonstrated that certain postnatal brain injuries such as trauma, infections, cerebrovascular accidents and tumors, significantly increase the incidence of seizures. The neurological impairment secondary to perinatal pathology, such as mental retardation and cerebral palsy, are also associated with a higher incidence of epilepsy. In spite of this, nearly 70% of epilepsy cases are idiopathic [3, 4, 12].

The etiology of epilepsy varies with age. In younger children, brain dysgenesis, perinatal disorders and inborn errors of metabolism are the most frequent causes. In older children and adolescents, infections and head trauma are also frequent causes [3, 4]. It is also important to consider precipitating factors in patients with epilepsy (i. e. drugs, alcohol, sleep deprivation, etc.) [3, 4, 10, 11].

Measures to Prevent Epilepsy

Epilepsy prevention can begin as early as in utero. Early diagnosis of congenital infections, brain dysgenesis, genetic and metabolic abnormalities of serious prognosis, can offer the parents the alternative to interrupt the pregnancy. This would decrease the number of refractory epilepsy cases associated with severe encephalopathy and poor quality of life [10-12]. In the future, better knowledge of the genetic basis of some epilepsies, will allow providing better genetic counseling and even specific genetic treatment [13]. Prenatal measures to prevent prematurity and perinatal asphyxia, as well as neuroprotective treatment of hypoxic-ischemic encephalopathy, are also preventive of post-neonatal epilepsy [12, 14, 15].

Early diagnosis of certain metabolic encephalopathies in the neonatal period may facilitate the use of specific treatments that prevent seizures. Examples are the use of benzoate and dextromethorfan, an anti-NMDA agent, in non-ketotic hyperglycinemia [16], and the treatment of pyridoxine-dependent seizures with vitamin B6 [17].

Certain measures of public health are very effective in the prevention of infectious causes of epilepsy. They include the prevention and treatment of prenatal infections and the vaccination against microorganisms causing meningoencephalitis like measles, rubella, haemophilus influenza or pneumococcus. Pharmacological treatments and hygiene measures also are very effective in the prevention of parasite infestations such as cysticercosis and echinococcosis, which are a frequent cause of epilepsy in some areas of the world [10, 11]. Early diagnosis and aggressive treatment of meningoencephalitis (i.e., early administration of acyclovir when suspecting herpes virus infection) can prevent the development of a severe encephalopathy associated with seizures [18].

A frequent cause of epilepsy in children and adolescents is head trauma. The majority can be prevented easily. There is a need to educate parents, children and adolescents about preventive measures (i.e., use of helmets when riding bicycles and motorcycles, appropriate use of lap belts and car seats). City councils are also responsible to participate in this public health problem (i.e., building recreation parks with minimum risk of accidents). Legislation is needed to assure that all these preventive measures are followed [10, 11, 19-21].

Although cerebrovascular accidents are not as frequent in children as in adults, appropriate treatment of diseases that produce cerebral infarcts can prevent this type of symptomatic epilepsy. Conditions that can cause cerebrovascular disease in children include coagulopathies, cardiac valve disease, sickle cell anemia and hypertension [22].

Febrile seizures, especially when they are atypical can slightly increase the potential risk to develop epilepsy. Treatment of febrile seizures to prevent future epilepsy has been controversial [10, 11, 23, 24]. It is now accepted that antiepileptic drug (AED) treatment can prevent the recurrence of febrile seizures but does not alter the risk of subsequent epilepsy [25].

Measures to Prevent Epileptic Seizures

People at risk for seizures have a predisposition due to inherent or acquired causes, so that they have a decrease threshold of neuronal excitability. Trigger factors include certain drugs, alcohol, sleep deprivation, stress, fatigue, depression, menstrual cycle, abrupt cessation of AED treatment, flickering lights, video games, hot water, etc. The identification and elimination of these factors may prevent seizures [10, 11, 26].

ANTIEPILEPTOGENESIS

AEDs have been used during the past 50 years to control seizures and also to avoid *epileptogenesis*, "the process by which a brain becomes epileptic and begins to generate spontaneous seizures" [27]. Epileptogenesis refers to acquired forms of epilepsy, not to the predisposition to chronic seizures secondary to genetic determination or anomalies of cerebral development [28]. Although there is a great interest in the subject, very little is known about the epileptogenic process. It is not known exactly what happens in the brain during the time interval between the injury and the moment when epileptic seizures begin [27, 28]. Several mechanisms are thought to be involved in epileptogenesis including neuronal loss, neurogenesis, gliosis, angiogenesis, inflammation, molecular reorganization, and axonal and dendritic plasticity [29]. Several experimental animal models allow studying the phenomenon of epileptogenesis. A widely accepted one is the *kindling model*, in which sub convulsive repeated electrical stimuli are produced until the animals develop spontaneous seizures. Other models use chemical compounds like pentylenetetrazol or flurothyl, which are administered systemically, or like penicillin and aluminum gel that are topically placed in the cerebral cortex. These models have a seizure free interval between the application and the initiation of seizures, which allows to investigate if the AEDs delay or eliminate the appearance of seizures [30].

Classic Antiepileptic Drugs

Table I shows the results of multiple studies on the action of classic AEDs in different models of epileptogenesis. The effect is greater with phenobarbital, valproic acid and diazepam than with phenytoin and carbamazepine. Ethosuximide has a positive effect in a kindling model with pentylenetetrazol [28, 31-36].

Although the information that is obtained from the experimental models of epileptogenesis is very useful, it is not clear that these results closely reflect what happens in humans. There is a need for good clinical studies; however, they must surpass some methodologic problems. For example, a decrease in the frequency of seizures during anticonvulsant treatment may reflect an antiepileptogenic effect, but also it can be due to an antiepileptic action. This problem can be clarified by establishing a period of observation after the discontinuation of the drug in study. Even when the treatment has not eliminated the seizures, a significant delay in its recurrence would indicate an anti-epileptogenic effect [27]. Although in principle any disease that increases the risk of seizures can be studied, the investigators have generally limited their studies to patients with diseases that confer at least a 20% of risk [28].

Table I. Experimental models of epileptogenesis: effect of classic antiepileptic drugs

AED	Model	Effect
Phenobarbital	Kindling-PTZ-Rats	Attenuation
	Kindling-amygdala-Rats	Attenuation
	Kindling-amygdala-Cats	Attenuation
	Penicillin-hippocampus-Rats	Attenuation
	Penicillin-hippocampus-Cats	Attenuation
	Gel aluminum-monkeys	Ineffective
Phenytoin	Penicillin-cortex-Rats	Attenuation
	Flurothyl-Mice	Attenuation
	Homocystein-thiolactone	Attenuation
	Gel aluminum-monkeys	Variable[a]
	Kindling-amygdala-Rats	Ineffective
	Kindling-amygdala-Cats	Ineffective
Valproic acid	Kindling-amygdala-rats	intense Attenuation
	Kindling-PTZ-rats	Attenuation
	Flurothyl-Mice	Attenuation
	Brain-slices-rats	Variable[b]
Carbamazepine	Kindling-amygdala-cats	Slight Attenuation
	Kindling-amygdala-Rats	Ineffective
	Kindling-PTZ-Rats	Ineffective
Diazepam	Kindling-PTZ-Rats	Attenuation
	Kindling-amygdala-Rats	Attenuation
Ethosuximide	Kindling-PTZ-Rats	Attenuation

* Modified from Temkin NR et al., 2001 (reference 28). PTZ: pentylenetetrazol; a: Attenuation with high dose, stimulation with normal dose; b: Attenuation if valproic acid is administered 20 minutes before, ineffective after 30 minutes.

Current and comprehensive information on the antiepileptogenic effect of classic AEDs in humans is provided by the studies of Temkin et al. [27]. A meta-analysis was conducted of 47 studies in which antiepileptic treatment was administered to prevent seizures. Etiology included fever, alcoholism, malaria, perinatal asphyxia, brain tumors, craniotomy, head trauma and administration of intravenous radiologic contrast. Studied AEDs, single or in combination, were phenobarbital, phenytoin, carbamazepine, valproic acid, diazepam, and lorazepam. The incidence of seizures in the treated group was compared with a control group (usually treated with placebo or without treatment). The relative risk (RR) indicates the proportion or rate of seizures between the two groups; the closer to 1 is the RR, the lesser is the anti-epileptogenic effect of the drug and vice versa.

The following drugs were effective in the prevention of acute symptomatic seizures: phenobarbital for the recurrence of febrile seizures (RR=0.51) and seizures induced by cerebral malaria (RR=0.36), diazepam for seizures associated with the administration of radiologic contrast (RR=0.10), phenytoin for seizures after craniotomy (RR=0.42) or head trauma (RR=0.33), carbamazepine for seizures after head trauma (RR=0.39) and lorazepam for seizures related to alcohol use (RR=0.12). None of the studied AEDs demonstrated a preventive effect of unprovoked seizures [27, 28].

Head Trauma

With a median annual incidence of 200 cases per 100,000 people-years, head trauma is responsible for 20% of symptomatic cases of epilepsy and 5% of all epilepsies. The risk of early post-traumatic epilepsy (within one week after head trauma) is approximately 2% to 15% and the risk of delayed epilepsy (after one week) is about 5% to 7%. The most important risk factor for the development of post-traumatic epilepsy is trauma severity For example, the incidence of epilepsy after 5 years of a closed head trauma is 0.6% in mild, 1.6% in moderate and 11.5% in severe trauma. In patients with severe head trauma, the incidence of epilepsy ranges from 7% to 39% if there is no dural penetration and increases to 20% to 57% if there is penetration of the dura [1, 37-39].

During the last four decades non-randomized, or double blind studies have suggested that phenobarbital, and phenytoin, have a prophylactic effect in post-traumatic epilepsy. Nevertheless, more recent, prospective, randomized and double blind studies, have found that oral administration of phenytoin, phenobarbital or carbamazepine do not have a preventive effect [38-40]. On the contrary, a study of Temkin et al. [41] demonstrated that intravenous administration of phenytoin within the first 24 hours after head injury diminishes the number of seizures during the first week post-trauma. Considering the results of these studies, in 1998 the Brain Injury Special Interest Group of the American Academy of Physical Medicine and Rehabilitation [42] recommended seizure prophylactic treatment only during the first week after the injury in patients at high risk. Routine prophylaxis for delayed post-traumatic seizures was not recommended, even in patients with severe penetrating injury [39-43].

Cerebral Infarct

The incidence of cerebral infarct ranges between 130 and 200 per 100,000 people-years, of which 52% to 77% are ischemic. Cerebral infarcts are the cause of seizures in 30% of patients older than 17 years and in 45% in patients above 60 years of age [44]. The incidence of seizures after cerebral infarct varies according to the different studies from 2,5% to 43%, whereas the epilepsy incidence ranges between 3% and 9%, one to ten years after cerebrovascular accident [1, 38, 44]. Risk factors include size of the infarct, cortex involvement, hemorrhagic infarct and persistence of motor deficits [1, 44].

Up to 78% of acute seizures occur in the first 72 hours and the majority within the first 48 hours after the infarct. Delayed seizures happen in a variable percentage from 2% to 24%, and in 79% of the cases they manifest in the first year after the cerebrovascular accident. These seizures must be treated according to the clinical and EEG diagnosis and usually respond well to AED monotherapy [38]. The prophylactic treatment of delayed post-infarct seizures is not indicated [1, 38, 44].

Vascular Malformations

The prevalence of cerebral arterio-venous and venous malformations is 0.1% and 4% of autopsies, respectively [45]. On the other hand, the incidence of aneurisms is approximately 25/100,000 people-years [46].

Aneurisms have minor epileptogenic effect. The postoperative risk for seizures is between 4% and 5% [38, 47]. In the case of arteriovenous malformations, the risk of seizures is 1% to 2% and the risk of epilepsy 18%, 20 years after the diagnosis. The surgical excision of the underlying epileptogenic tissue cures the epilepsy in 70% of patients, improves the seizures in 20%, and worsens the seizures in 10%. In the case of venous malformations, 40% to 70% of the patients can develop medically refractory seizures. An early antiepileptic treatment is indicated along with a plan for surgical treatment [38]. In some cases of vascular malformations, radio surgical treatment may be an alternative to regular surgery [48].

The use of perioperative benzodiazepines is suggested for prophylactic treatment. Chronic AED use to prevent the development of seizures or epilepsy is not recommended [38, 45, 47].

Brain Tumors

Epidemiological studies have found that 3.5% of patients with refractory epilepsy have a brain tumor. The use of magnetic resonance imaging has demonstrated that this incidence is probably higher (14% to 16%). On the other hand, the incidence of seizures in patients with brain tumors is approximately 35% [49]. Seizures are more frequent in benign slow growing tumors (70% to 80%) than in malignant ones (30% to 40%) [38].

The effectiveness of the surgical treatment on seizures depends on the type of tumor, the extension of the resection, including the epileptogenic zone demonstrated by electrocorticography, and the degree of damage during surgery. Radiotherapy can significantly decrease the number of seizures in patients with tumors that cannot be completely removed. The frequency of postoperative seizures varies from 15% to 35%, generally appearing in the first 6 months after the surgery and they often are refractory to AEDs. In the absence of seizures during the first 6 months after surgery, prophylactic antiepileptic treatment is not indicated [38, 49].

Febrile Seizures

Febrile seizures usually appear in children between 6 months and 5 years of age. Although they can appear before the age of 6 months, other infectious etiologies like meningitis or encephalitis should be ruled out. There has also been description of seizures associated with fever that extend, or even appear, after the 5 years [1, 24, 50], like in the case of the recently described syndrome of generalized epilepsy and febrile seizures plus [51, 52]. Approximately 30% of patients with a first febrile seizure have a second febrile seizure and 15% have a third one. The incidence of nonfebrile seizures, unprovoked seizures or epilepsy in these patients ranges from 2% to 6% and reaches 13% in those with two risk factors (less than 6 months of age, neurological abnormality or complex febrile seizures: duration greater than 15 minutes, focal or recurrent in the same febrile episode) [1, 50].

The treatment with oral or rectal diazepam during the febrile process can decrease the incidence of febrile seizures [23, 24, 50, 53]. Although chronic treatment with phenobarbital or valproic acid reduces the recurrence of febrile seizures, side effects, including cognitive and behavior alterations, have made this therapeutic alternative less attractive. Moreover, it has not been demonstrated that the treatment of patients with febrile seizures with phenobarbital or valproic acid diminishes the development of epilepsy [1, 50, 53].

Absence Epilepsy

Some patients with generalized epilepsy, absence type or "petit mal", develop generalized tonic-clonic seizures. In these patients, absences start in late childhood or at the beginning of adolescence [54]. It has been suggested that the use of ethosuximide as first line AED in this group of patients can make them vulnerable to the development of generalized tonic-clonic seizures. Therefore, it has been hypothesized that the use of broad-spectrum AEDs, like valproic acid, to treat absences can have a prophylactic effect of future tonic-clonic seizures [1,10].

First Unprovoked Seizure

The risk of epilepsy, or recurrence of seizures, after the first unprovoked seizure in children is 29%, 37%, 43% and 46% at 1, 2, 5 and 10 years of follow up, respectively. Recurrence happens more frequently during the first 6 months after the initial seizure [55]. The effect of treatment on the natural history of the first unprovoked seizure is unknown. When several etiologic factors are present, the risk of recurrence is high and the chronic treatment with AEDs may be justified [1, 55, 56]. If one knew that antiepileptic treatment modifies epileptogenesis in patients without risk factors, prophylactic antiepileptic treatment should be started in every patient after the first unprovoked seizure [1]. Unfortunately, there is no convincing scientific data demonstrating that chronic antiepileptic treatment after the first seizure prevents the development of epilepsy [1].

Data on the natural history of seizures and epilepsy are controversial. Gowers [57] suggested that the tendency of epilepsy is towards self-perpetuation, where the repetition of seizures facilitates the occurrence of more seizures. In contrast, epidemiological studies in developing countries have demonstrated that in approximately 28% of patients epilepsy reaches remission, whether they were treated with AEDs or not [58].

First Epileptic Seizures

Some observations suggest that anatomic substrate is probably more important than frequency of seizures in the development of epilepsy [1]. Nevertheless, a recent study in children has demonstrated that frequency of seizures at the moment of diagnosis is a very significant factor predicting the development of refractory epilepsy. Accordingly, early diagnosis and aggressive treatment of epilepsy in these high-risk patients may prevent a negative clinical progression [59].

New Antiepileptic Drugs

Table II shows the results of multiple studies on the action of the new AEDs in different models of kindling. Vigabatrin, levetiracetam, tiagabine and zonisamide attenuate seizures. Levetiracetam has recently raised interest due to its antiepileptogenic effect. This medication was discovered using non-conventional drug screening methods. It markedly suppresses kindling development in the amygdala rat-kindling model, but it is ineffective in other traditional animal models like the acute maximal electroshock and the pentylenetetrazol model [60-62]. Felbamate has a slight effect and lamotrigine and topiramate are not effective.

Table II. Experimental models of epileptogenesis: effect of new antiepileptic drugs

Drug	Model	Effect
Vigabatrin	Kindling-amygdala-Mice	Attenuation
	Kindling-cornea-Rats	Attenuation
	Kindling-amygdala-Mice	Ineffective
Levetiracetam	Kindling-cornea-Rats	Protection
	Kindling-amygdala-Rats	Attenuation
Tiagabine	Kindling-amygdala-Rats	Attenuation
Zonisamide	Kindling-visual cortex-cats	Attenuation
Felbamate	Kindling-amygdala-rats	Slight Attenuation
Lamotrigine	Thiolactone Homocystein	Ineffective
	Kindling-amygdala-Rats	Ineffective
Topiramate	Kindling-amygdala-Rats	Ineffective

* Modified from Temkin NR et al., 2001 (reference #28)

A better understanding of the molecular basis of epileptogenesis can help the development of specific drugs. Thus, it is known that norepinephrine has a great antiepileptogenic effect, as demonstrated by kindling inhibition. Based on this knowledge, Janumpalli et al. [63] produced a mutation in the gene of the mouse adrenergic receptor α2A subtype. The mutation caused an important increase in epileptogenesis, emphasizing the importance of the α2A receptor in the suppression of epileptogenesis. These findings open the possibility of developing drugs that would act specifically at the level of this adrenergic receptor subtype. They could demonstrate their anti-kindling effect in experimental models and eventually could prevent epileptogenesis in humans.

There is a need for clinical studies with the specific objective of demonstrating the antiepileptogenic effect of old, current and new AEDs. A pilot study evaluated the antiepileptogenic effect of valproic acid administered within a period of one hour after head trauma. The antiepileptogenic effect of magnesium sulphate is also being evaluated in patients who have suffered head injury. These studies must consider the complex developmental process of the Central Nervous System (CNS), which can influence the response to AEDs at different ages [64]. Only when the antiepileptogenic efficacy of a certain drug will be demonstrated clinically, it will be used with a clear prophylactic indication [27, 28].

NEUROPROTECTION

Many of the causes of symptomatic epilepsy (i.e. head trauma, hypoxic-ischemic injury) produce CNS neuronal destruction. Even prolonged seizures or status epilepticus can produce neuronal injury, without ischemia or hypoxia. The concept of neuroprotection refers to the preservation and rescue of injured neurons [65].

Antiepileptic Drugs

The neuronal injury mechanisms involved in epilepsy and hypoxic-ischemic injury are similar, although not identical: 1) Energy failure, 2) Activation of glutamate receptors with intracellular penetration of Ca^{++}, activation of nitric oxide synthase and production of free radicals and 3) Inflammatory response, leukocyte adhesion, arachidonic acid production and free radicals release [65-68]. As there is more research in the area of in-vitro and in-vivo experimental models of epilepsy, there is increased knowledge of these pathogenic effects of neuronal damage. Also, AED mechanisms of action are better known everyday. Some of them may have important implications for the AED use as neuroprotective agents. In general, AEDs act blocking the action potentials or interfering with the synaptic transmission. These effects occur through the following mechanisms: 1) Decreasing repeated and sustained neuronal discharges (i.e., Na^+ channel blockers), 2) Increasing gamma-amino butyric acid (GABA)-mediated inhibition, 3) Attenuating voltage-sensitive Ca^{++} channels, 4) Decreasing glutamate-mediated excitation [65].

In addition to the regular mechanisms of action, some of the new AEDs have further interesting neuroprotective functions. For example, zonisamide has been shown to scavenge hydroxyl radicals and nitric oxide in a dose-dependent manner [69]. It may protect neurons from free radical damage and produce stabilization of the membrane. Lamotrigine may have a concomitant inhibitory effect on both N-type Ca^{2+} channels and Na^+ channels with inhibitory action on the release of glutamate from the nerve terminals. Levetiracetam also modulates the N-type Ca^{2+} channel [70].

The neuroprotective effect of different AEDs has been investigated in animal models of brain ischemia. AEDs that showed a positive effect include felbamate, fosphenytoin, lamotrigine, levetiracetam, phenytoin, remacemide, tiagabine, topiramate, vigabatrin and zonisamide [70].

The neuronal injury secondary to seizures is mediated through different mechanisms, and it is possible that AEDs with multiple mechanisms of action may be more effective against various types of injuries [65] (Table III).

Other Neuroprotective Drugs

One of the best-studied experimental models of epilepsy in the area of neuroprotection is post-traumatic epilepsy. Its pathogenic mechanisms are to some extent similar to those of other epilepsy models [65-68]. In addition, there are specific mechanisms related to the consequences of trauma. Secondary hemorrhage produces hemoglobin deposition in neurons. A characteristic pathologic finding in post-traumatic epilepsy is the sequestered hemosiderin from released iron of hemoglobin and transferrin. The oxidation of iron from ferrous to ferric, through oxidative reactions in the brain produces free oxygen radicals. These are unstable intermediate compounds with an unpaired electron that have great biological activity. The super oxide (O2*) radical is formed through several mechanisms, including the process of mitochondrial metabolism in activated leukocytes, the xanthin-oxidase and arachidonic acid pathways and also directly by a single redox reaction catalyzed by free iron. In the presence of free iron the super oxide radical is combined with hydrogen peroxide, its own metabolite, forming the hydroxyl radical (OH*), which is even more destructive. This radical has an intense affinity for lipids and produces a lipidic peroxidation that releases arachidonic acid. This release produces a vicious circle that originates more free radicals through the cyclooxygenase pathway [71, 72].

Table III. Mechanisms of action of antiepileptic drugs*

Mechanism of action		**Antiepileptic Drugs**	
		Classic	**New**
Inhibition of Na^+ channels and stabilization of neuronal membranes		Phenytoin Carbamazepine Valproic acid	Felbamate Lamotrigine Oxcarbazepine Topiramate Gabapentin
Increase inhibition mediated by GABA		Phenobarbital Benzodiazepines Valproic Acid	Felbamate Topiramate Gabapentin Vigabatrin Tiagabine Zonisamide
Decrease glutamate mediated excitation	NMDA receptor	None	Felbamate
	AMPA / kainate receptors	Phenobarbital	Topiramate
Voltage sensitive calcium channel interaction	Type-T	Ethosuximide Valproic acid	Zonisamide
	Type-L, high voltage	None	Felbamate Lamotrigine Topiramate Gabapentin[a]

* Modified from Moshé SL, 2000 (reference #65); a: it binds to the alpha-2-delta subunit

Table IV shows a list of pharmacological compounds along with their mechanism of action, the neuroprotective effect of which has been studied in different post-traumatic epilepsy experimental models. Anti-oxidant compounds have been widely studied [39].

Table IV. Neuroprotective drugs studied in experimental models of post-traumatic epilepsy *

Mechanism of action	Drugs
Glutamate receptors antagonist	Selfotel, Aptiganel, Eliprodil, Lubeluzole, Licostinel (Acea-1021), Gavestinel (Gv-150526), Sipatrigine (619C89)
Opiate -κ receptors antagonist	Nalmetene
Lipidic peroxidation inhibitor	Trilazad
TRH analog	Montirelin (Cg-2703)
Antioxidant	S-nitrosoglutathione
Vitamin E analog	MDL-74180
Superoxide radicals scavenger	Pergorgotein (PEG-SOD), TJ-960, Dizocilpine, Melatonin, EUK-8, EUK-134
Nitric oxide synthase inhibitor	NG-mono-methyl-l-arginine (NMMA)

* Modified from Iudice, A. and Murri L, 2000 (reference #39)

In the next coming years there will be a continuous effort to identify effective neuroprotective drugs in the treatment of epilepsy. The currently available AEDs will be studied first, but other chemical compounds may also be good candidates. Table V summarizes the possible strategies for neuroprotective drug development [65]. The use of experimental models in-vitro and in-vivo will facilitate the investigations, although the results obtained may not always be applicable to the clinical treatment of epileptic patients. The neuroprotective effect is relatively easy to demonstrate in animal models when the drug to be studied is administered before producing the epileptogenic damage. Nevertheless, a great interest and hope exists in being able to develop neuroprotective treatments that are effective when applied after the epileptogenic injury has occurred. In this regard, two important questions to be answered are: how long should the treatment last, and which is the marker to assess response to the treatment [65].

Table V. Strategies for the development of neuroprotective drugs *

Na^{+} channels blockers
Ca^{++} channels blockers
Glutamate inhibitors
Neurotrophic factors
Nitric oxide Inhibitors
Antioxidants/ free radicals scavengers
Inhibitors of apoptosis-related proteases
New protein synthesis inducers or blockers
Agents that simulate the intracellular action of proteins that are decreased before cellular death
Agents that increase cerebral blood flow
Genetic modulators
Hormonal factors

* Moshé SL, 2000 (reference #65)

New Therapeutic Modalities

Vagus Nerve Stimulator

The vagus nerve stimulator (VNS) was introduced for the treatment of epileptic patients in 1990. Since then, its use in cases of refractory epilepsy has progressively increased. Cyberonics, the company that makes the device created a follow-up registry of implanted adults and children. As of December 2003, the database shows that 6,915 patients have been implanted with the device. Of these, 4,310 have been followed for 3 months and 2,584 for 12 months. Median seizure reduction at 12 month of follow up is 57%. The percentage decrease in seizures of more than 50%, 75% and 90% at 12-month follow-up is 57%, 36% and 20%, respectively. There are 2,330 children implanted with the VNS in the registry. In adults and children there appears to be an increase in efficacy with time. The median seizure reduction increased from 50% at 3 months to 70% at 24 months in patients less than 18 years old. The VNS efficacy in pediatric patients has also been shown in other series [74, 75].

Cyberonics data indicate that there may be a better control of seizures when implanted early in the course of the epilepsy [73]. This suggests that VNS may prevent the epileptogenic effect of repeated seizures [57]. Further studies are needed to specifically investigate the possible antiepileptogenic effect of this new therapeutic modality [27, 28].

Surgical Treatment

Throughout the years, surgical treatment of refractory epilepsy in pediatric patients is being more frequently considered. The results of different published series are promising: the percentage of seizure-free patients ranges from 60% to 65% in infants, from 59% to 67% in children and around 69% in adolescents [76-80]. In general, the results are better in the resection of a temporal lobe focus, compared with extra-temporal one. Hemispherectomy results are intermediate. Nevertheless, these differences disappear when the data are analyzed according to the etiologic factors [80]. The centers with most experience in epilepsy surgery of small children recommend an aggressive and precocious surgical treatment to improve the prognosis of the epilepsy and the neurological and psychosocial development [80]. Thus, epilepsy surgery acquires a preventive and not only therapeutic role.

Another example of the preventive role of epilepsy surgery is the temporal lobe epilepsy secondary to mesial sclerosis (MTLE). The partial epilepsy secondary to this common lesion is typically resistant to AEDs. However, early surgical excision is curative and can prevent the development of a typical refractory epileptic syndrome including serious complications such as drug side effects, behavior abnormalities, decreased quality of life, etc. [6, 7] Therefore surgery should be considered as the treatment of choice when curative, as it is the case of MTLE. However, questions remain about the neurological consequences of both medical and surgical treatment, the ultimate gains in quality of life parameters, and the precise predictors of success. Long-term follow-up and analyses of multiple factors in large groups of contemporary patient populations will be necessary to fully answer the question, "is temporal lobe epilepsy a surgical disease?" Right now it should be considered one in most cases [81].

FUTURE THERAPEUTIC MODALITIES

The following is a discussion on therapeutic aspects of epilepsy with preventive implications. In some cases there are preliminary data suggesting a positive effect. In other cases, the hypotheses are based on how people think that the science is going to evolve in the future. It is possible that some of these therapeutic modalities will be a reality someday.

Alternative Therapies

Natural Medicine

Sugaya at al. [82] recently demonstrated that a combination of Japanese herbs called Saiko-keishi-to-kashakuyaku (SK, TJ-960) has a regulating effect on the expression of different genes, which are implicated in important functions in the CNS. Using experimental models of epilepsy and hypoxic-ischemic injury, they proved that SK regulates the gene PTZ-17 that is related to seizures, the early gene product c-fos and the "heat-shock" HSP72 protein. The authors hypothesized that SK can have preventive properties in the development of neurological diseases, including epilepsy. According to them, all human beings have genes related to seizures; a low threshold expression favors breakthrough seizures by certain environmental stimuli (fever, fatigue, stress, etc.). It is possible that the continuous administration of SK stabilizes the threshold expression of the PTZ-17 gene and other seizure-associated genes, so that they protect the brain from developing epilepsy.

Psychological Treatment

A recent meta-analysis study by Müller [83], reviewed the effect of psychological treatment in the prevention of nocturnal seizures in 70 patients with an average age of 19 years (range 5-41). Patients with non-epileptic seizures were not included. Frequently associated precipitating factors were sleep deprivation, stress, anxiety, fear, or abnormal psychological dependency to another person. Therapeutic interventions included combinations of the following: behavioral, family, group, psychodynamic and pedagogic therapy, massage, relaxation, biofeedback, desensitization or exercise. Altogether a positive response was seen in 33 (47%) patients with reliable follow-up: 19 remained without seizures after 6 months and 4 after 3 months, whereas 10 had a decrease of more than 50% in the number of seizures. These data are very provocative, but they clearly indicate the importance to develop more studies to investigate the role of psychological treatment in the control of nocturnal, or even diurnal, seizures.

Automated Pharmacological Treatment of the Epileptic Focus

Stein et al. [84] have investigated an experimental model of epilepsy with a local delivery system of AEDs, and another seizure detection system as feedback. The authors induced seizures with bicuculline, an antagonist of GABA, in Sprague-Dawley rats. The number and duration of seizures were significantly decreased after the administration of diazepam in the treated group compared to a control. In theory, a similar system could be eventually used for the treatment, and prevention, of the refractory epilepsy in humans.

The actual development of this system probably will be parallel to advances in understanding the theory of "chaos" and the role of non-linear EEG in the early detection of seizure activity [85].

Genetic Treatment

The ultimate objective of genetic treatment in any disease (i.e., epilepsy) is its abolition by introducing new genetic material in the patient's somatic cells. This can be achieved when the three following conditions are fulfilled: a) the specific DNA sequence is selectively introduced in the desired eucariotic cells, b) the expression of intracellular DNA is regulated in a physiologic way and c) the expression of this DNA persists during the vital cycle of the cells [86].

Experimental studies have demonstrated the possibility of transferring genes to the hippocampus obtained from surgical resection of patients with refractory epilepsy. Adenovirus was used as a vector. The expression of the gene was demonstrated within 5 hours after its injection and persisted through the viable lifetime of the hippocampus [87]. In animal models of epilepsy, it has also been demonstrated that the treatment with the gene of "heat-shock" HSP72 protein [88] or the apoptosis inhibitor Bcl2 [89] produces a neuroprotective effect during or after the induction of seizures. These experimental results should lead to future investigation and application for the treatment of epilepsy in humans. This could be done with administration of specific genes in the epileptogenic zone.

Genetic treatment also includes the therapeutic correction of gene anomalies specifically linked to certain types of epilepsy. This could be done as early as in utero or during the first years of the life when the disease manifests [86].

Immunization

In 2000, During et al. [90] suggested an original idea for the treatment and prevention of epilepsy. Even though the brain is in general an inaccessible organ to the immune system, and in spite of known autoimmunity, the group of investigators built a vaccine including a plasmid, an adenovirus and the NR1 subunit of the NMDA receptor. The vaccine was administered in a single oral dose to rats. The transgenic expression of the vaccine persisted for 5 months and it was associated with a strong humoral immunity without affecting the cellular response. The vaccine was associated with a great antiepileptic effect in rat model of kainic acid induced seizures. It also produced a powerful neuroprotective effect in a focal model of ischemia. Therefore, a strategy to give vaccine against specific cerebral proteins is feasible, which offers therapeutic and preventive possibilities of many neurological diseases, including epilepsy.

CONCLUSIONS

The first step in the prevention of epilepsy is to avoid the causes or risk factors. This requires a multidisciplinary approach that includes good medical attention of different specialists, effective public health infrastructure and efficient methods for education of patients and people in general.

Some classic AEDs have demonstrated their efficacy in the prophylaxis of provoked (acute symptomatic) seizures, but none of them has proven to be useful in the prevention of unprovoked seizures.

The majority of investigations have not demonstrated a clear prophylactic effect of classic AEDs in patients with brain trauma, infarct, vascular malformations or tumors.

It is not clear that the treatment with AEDs following a first seizure in patients with risk factors has a future prophylactic effect. Diazepam prevents febrile seizures in patients with increased risk.

Better knowledge of the pathogenesis and molecular basis of epileptogenesis secondary to various lesional causes, suggests that antioxidant and neuroprotective agents like the new AEDs may prevent the development of epilepsy. There is a need to design clinical studies to demonstrate the antiepileptogenic activity of new medications at different life stages.

Future development of new therapeutic modalities, aimed to preventing neuronal injury secondary to seizures or their causes, will emphasize the importance of prevention, prophylaxis and neuroprotection in the treatment of epilepsy.

BIBLIOGRAPHY

[1] Willmore LJ. Prophylactic treatment. In Engel J, Pedley TA, ed. *Epilepsy: A comprehensive textbook*. Philadelphia: Lipincott-Raven Publishers 1997; p.1333-7.

[2] Aicardi J. *Epilepsy in Children*. New York: Raven Press 1994; p.1-8.

[3] Hauser WA. Epidemiology of epilepsy in children. In Pellock JM, Dodson WE, Bourgeois BFD, ed. *Pediatric epilepsy. Diagnosis and therapy*. New York: Demos 2001; p. 81-96.

[4] Annegers JF. The epidemiology of epilepsy. In Wyllie E, ed. *The treatment of epilepsy. Principles and practice*. Philadelphia: Lippicontt Williams & Wilkins 2001; p.131-8.
[5] Langan Y, Nashef L, Sander JWA. Sudden unexpected death in epilepsy: a series of witnessed deaths. *J Neurol Neurosurg Psychiatry* 2000; 68:211-3.
[6] Perucca E, Beghi E, Dulac O, Shorvon S, Tomson T. Assessing risk to benefit ratio in antiepileptic drug therapy. *Epilepsy Res* 2000; 41:107-39.
[7] Hauser A, Hesdoffer DC. Remission, intractability, mortality, and comorbidity of seizures. In Wyllie E, ed. *The treatment of epilepsy. Principles and practice*. Lippicontt Williams & Wilkins 2001; p.139-45.
[8] Kotsopoulos IA, Evers SM, Amen AJ, de Krom MC. Stimating the costs of epilepsy: an international comparison of epilepsy cost studies. *Epilepsia* 2001; 42:634-40.
[9] Guerrini R, Battini R, Ferrari AR, Veggiotti P, Besana D, Gobbi G, et al. The costs of childhood epilepsy in Italy: comparative findings in three health care settings. *Epilepsia* 2001; 42:641-6.
[10] Dreifuss FE. Prevention as it pertains to epilepsy. *Arch Neurol* 1995; 52:363-6.
[11] Dreifuss FE. Critical review of health care for epilepsy. In Engel J, Pedley TA, ed. *Epilepsy: A comprehensive textbook*. Philadelphia: Lipincott-Raven Publishers 1997: p. 2903-6.
[12] Clancy R, Legido A. Postnatal epilepsy following EEG confirmed neonatal seizures. *Epilepsia* 1991; 32:69-76.
[13] Delgado-Escueta AV, Wilson WA, Olsen RW, Porter RJ. New waves of research in the epilepsies: crossing into the third millenium. *Adv Neurol* 1999; 79:3-58.
[14] Legido A, Katsetos CD, Mishra OP, Delivoria-Papadopoulos M. Perinatal hypoxic-ischemic encephalopathy: Current and future treatments. *Int Pediatr* 2000; 15:143-51.
[15] Clancy RR, McGaurn SA, goin JE, Hirtz DG, Norwood WI, Gaynor JW, et al. Allopurinol neurocardiac protection trial in infants undergoing heart surgery using deep hypothermic circulatory arrest. *Pediatrics* 2001; 108:61-70.
[16] Hamosh A, Maher JF, Bellus GA, Rasmussen SA, Johnston MV. Long-term use of high-dose benzoate and dextromethorphan for the treatment of nonketotic hyperglycinemia. *J Pediatr* 1998; 132:709-13.
[17] Baxter P. Pyridoxine-dependent and pyridoxine-responsive seizures. *Dev Med Child Neurol* 2001; 43:416-20.
[18] Chaudhuri A, Kennedy PG. Diagnosis and treatment of viral encephalitis. *Postgrad Med J* 2002;78:575-83.
[19] Tsai MC, Hemenway D. Effect of the mandatory helmet law in Taiwan. *Inj Prev* 1999; 5: 290-1.
[20] Lestina DC, Williams AF, Lund AK, Zador P, Kuhlmann TP. Motor vehicle crash injury patterns and the Virginia seat belt law. *JAMA* 1991; 265: 1409-13.
[21] Durkin MS, Laraque D, Lubman I, Barlow B. Epidemiology and prevention of traffic injuries to urban children and adolescents. *Pediatrics* 1999; 103: E74.
[22] Gorelick PB, Sacco RL, Smith DB, Alberts M, Mustone-Alexander L, Rader D, et al. Prevention of a first stroke: review of guidelines and a multidisciplinary consensus statement from the National Stroke Association. *JAMA* 1999; 281: 1112-20.
[23] Rosman NP, Colton T, Labazzo J, Gilbert PL, Gardella NB, Kaye EM, et al. A controlled trial of diazepam administered during febrile illness to prevent recurrence of febrile seizures. *N Engl J Med* 1993; 329: 79-84.

[24] Rantala H, Tarkka R, Uhari M. Preventive treatment for recurrent febrile seizures. *Ann Med 2000; 32*: 177-80.

[25] Shinnar S. Glauser TA. Febrile seizures. *J Child Neurol* 2002; 17: S44-52

[26] Spector S, Cull C, Goldstein LH. Seizure precipitants and perceived self-control of seizures in adults with poorly-controlled epilepsy. *Epilepsy Res* 2000: 38: 207-16.

[27] Temkin NR. Antiepileptogenesis and seizure prevention trials with antiepileptic drugs. *Epilepsia* 2001; 42: 515-24.

[28] Temkin NR, Jarel AD, Anderson GD. Antiepileptogenic agents. How close are we? *Drugs* 2001; 61:1045-55.

[29] Pitkanen A. Drug-mediated neuroprotection and epileptogenesis: Animal data. *Neurology* 2002; 59 (Suppl. 5): S27-S33.

[30] Loscher W. Animal models of intractable epilepsy. Prog Neurobiol 1997; 53: 239-58.

[31] Applegate CD, Smoriski GM, Ozduman K. Effects of valproate, phenytoin, and MK-801 in a novel model of epileptogenesis. *Epilepsia* 1997; 38: 631-6.

[32] Racine RJ, Livingston K, Joaquin A. Effects of procaine hydrochloride, diazepam and diphenylhydantoin on seizure development in cortical and subcortical structures in rat. *Electroencephalogr Clin Neurophysiol* 38; 355-65.

[33] Schmutz m, Klebs K, Baltzer V. Inhibition or enhancement of kindling evolution by antiepileptics. *J Neural Transm* 1988; 72: 245-57.

[34] Silver JM, Shin C, McNamara JO. Antiepileptogenetic effects of conventional anticonvulsants in the kindling model of epilepsy. *Ann Neurol* 1991; 29: 356-63.

[35] Wada J, Sato M, Wake A. Prophylactic effects of phenytoin, phenobarbital and carbamazepine examined in kindling cat preparations. *Arch Neurol* 1976; 17: 49-57.

[36] Lockard JS, DuCharme LL, Congdon WC, Franklin SC. Prophylaxis with diphenylhydantoin and phenobarbital in alumina-gel monkey model. II. Four-month follow-up period: seizure, EEG, blood, and behavioral data. *Epilepsia* 1976; 17:49-57.

[37] Barry E. Postraumatic epilepsy. In Wyllie E, ed. *The treatment of epilepsy. Principles and practice.* Philadelphia: Lippicontt Williams & Wilkins 2001; p. 609-13.

[38] Lemesle-Martin M. Traitements antiépileptiques dans les lésions cérébrales: quelles sont les indications et les principales attitudes pratiques? *Ann Fr Anesth Réanim* 2001; 20: 115-22.

[39] Iudice A, Murri L. Pharmacological prophylaxis of post-traumatic epilepsy. *Drugs 2000; 59*: 1091-9.

[40] Roberts SG. Anti-epileptic drugs for preventing seizures following acute traumatic brain injury. *Cochrane Database Syst Rev* 2000; 2: CD000173.

[41] Temkin NR, Dikmen SS, Wilensky AJ, Keihm J, Chabal S, Winn HR. A randomized, doulbe-blind study of phenytoin for the prevention of post-traumatic seizures. *N Engl J Med* 1999; 23: 497-502.

[42] Brain Injury Special Interest Group of the American Academy of Physical Medicine and Rehabilitation. Practice parameter: antiepileptic drug treatment of postraumatic seizures. *Arch Phys Med Rehabil* 1998; 79: 594-7.

[43] Beghi E. Overview of studies to prevent posttraumatic epilepsy. *Epilepsia* 2003; 44 (Suppl 10): 21-6.

[44] Lancman ME. Stroke-related epilepsy. In Kotagal P, Lüders HO, ed. *The epilepsies. Etiologies and prevention.* San Diego: Academic Press 1999; p. 399-407.

[45] Vives KP, Awad IA. Vascular causes of epilepsy. Overview. In Kotagal P, Lüders HO, ed. *The epilepsies. Etiologies and prevention*. San Diego: Academic Press 1999; p. 371-83.

[46] Inagawa T. Trends in incidence and case fatality rates of aneurysmal subarachnoid hemorrhage in Izumo City, Japan, between 198-1989 and 1990-1998. *Stroke* 2001; 32: 1499-507.

[47] Hayashi T, Hadeishi H, Kawamura S, Nonoyama Y, Suzuki A, Yasui N. Postoperative anticonvulsant prophylaxis for patients treated for cerebral aneurysms. *Neurol Med Chir* 1999; 39: 828-34.

[48] Régis J, Bartolomei F, Kida Y, Kobayashi T, Vladyka V, Liscàk R, et al. Radiosurgery for epilepsy associated with cavernous malformation: retrospective study in 49 patients. *Neurosurgery* 2000; 47:1091-7.

[49] Morris HH, Estes ML. Brain tumors and epilepsy. In Wyllie E, ed. *The treatment of epilepsy. Principles and practice*. Philadelphia: Lippicontt Williams & Wilkins 2001; p.615-26.

[50] Duchowny M. Febrile seizures. In Wyllie E, ed. *The treatment of epilepsy. Principles and practice*. Philadelphia: Lippicontt Williams & Wilkins 2001; p.601-8.

[51] Wallace RH. Scheffer IE. Parasivam G. Barnett S. Wallace GB. Sutherland GR. Berkovic SF. Mulley JC. Generalized epilepsy with febrile seizures plus: mutation of the sodium channel subunit SCN1B. *Neurology* 2002; 58: 1426-9.

[52] Scheffer IE. Berkovic SF. Generalized epilepsy with febrile seizures plus. A genetic disorder with heterogeneous clinical phenotypes. *Brain* 1997; 120: 479-90.

[53] Baumann RJ, Duffner PK. Treatment of children with simple febrile seizures. The AAP practice parameter. American Academy of Pediatrics. *Pediatr Neurol* 2000; 23: 11-7.

[54] Rocca WA, Sharbrough FW, Hauser WA, Annegers JF, Schoenberg BS. Risk factors for absence seizures: a population-based case-control study in Rochester, Minnesota. *Neurology* 1987; 37: 1309-14.

[55] Shinnar S, Berg At, O'Dell C, Newstein D, Moshe SL, Hauser WA. Predictors of multiple seizures in a cohort of children porspectively followed from the time of their first unprovoked seizure. *Ann Neurol* 2000; 48: 140-7.

[56] O'Dell C, Shinnar S. Initiation and discontinuation of antiepileptic drugs. *Neurol Clin* 2001; 19: 289-311.

[57] Gowers WR. *Epilepsy and other chronic convulsive disorders*. London: Ed. J&A Churchill; 1881.

[58] Placencia M, Shorvon SD, Paredes V, Bimos C, Sander JW, Suarez JC, et al. Epileptic seizures in an Andean region of Ecuador: prevalence and incidence and regional variation. *Brain* 1992; 115: 771-82.

[59] Berg AT, Shinnar S, Levy SR, Testa FM, Smith-Rapaport S, Beckerman B. Early development of intractable epilepsy in children. A prospective study. *Neurology* 2001; 56: 1445-52.

[60] Stratton SC. Large CH. Cox B. Davies G. Hagan RM. Effects of lamotrigine and levetiracetam on seizure development in a rat amygdala kindling model. *Epilepsy Research*. 53: 95-106, 2003

[61] Klitgaard H. Matagne A. Gobert J. Wulfert E. Evidence for a unique profile of levetiracetam in rodent models of seizures and epilepsy. *European Journal of Pharmacology*. 353: 191-206, 1998

[62] Klitgaard H, Pitkanen A. Antiepileptogenesis, neuroprotection, and disease modification in the treatment of epilepsy: focus on levetiracetam. *Epileptic Disord* 2003; 5: S9-16.

[63] Janumpalli S, Butler LS, MacMillan LB, Limbird LE, McNamara JO. A point mutation (D79N) of the α2A receptor abolishes the antiepileptogenic action of endogenous norepinephrine. *J Neurosci* 1998; 18: 2004-8.

[64] Kuvobá H. Ontogenesis and treatment efficacy: prevention of seizures in the immature brain. *Adv Neurol* 1999; 81: 357-61.

[65] Moshé SL. Neuroprotection and epilepsy. Medscape 2000; [www.medscape.com], January 19:1-12.

[66] Legido A. Perinatal hypoxic-ischemic encephalopathy: current advances in diagnosis and treatment. *Int Pediatr* 1994; 9: 114-36.

[67] Volpe JJ. Perinatal brain injury: from pathogenesis to neuroprotection. *Ment Retard Dev Disabil Res Rev* 2001:56-64.

[68] Katsetos CD, Spandou E, Legido A, Taylor ML, de Chadarevian JP, Mishra OP, et al. Acute hypoxia induced alterations of calbindin-D28k in Purkinje cells and subcellular fractions of fetal guinea pig cerebellum at term. *J Neuropathol Exp Neurol* 2001; 60: 470-82.

[69] Noda Y, Mori A, Packer L. Zonisamide inhibits nitric oxide synthase activity induced by N-methyl-D-aspartate and buthionine sulfoximine in the rat hippocampus. *Res Commun Mol Pathol Pharmacol* 1999; 105: 23-33.

[70] Calabresi P, Cupini LM, Centonze D, Pisani F, Bernardi G. Antiepileptic drugs as a possible neuroprotective strategy in brain ischemia. *Ann Neurol* 2003; 53: 693-702.

[71] Willmore LJ. How does trauma cause epilepsy? In Kotagal P, Lüders HO, ed. *The Epilepsies. Etiologies and prevention*. San Diego: Academic Press 1999; p. 289-91.

[72] Salazar AM, Ellenbogen R. Posttraumatic epilepsy prevention. In Kotagal P, Lüders HO, ed. *The Epilepsies. Etiologies and prevention*. San Diego: Academic Press 1999; p. 293-6.

[73] *Cyberonics VNS patient outcome registry.*

[74] Farooqui S, Boswel W, Hemphill JM, Pearlman E. Vagus nerve stimulation in pediatric patients with intractable epilepsy: case series and operative technique. *Am Surg* 2001; 67: 119-21.

[75] Wheless JW, Maggio V. Vagus nerve stimulation therapy in patients younger than 18 years. *Neurology* 2002;59:S21-5.

[76] Chugani HT, Shields WD, Shewmon DA, et al. Surgery for intractable infantile spasms: neuroimaging perspectives. *Epilepsia* 1993; 34: 764-71.

[77] Wyllie E, Comair YG, Kotagal P, et al. Seizure outcome after epilepsy surgery in children and adolescents. *Ann Neurol* 1998; 44: 740-8.

[78] Duchowny M, Jayakar P, Resnick T, Harvey AS, Alvarez L, Dean P, et al. Epilepsy surgery in the first three years of life. *Epilepsia* 1998; 39: 737-43.

[79] Paolicchi JM, Jayakar P, Dean P, Yaylali I, Morrison G, Prats A, et al. Predictors of outcome in pediatric epilepsy surgery. *Neurology* 2000; 54: 642-7.

[80] Wyllie E, Bingaman WE. Epilepsy surgery in infants and children. In Wyllie E, ed. *The treatment of epilepsy. Principles and practice*. Philadelphia: Lippicontt Williams & Wilkins 2001; p.1161-73.

[81] Spencer SS. When should temporal-lobe epilepsy be treated surgically? *Lancet Neurol* 2002:1:375-82.

[82] Sugaya A, Yuyama N, Kajiwara K, Tsuda T, Ohguchi H, Shimizu-Nishikawa K, et al. Regulation of gene expression by herbal medicines. A new paradigm of gene therapy for multifocal abnormalities of genes. *Res Commun Mol Pathol Pharmacol* 1999; 106: 171-80.

[83] Müller B. Psychological approaches to the prevention and inhibition of nocturnal epileptic seizures: a meta-analysis of 70 case studies. *Seizure* 2001;10:13-33.

[84] Stein AG, Eder HG, Blum DE, Drachev A, Fisher RS. An automated system for focal epilepsy. *Epilepsy Res* 2000; 39: 103-14.

[85] Elger CE, Widman G, Andrzjak R, Arnhold J, David P, Lehnertz K. Nonlinear EEG analysis and its potential role in epileptology. *Epilepsia* 2000; 41: S34-8.

[86] McNamara JO. Identification of genetic defect of epilepsy: strategies for therapeutic advances. *Epilepsia* 1994; 35: S51-7.

[87] Freese A, Kaplitt MG, O'Connor WM, Abbey M, Langer D, Leone P. et al. Direct gene transfer into human epileptogenic hippocampal tissue with an adeno-associated virus vector: implications for a gene therapy approach to epilepsy. *Epilepsia* 1997; 38: 759-66

[88] Yenari MA, Fink SL, Sun GH, Chang LK, Patel MK, Kunis DM, et al. Gene therapy with HSP72 is neuroprotective in rat models of stroke and epilepsy. *Ann Neurol* 1998; 44: 584-91.

[89] McLaughlin J, Roozendaal B, Dumas T, Gupta A, Ajiolre O, Hsieh J, et al. Sparing of neuronal function postseizure with gene therapy. *Proc Natl Acad Sci USA* 2000; 97: 12804-9.

[90] During MJ, Symes CW, Lawlor PA, Lin J, Dunning J, Fitzsimons HL, et al. An oral vaccine against NMDR1 with efficacy in experimental stroke and epilepsy. *Science* 2000; 287: 1453-60.

In: Focus on Epilepsy Research
Editor: Shawn M. Benjamin, pp. 23-58

ISBN 1-59454-087-X

Chapter II

The Importance of Age in the Development of Mesial Temporal Lobe Epilepsy

Aristea S. Galanopoulo[1,2,4,*], Andreas Kyrozis[1], Filippo S. Giorgi[1] and Solomon L Moshé[1-4]

Departments of Neurology[1], Neuroscience[2] and Pediatrics[3],
Albert Einstein College of Medicine, Bronx NY and
Einstein Comprehensive Epilepsy Management Center[4],
Montefiore Medical Center, Bronx NY.

Abstract

Mesial temporal lobe epilepsy (MTLE) is the commonest form of epilepsy. Seizures usually start during childhood, remit for a period of time, and then reappear and become more frequent and harder to control during adulthood. Although mesial temporal sclerosis (MTS) is the characteristic pathological finding in adults with intractable MTLE, it is rarely present in children. Both clinical and experimental evidence support that the immature brain is more resistant to the development of seizure-induced hippocampal pathology akin to MTS compared with the mature brain, although functional changes may occur. A variety of factors may alter the susceptibility of the brain to seizures and their consequences. These include genetic predisposition, prior neurological abnormalities, sex, etiology and severity of seizures. The impact of these factors changes through development. We will summarize the current knowledge on the pathological and functional consequences of seizures on the immature and mature brain, the age-specific role of the known modifying factors and will discuss how this knowledge may be implemented in the design of age-appropriate preventative or therapeutic interventions.

* Corresponding Author: Aristea S Galanopoulou, MD PhD, Albert Einstein College of Medicine, 1410 Pelham Parkway South, Kennedy Center Rm 311, Bronx, NY 10461, Tel: 718-430-3791 or 2620, Fax: 718-430-8899, e-mail: agalan@aecom.yu.edu

Mesial temporal lobe epilepsy (MTLE) is the commonest form of epilepsy and accounts for 70% of intractable epilepsy cases (Babb, 1987; Pasquier, 2002). It is diagnosed when behavioral, electrophysiological and anatomical data suggest that its origin lies within the mesial temporal lobe structures. MTLE is associated with a characteristic hippocampal pathology called *mesial temporal sclerosis* (MTS) or *hippocampal sclerosis*, which is particularly common in temporal lobectomy specimens of patients with intractable MTLE. The striking morphological and pathological features of MTS, which are now easily identifiable with specific neuroimaging studies or histological stains, and the hope that it can possibly serve as both a surrogate marker of intractable MTLE and a guide for selecting appropriate candidates for surgical therapies have rendered it the focus of intense scientific research. Such efforts aim to clarify its role in the pathogenesis and course of MTLE, as well as identify neuroprotective treatments that could prevent or halt its development. Several of these studies have made clear that age-specific factors can modify the development of MTS. In this review, we will summarize the relevant literature focusing in particular on the importance of age on the development of MTS and MTLE.

HIPPOCAMPAL ANATOMY AND MTS

Hippocampal Anatomy

Mesial temporal lobe structures include the amygdala, the temporal segment of the prepiriform cortex and the hippocampal allocortex (Gloor, 1997). The hippocampal formation includes the subiculum, dentate gyrus and hippocampus proper. In humans, the dentate gyrus is C-shaped and consists of 3 layers: a compact layer of dentate granule cells, which are the excitatory projection neurons of the gyrus, the molecular layer and the *end folium*, which comprises the polymorph layer of the dentate (CA4 area) and the hilus. The hippocampus proper (cornu ammonis, CA) is C-shaped and consists of 4 layers: the stratum oriens (so), a compact layer of pyramidal cells (excitatory projection neurons), the stratum radiatum (*sr*) and stratum lacunosum-moleculare (*slm*) (see Figure 1).

The circuit of connectivity between these structures, as well as with other brain regions, enables them to easily engage into a seizure activity but also to sustain and propagate it. First described in 1911 by Ramon y Cajal, the unidirectional nature of the excitatory connections between the different hippocampal regions was emphasized in 1971 by Andersen and colleagues (Andersen, 1971). The hippocampus receives afferents from layer II of the entorhinal cortex through the *perforant pathway*, which terminates in the dentate gurus and the CA2 / CA3 region. Afferents from entorhinal layer III terminate at the CA1 sector and subiculum. *Mossy fibers* propagate the input from the dentate granular neurons to the CA3 or CA4 neurons. CA3 pyramidal cells then project to CA1 neurons (*Schaffer collaterals*) or to other CA3 neurons. Finally, CA1 neurons project to the subiculum or the entorhinal cortex, completing thus this circuit. Interhippocampal communications take place via the commissural connections, whereas reciprocal communication with other cortical areas occurs through the entorhinal cortex. This extensive network renders therefore the hippocampus both a receiver and broadcaster of activities generated within other brain structures, but also enables it to sustain these activities via a feedforward circuit. Furthermore, the interaction between inhibitory interneurons and excitatory neurons within the hippocampus also enables the synchronization of the epileptiform activities that is required for seizure generation. These features form the basis for the generation, propagation and maintenance of epileptic activity.

Mesial Temporal Sclerosis

The histologic hallmark of MTLE is *mesial temporal sclerosis* (MTS), a term interchangeably used with *hippocampal sclerosis*, although the former implies damage beyond the hippocampus. In a recent workshop (2002) organized by the International League Against Epilepsy, MTS was defined by the following features: 1) CA1 and dentate hilar neuronal loss and gliosis with relative sparing of transitional cortex, although with detailed counting all hippocampal regions may show variable degrees of neuronal loss and gliosis (Sommer, 1880; Bratz, 1899; Mathern, 1997); 2) short- and long-term structural and functional glial changes (Bratz, 1899; Mathern, 1997); 3) structural and functional reorganization including but not limited to mossy fibers (Mathern, 1997; Thom, 2002); 4) granular cell dispersion (Thom, 2002); 5) extrahippocampal lesions or atrophy (Mathern, 1997); 6) dysplastic or structurally altered neurons may also be seen (Blumcke, 1999; Thom, 2002). An increased number of proliferating neuronal precursors has also been demonstrated in the subgranular matrix of the dentate gyrus (Mathern, 1997; Blumcke, 2002). A pathology revealed much less commonly than MTS in surgical specimens is *end-folium sclerosis*, in which the pathological changes are confined to the end folium (Margerison, 1966; Van Paesschen, 1997). Finally, in a minority of cases no significant hippocampal pathology is found.

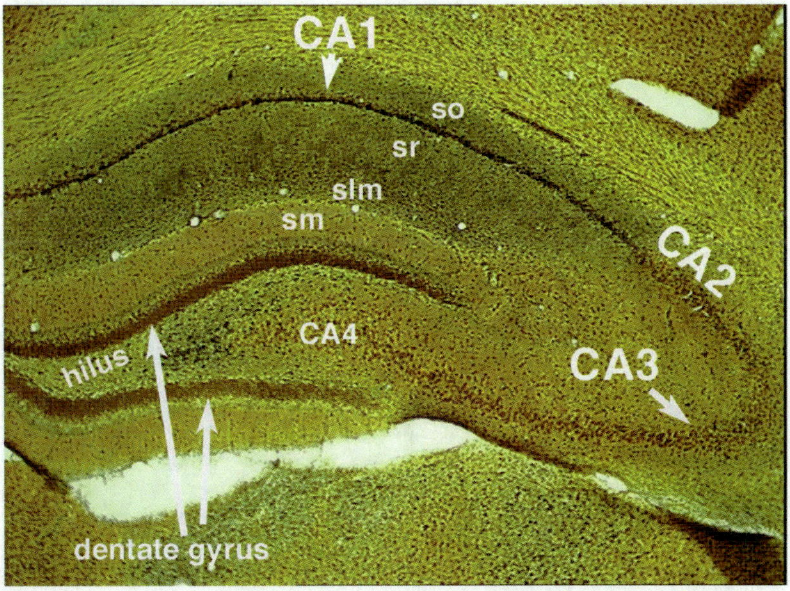

Figure 1: Lithium-pilocarpine induced status epilepticus induces neurodegeneration in adult rat hippocampus, typical of MTS. Silver impregnation staining reveals abundant degenerating neurons (stained black) in the CA1, CA4 pyramidal areas and the dentate hilus. Although not clearly shown in this magnification, variable numbers of degenerating neurons are present in the CA3 region as well. Normal neurons are stained brown. *Abbreviations*: so: stratum oriens; sr: stratum radiatum; slm: stratum lacunosum moleculare; sm: stratum moleculare.

MTS is found in 60-80% of adult TLE cases undergoing surgery in most large series (Babb, 1987; Williamson, 1993; Kalviainen, 2002; Mathern, 2002). Most of the reports in children however document lower incidence rates of MTS (15% - 43%) (Mizrahi, 1990; Adelson, 1992; Duchowny, 1992; Kuzniecky, 1993; Harvey, 1997; Wang, 1997; Berg, 1999; Sinclair, 2001; Sztriha, 2002). In the Cleveland Clinic pediatric cohort, TLE accounted for half of the cases of intractable epilepsy requiring surgery, but MTS was a rare finding (Wyllie, 1998). Instead, cortical dysplasias, migrational disorders, low-grade tumors, hamartomas were more prevalent in children (Bourgeois, 1998; Wyllie, 1998). Occasionally however higher incidence rates are reported, which may probably be related to different population characteristics (Grattan-Smith, 1993; Bocti, 2003). For instance, the higher incidence of MTS in the pediatric population studied by Bocti et al (80%), was attributed to a more rapid progression and severe course of their epilepsy (Bocti, 2003). Interestingly, the majority (80%) of these patients were 5 years old or younger at the time of their first seizure, which may predispose to the development of MTS (Mathern, 1995c). Furthermore, although in the study by Kuzniecky et al half of the patients undergoing surgery for intractable epilepsy had MTS, only a minority of those younger than 12 years of age had MTS (Kuzniecky, 1993). The youngest probable cases of pathologically or MRI-proven hippocampal sclerosis were in 2-year old patients (Harvey, 1995; Murakami, 1996a; Kanos, 2000).

Virtually all mesial temporal lobe structures can display damage in MTLE, as do additional extratemporal structures to a lesser degree. The hippocampus, subiculum and amygdala are apparently most consistently affected, but hippocampus is by far the best studied, partially due to its characteristic anatomy that facilitates quantitative histological and imaging studies. The common co-existence of MTS and extra-hippocampal pathology led to the introduction of the term *dual pathology* (Babb, 1987; Grattan-Smith, 1993; Cendes, 1995; Raymond, 1995; Ho, 1998; Bocti, 2003).

The Syndrome of Mesial Temporal Lobe Epilepsy (MTLE)

Clinical Presentation

Even if classically identified in adults, MTLE often begins in childhood, and typically between 5 and 10 years of age (French, 1993; Engel, 1996; Foldvary, 1997; Bourgeois, 1998). The incidence of MTLE among children with epilepsy varies in different statistics, but usually accounts for less than 1% (Murakami, 1996b). Temporal lobe resections however account for almost half of the surgeries performed for intractable complex partial seizures in childhood (Wyllie, 1998).

It is estimated that the majority (60-88%) of patients with intractable MTLE manifest their first unprovoked seizure at or before the age of 16 years (French, 1993; Berg, 2003), in contrast to patients with neocortical TLE who manifest their first seizure after this age (Kotagal, 2001). Seizures are typically complex partial, very often preceded by auras. Approximately half of the patients will additionally exhibit secondarily generalized seizures (French, 1993). The semiology and characteristics of MTLE seizures change with age (Brockhaus, 1995; Bourgeois, 1998). In children younger than 42 months, motoric seizures are more prevalent (Fogarasi, 2002) and consist of tonic or myoclonic movements of the limbs, postures reminiscent of frontal lobe seizures or head nodding similar to infantile spasms (Brockhaus, 1995). As a result, diagnosis of MTLE at this young age may be more difficult. In children older than 3 years, motoric seizures become less frequent (Fogarasi, 2002), whereas after the age of 6 years, seizures are semiologically similar to adults (Brockhaus, 1995). Initially patients may experience psychic or epigastric auras (90%), followed by behavioral arrest or staring, decrease in the level of consciousness, automatisms (oroalimentary, manual or ambulatory) and autonomic symptoms (Nahm, 2001). A variety of additional neuropsychological manifestations, such as depression and memory disturbances, are often present.

Initial Precipitating Injuries

In the majority of intractable MTLE patients (80-90%), careful history may reveal the occurrence of antecedent events, which may represent an "initial precipitating injury" (IPI) (French, 1993; Mathern, 1995c). The most common IPI is childhood or infantile seizures, and particularly complex febrile seizures (Falconer, 1964; Cendes, 1993a; French, 1993; Kuks, 1993; Mathern, 1995c; Bower, 2000). Other common IPIs include viral or bacterial central nervous system infections, head trauma or birth trauma, perinatal hypoxia (Marks, 1992; French, 1993; Mathern, 1995c; Mathern, 1997). A minority of cases have no identifiable or suspected IPI, and are thus classified as idiopathic.

Whereas it may sometimes be the case that a single potent IPI may be enough to cause epilepsy and histologic damage in any host, MTLE is generally viewed as a multifactorial process where the direct sequelae of the IPI are in complex interaction with additional important factors including age, sex, genetic background, prior neurologic abnormalities as well as frequency and severity of seizures. Therefore, poor understanding of causal factors in human MTLE complicates studies addressing the effects of seizures and their age dependence on disease progression. Prospective studies are needed to address the importance of each of these IPIs on the generation of MTLE. Animal models, which will be discussed in the subsequent sections, offer the advantage of testing the effects of well defined IPI in naïve or genetically altered animals and address thus the age-dependence of seizure and IPI effects on MTLE pathogenesis.

Imaging Studies in the Diagnosis of MTLE

The development of high resolution magnetic resonance techniques has immensely contributed to the non-invasive assessment of structural abnormalities associated with MTLE. An important benefit of magnetic resonance imaging (MRI) from a clinical point of view is the increased confidence in identifying the side and exact location of the presumed epileptogenic focus during presurgical assessment. From a research point of view, MRI studies have complemented histological studies in providing a wealth of data on the role of seizures and other factors in the development of structural damage in MTLE. Three quantitative MR indices are commonly employed in the localization of the TLE focus. Hippocampal volumetry is the most widely used. Several studies have established that reduced hippocampal volume is well correlated with neuronal loss and gliosis that define MTS (Kuzniecky, 1987; Berkovic, 1991; Cascino, 1991; Van Paesschen, 1997; Watson, 1997). A second valuable MRI parameter is the hippocampal T2-weighted signal. It is considered to be slightly less well correlated with MTS, but is highly correlated with dentate gliosis (Van Paesschen, 1997; Briellmann, 2002b) and can occasionally be abnormal in proven TLE cases with normal volumetry (Jackson, 1994). A third and most recent technique now commonly used is MR spectroscopy with measurement of N-acetyl aspartate / creatinine (NAA/Cr) ratio, which reflects neuronal metabolism and assesses for the presence of neuronal loss (Cendes, 1997; Namer, 1999; Li, 2000; Miller, 2000; Kikuchi, 2001; Bernasconi, 2002).

MTLE: Current Therapeutic Options

From studies retrospectively describing the natural history of intractable MTLE, we know that seizures are initially infrequent, easily controlled with antiepileptics and as a result they may remit for a period of time (Berg, 2003). Although the currently available antiepileptic drugs can be efficient anticonvulsants, there is no convincing evidence from the available clinical trials that they may act as antiepileptogenic drugs [reviewed in (Temkin, 2001)]. It is not thus unusual that, despite an initial period of remission which is present in 26% of patients with intractable epilepsy (Berg, 2003), seizures reappear, become more frequent and require increase in dosage or combination regimens (Engel, 1996).

In most cases, diagnosis of MTLE is instituted only during the presurgical evaluation in patients with intractable TLE, and thus there is insufficient amount of information as to what percent of patients do not develop drug-refractory MTLE. In a study of 104 MTLE patients diagnosed with MRI scans, it was estimated that 25% were completely controlled with medications over the course of 2-year follow up, 37% had partial seizure control, whereas 38% were deemed intractable (Kim, 1999). From the patients' perspective however the distinction between partial seizure control and intractability are often not as clear, given the impact and restrictions posed by the diagnosis of epilepsy on their everyday life. Average latency time between epilepsy onset and declaration of "intractability" was 9 years in a recently reported large series (Berg, 2003).

The majority of outcome studies on MTLE patients have been done on patients being evaluated for possible surgery, and therefore show a selection bias towards those that have not responded to initial pharmacotherapy. The first randomized study of surgery versus medical treatment efficacy in intractable MTLE patients shows the superiority of surgical resection, since 58% of surgically versus 8% of medically treated MTLE patients became seizure-free within one year (Wiebe, 2001). The report of the *Quality Standards Subcommittee* of the American Academy of Neurology in association with the American Epilepsy Society and the American Association of Neurological Surgeons has presented an extensive summary of the current literature and concludes with a recommendation that patients fulfilling the selection criteria for anteromesial temporal lobe resection should be offered surgical treatment (Engel, 2003). Such presurgical evaluation is aimed at identifying the primary epileptogenic focus, investigating whether it colocalizes with the hippocampus showing evidence of MTS, and limiting the associated surgery-related morbidities. This workup includes clinical and electroencephalographic data as well as corroborating evidence from adjunctive tests, namely MRI, ictal and / or interictal single photon emission tomography (SPECT) and positron emission tomography (PET) imaging, WADA studies, and neuropsychological evaluation (Williamson, 1993; Benbadis, 1995; Ho, 1997; Sirven, 1997; Theodore, 1997; Holmes, 2000).

The two common resective surgeries are anterior temporal lobectomy with resection of adjacent mesial temporal lobe structures and selective amygdalohippocampectomy (Nahm, 2001). The anterior temporal lobectomy, as developed at Yale, involves resection up to 3.5cm from the pole of the temporal lobe, including neocortical tissue and a substantial part of the amygdala, hippocampus and parahippocampus, but sparing the superior temporal gyrus (Kim, 2001). Variations of the selective amygdalohippocampectomy allow resection of significant portions of the amygdala, hippocampus and parahippocampus accessed through the sylvian fissure, or the temporal neocortex or via subtemporal access (Kim, 2001). A comprehensive review of the surgical literature reveals that a seizure-free outcome after anterior temporal lobectomy is expected in approximately 65% of patients and improvement in 21% (Engel, 2003). The presence of MTS in MTLE patients is associated with a much higher probability of remaining seizure-free post-operatively compared to patients with normal MRIs (36% seizure-free outcome (Berkovic, 1995).

MTS AND INTRACTABLE MTLE

Many questions regarding the role of MTS in the pathogenesis, co-morbidities and outcome of MTLE still need to be answered. As discussed previously, MTS is not only very frequently encountered in adults with intractable epilepsy but can also predict an excellent outcome in response to surgical treatment, underlining thus the importance of early detection. On the other hand, MTS appears to be less prevalent in surgical series of children with intractable TLE, in which other causalities dominate, such as neurodevelopmental disorders or tumors. It is possible that a spectrum of MTLE variants may exist to explain these data. First, the benign MTLE variants (childhood or adult onset) may have no overt temporal lobe pathologies in neuroimaging studies and are associated with excellent response to antiepileptics. In this category belong certain idiopathic MTLEs (Berkovic, 1996a; Nelson, 2002; Regesta, 2002; Ward, 2002). Second, the presence of neurodevelopmental abnormalities or tumors may accelerate the development of intractable epilepsy and lead thus to epilepsy surgery during the childhood years. Third, MTLE associated with MTS only, may have a slower course, leading to the diagnosis of intractable epilepsy mostly during the adult years. If MTS is limited to the epileptogenic focus excellent post-operative surgical outcome is expected. Finally, an intractable MTLE group without associated hippocampal pathologies on neuroimaging may not respond as well to epilepsy surgery (Garcia, 1994; Berkovic, 1995; Ho, 1997; Theodore, 1997; Holmes, 2000). Definitive answers however are needed to delineate the natural history and characteristics of these groups. Due to the known limitations of the retrospective studies mentioned above, in recent years many authors have started to address these issues using prospective studies with longitudinal MRI evaluations of patients with newly-diagnosed epilepsy, especially children (Berg, 2000; Shinnar, 2001), and hopefully the real incidence and temporal evolution of MTS will be defined in more detail in the future.

Clinicopathological Correlations: Role of Seizures and Age in the Development of MTS

Correlations among several clinical / behavioral parameters and hippocampal damage have been investigated by MRI and histological studies from patients with MTLE. The following sections will discuss whether certain parameters play a causative role in histologic damage, namely the age of seizure onset, duration of disease, total seizure number and frequency and seizure etiology as a function of age.

Age of Seizure Onset

Assessment of hippocampal damage as a function of age of TLE onset can provide strong clues concerning the age dependence of seizure-induced hippocampal damage. A younger age of onset has been correlated with more severe hippocampal abnormalities (Kodama, 1995; Davies, 1996a; Duc, 1998; Fuerst, 2001; Salmenpera, 2001) and epilepsy course (Aguglia, 1998) suggesting that seizures early in life may be more harmful. In one study (Trenerry, 1993), young age at onset was correlated with decreased hippocampal volume only in left lobectomy patients. Other studies have failed to detect a correlation between age at onset and hippocampal damage (Theodore, 1999; Bower, 2000; Keller, 2002). However, as for other assessed parameters, any correlation between age at onset and histologic damage must be viewed with caution because of several confounding factors that are generally difficult to simultaneously control. For example, early age of onset is often correlated with increased duration of disease, or a history of IPIs, such as prolonged febrile seizures (Kodama, 1995; Davies, 1996a) which may by themselves increase the likelihood of developing MTS. Some studies explicitly control for these factors whereas others do not. It must also be noted that a correlation may not necessarily reflect an age-dependent effect of seizures but rather the different etiologic and pathogenic mechanisms that are believed to be associated with TLE onset at different ages.

Duration of Epilepsy

Several studies have investigated whether the development of MTS is progressive, by correlating the duration of clinically overt TLE with the degree of hippocampal damage. A positive correlation was reported in retrospective studies (Duc, 1998; Kalviainen, 1998; Theodore, 1999; Fuerst, 2001; Salmenpera, 2001; Bernasconi, 2002). Comparing hippocampal pathology from surgical specimens obtained from patients with temporal or extratemporal seizures, Mathern and colleagues reported progressive neuronal loss in all hippocampal subfields, that correlated with seizure duration (Mathern, 2002). Contrary however to these findings, there are studies that find either no significant effect of epilepsy duration over the degree of hippocampal atrophy (Cendes, 1993b; Bower, 2000; Keller, 2002) or attribute the apparent negative impact of long epilepsy duration upon the younger age of seizure onset in these patients (Davies, 1996a).

Most of the above studies are retrospective and dealing primarily with established and usually intractable TLE cases. Information during earlier stages of the disease and longitudinal follow up of the evolution of hippocampal abnormalities during the course of epilepsy are very helpful in determining the impact of seizures on MTS. The progressive nature of MTS was thus supported with follow up MRI studies in 12 patients with medically refractory MTLE who eventually either became seizure-free (3 patients) or continued having seizures (9 patients) (Fuerst, 2003). Progressive volume loss in the affected hippocampus was documented only in those who continued having seizures and correlated with seizure frequency. Similar results were obtained in a longitudinal MRI studies of TLE patients, in which progressive hippocampal atrophy was documented over a period of 3-5 years (Wieshmann, 1997; O'Brien, 1999; Briellmann, 2002a; Worrell, 2002). In one large series (Kalviainen, 2002), hippocampal or amygdala damage as assessed by MRI was rare at the time of first spontaneous seizures but frequent in chronic TLE adult patients. In another, 1 out of 4 patients with hippocampal atrophy had progression of the MRI abnormalities within one year of follow up (Van Paesschen, 1998).

Severity of Seizures

Hippocampal damage has been positively correlated with the total number and / or frequency of complex partial seizures (Kalviainen, 1998; Salmenpera, 2001; Fuerst, 2003) or secondarily generalized seizures (Kalviainen, 1998; Tasch, 1999; Salmenpera, 2001; Briellmann, 2002a). Other studies however have found no effect of seizure frequency (Cendes, 1993b; Bower, 2000) or the presence of generalized tonic-clonic seizures (Cendes, 1993b) on hippocampal pathology.

Sex

It has long been known that sex hormones influence neuronal excitability and synaptic plasticity in the hippocampus (Woolley, 1992, 1994; Herzog, 1999). Sex does not appear to influence the age at onset of epilepsy. Interestingly, in the same study, the left hemisphere appeared to be more vulnerable to seizure onset in childhood (Strauss, 1997). Men with MTLE showed more extramesiotemporal hypometabolism assessed by regional cerebral glucose utilization studies (Nickel, 2003). Sex differences in hypometabolism and seizure spread patterns were shown by Savic et al (Savic, 1998). Men with MTLE had more frequently hypometabolism as well as seizure spread at the frontal lobe ipsilaterally, in contrast to women who had hypometabolism and seizure spread at the contralateral hippocampus. Moreover, following left temporal lobectomy, women had improvement of verbal memory, in contrast to men (Trenerry, 1995). These suggest the existence of sexual dimorphism in function and connectivity of brain structures that are implicated in MTLE, which may impact upon the course of MTLE. However no definite evidence of sex differences in MTS pathology exists in humans. It appears though that men develop more diffuse brain atrophy compared to women with MTLE and that they are more prone to seizure-induced injury (Briellmann, 2000a).

Etiology of First Seizure

In a retrospective study comparing the hippocampal pathologies of epileptic patients with or without a history of IPI who eventually developed either temporal or extratemporal seizures, Mathern and colleagues reported that MTS is strongly linked with a history of an IPI (Mathern, 2002). The authors concluded that there is an initial neuronal loss associated with the occurrence of IPI but during the course of epilepsy further progressive hippocampal damage ensues (Mathern, 2002). Patients with a prolonged initial seizure or a nonseizure IPI occurring prior to 5 years of age were more likely to have MTS compared to those with an IPI after that age (Mathern, 1995c). Nonseizure IPIs prior to 5 years of age had significantly longer latent period and less favorable response to surgery (Mathern, 1995c).

The largest volume of literature pertains to the role of childhood febrile seizures as triggers of MTS and MTLE. MRI evidence of hippocampal injury following prolonged, lateralized febrile seizures was demonstrated in few infants by VanLandingham et al (VanLandingham, 1998). In a follow up study, the same investigators reported a 30% incidence of acute MRI abnormalities, within the first 72 hours of a prolonged febrile seizure (Lewis, 2002). From 8 of the infants with acute MRI abnormalities that had follow up MRI later on, 3 developed evidence of MTS and only one manifested TLE. Interestingly, all three patients with MTS belonged to the group of 4 infants with abnormal hippocampal T2 signal in their initial MRI. Although the number of cases in this report is small, these data suggest the need for further prospective studies to evaluate not only the impact of prolonged febrile seizures in the development of MTS and MTLE but also the role of MRI as a surrogate marker of future development of MTS and MTLE. Although certain retrospective studies have shown that a history of childhood febrile seizures in general correlates with the degree of hippocampal damage (Trenerry, 1993; Keller, 2002) or more severe seizures (Aguglia, 1998), most studies implicate the complex, and especially the prolonged, febrile seizures as risk factors for the development of MTS in MTLE patients (Sagar, 1987; Cendes, 1993b; Kuks, 1993; Mathern, 1995a; Mathern, 1995b; Fuerst, 2001; Salmenpera, 2001; Scott, 2001; Trinka, 2002; Saltik, 2003). The interpretation of these data however is often skewed by confounding factors that are not always eliminated (Annegers, 1996; Berg, 1997; Shinnar, 1998). For instance, a history of complex febrile seizures is often found in patients with younger age at epilepsy onset (Berg, 1999), which as discussed above may predispose to more severe hippocampal damage. In the study of Davies et al, the impact of complex febrile seizure on the development of MTS was lost after controlling for age at onset (Davies, 1996a). In other series, there was no correlation between febrile seizure history and the presence or severity of hippocampal atrophy (Berg, 1999; Bower, 2000). An elegant discussion on the link between febrile seizures and MTS and the limitations of the existing retrospective studies was recently presented by Shinnar (Shinnar, 2003).

A history of prior infection of the central nervous system (CNS) is encountered in 1.9% (Davies, 1996b) to 9.5% (French, 1993) of patients with intractable epilepsy. The vast majority of patients with intractable epilepsy preceded by meningitis develop TLE associated with either hippocampal sclerosis or gliosis (Davies, 1996b). 48-67% of intractable TLE patients with a prior history of CNS infection have MTS, whereas 20-33% have neocortical epilepsy (Lancman, 1996; Lee, 1997). Patients with MTLE following CNS infection were differentiated from the group with neocortical epilepsy by a younger age at the time of the CNS infection, a prolonged latent period, and a higher frequency of meningitis (Marks, 1992;

Lee, 1997). The development of MTS has been found to be more common among children who develop meningitis or encephalitis in the first 4 years of life (Marks, 1992).

Other important IPIs are perinatal events, such as neonatal seizures. A common cause of neonatal seizures is hypoxic / ischemic encephalopathy (30% of cases), and is associated with a less favorable course, often refractory to treatment seizures, and higher risk for subsequent epilepsy (Bergamasco, 1984; Connell, 1989; Strober, 1997; Arpino, 2001; Tharp, 2002). Other causes of acute symptomatic neonatal seizures are intracerebral hemorrhages, strokes, infections or metabolic disorders including hypoglycemia. The Collaborative Perinatal Project reported that 30% of the survivors of neonatal seizures had neurologic sequelae, including mental retardation (19%), epilepsy (20%) or a combination of mental retardation, cerebral palsy or epilepsy (13%) (Holden, 1982). Neonatal seizures are usually focal or multifocal and half of them originate from the temporal lobes (Green, 1993; Koc, 1997; Patrizi, 2003), which may explain the higher risk for the subsequent development of epilepsy, including temporal lobe epilepsy (Nevo, 1995; Berg, 1996).

A common IPI that usually occurs in the older ages is traumatic brain injury. Post-traumatic or post-craniotomy seizures are associated with a high risk for epilepsy (Annegers, 1980). The risk for posttraumatic epilepsy correlates positively with a history of penetrating head trauma, prolonged posttraumatic amnesia, and the extent of the sustained focal brain lesions (Pohlmann-Eden, 1997). In a series of 23 patients with intractable epilepsy and history of BTI after the age of 10 years, 35% had MRI evidence of MTS (Diaz-Arrastia, 2000). Patients with a history of significant head trauma were less likely to become seizure free following anterior temporal lobectomy (Schuh, 1998).

Genetic Factors Implicated in MTLE

A variety of genetic factors may control the susceptibility to MTLE by influencing the vulnerability to specific environmental triggers, such as infections or fever, or the ability to suppress or propagate excitatory insults. An autosomal dominant mode of inheritance for TLE has been described in several families (Berkovic, 1996a; Cendes, 1998; Gambardella, 2000; Ikeda, 2000). Familial MTLE may start at any age, with a mean age at onset at 10 years (Kobayashi, 2003). In the families described by Kobayashi et al, 30% of familial MTLE patients developed intractable features. MRI evidence of hippocampal atrophy was more frequently seen in refractory MTLE patients (88%) than in those that had a benign course or other seizures types (65% and 62% respectively) (Kobayashi, 2003). Interestingly, 30% of asymptomatic first degree relatives of patients with familial MTLE also had MRI evidence of hippocampal atrophy and T2 signal abnormalities (Kobayashi, 2002). The authors conclude that genetic determinants may contribute to the presence of hippocampal atrophy, which does not always predict refractoriness to medical treatment. Although these observation are only based on MRI apparent morphological abnormalities, these observations support the idea that MTS is not sufficient to cause MTLE or intractable epilepsy. The finding that 4% of the general population may have MRI evidence of MTS without seizures also corroborates these data (Benbadis, 2002). However caution has to be exercised when extending the observations made on a population genetically predisposed to manifest MTS to the general population, which needs additional triggers, such as an IPI at a vulnerable age, prolonged seizures or other genetic traits, to develop MTS. Further studies are needed to elucidate how each of these precipitating factors may modify the role MTS plays in the course of sporadic MTLE and particularly in intractable MTLE.

Familial TLE may be associated with febrile seizures (Abou-Khalil, 2001; Baulac, 2001b; Briellmann, 2001; Depondt, 2002; Ward, 2002; Kobayashi, 2003) or MTS (Briellmann, 2001; Kobayashi, 2001) and in some families may have a benign course (Depondt, 2002; Ward, 2002) without being associated with MTS (Baulac, 2001b; Ward, 2002). TLE may occur in families with the generalized epilepsy with febrile seizure plus syndrome (GEFS+) which has been linked to either sodium channel SCN1A mutations (Abou-Khalil, 2001), or to mutations of the gamma 2 subunit of $GABA_A$ receptors (Baulac, 2001a). The G1465A polymorphism of $GABA_{B1}$ receptor was recently linked with non-lesional TLE (Gambardella, 2003). In particular TLE patients with this polymorphism exhibited a more intractable course and earlier age at onset of epilepsy.

Other genes implicated in the development of MTLE with MTS are certain HLA class II antigens (Ozkara, 2002), a low expressing prodynorphin promoter allele (Stogmann, 2002) and a high IL-1β producer allele (Kanemoto, 2000), at least in certain populations (Buono, 2001). The Asn171Ser allele of prion protein was recently found to be present in 23% of MTLE patients with MTS and linked with persistence of seizures following temporal lobectomy (Walz, 2003). The APOE epsilon 4 genotype has been associated with earlier age at epilepsy onset in patients with intractable TLE (Briellmann, 2000b). The transgenic mice research has implicated genes like neuropeptide Y (Vezzani, 2002), cytokines (Vezzani, 2000), or the neuronal specific potassium chloride cotransporter KCC2 (Woo, 2002) in seizure susceptibility, although it is not yet clear how these factors contribute to MTS and MTLE.

Effects of SE on the Adult Hippocampus

Epidemiological studies have thus implicated several genetic and clinico-pathogenetic factors in the pathogenesis of MTS. The difficulty in controlling for certain confounding factors, which are often inter-dependent, poses an obstacle in attempts to obtain definitive answers on the specific role of each of these factors. The opportunity to test each of these factors individually was presented with the availability of experimental animal models of TLE. In these models, it is possible to induce a prolonged status epilepticus (SE) in developing or adult rodents and evaluate the behavioral effects and pathological consequences – such as MTS development – at different time points. SE can be induced via administration of chemoconvulsants, such as kainic acid (Nadler, 1978; Schwarcz, 1978; Pisa, 1980; Lothman, 1981b; Nadler, 1981a; Tanaka, 1982; Tremblay, 1984a; Ben-Ari, 1985; Sperk, 1985; Nitecka, 1986; Holmes, 1988), pilocarpine (Molnar, 1967; Honchar, 1983; Turski, 1983a; Turski, 1983b; Jope, 1986; Millan, 1986; Cavalheiro, 1987; Clifford, 1987; Hosford, 1988) or lithium-pilocarpine (Clifford, 1987), via electrical stimulation (Burnham, 1975; McCaughran, 1977; Pinel, 1978; Rose, 1979; McNamara, 1980a; McNamara, 1980b; Lopes da Silva, 1982; McIntyre, 1982; Moshe, 1983), or via intrahippocampal injections of tetanus toxins or other chemoconvulsants (Mellanby, 1977; Jefferys, 1989; Lee, 1995; Mitchell, 1995). Typically, most of the models using chemoconvulsant to induce SE in adult rats reproduce in the hippocampus pathological changes similar to MTS. After a latent period of a few weeks spontaneous seizures appear that herald the onset of the epileptic state

(Cavalheiro, 1982; Cronin, 1988; Hamani, 1997; Hellier, 1998; Dudek, 2002; Riban, 2002). These experimental models are an unbiased way to assess the susceptibility of the hippocampus to epileptic damage, under different experimental settings, and monitor the development of MTS and epilepsy. Most of these models show age-specific differences in the seizure threshold, semiological and pathological features.

The first experimental evidence of neuronal death induced by prolonged seizures rather than hypoxia was provided by Meldrum et al, who used ventilated and paralyzed baboons (Meldrum, 1973a; Meldrum, 1973b) or rats (Blennow, 1978). The investigators proposed that the neuronal damage associated with prolonged seizures was due to oxidative mechanisms in cells with enhanced neuronal activity and failing energy production (Blennow, 1978). The neuropathological changes ensuing following SE in adult rats resemble human MTS (Ben-Ari, 1980; Turski, 1983b; Clifford, 1987; Hopkins, 2000; Wall, 2000) (Figure 1). They consist of gliosis associated with profound loss of pyramidal CA1 and CA4 neurons, hilar dentate neurons and to a lesser degree of CA3 pyramidal neurons and dentate granule cells. Neuronal loss occurs as early as 2.5 hours following the onset of SE but manifests faster in the pilocarpine model (Tuunanen, 1999; Covolan, 2000a; Hopkins, 2000). There are individual variations in the extent of neuropathological features. Extrahippocampal structures are often affected, especially in pilocarpine-treated rats (Ben-Ari, 1980; Turski, 1984; Clifford, 1987; Du, 1993; Hopkins, 2000; Wall, 2000). In addition, the formation of collateral connections of mossy fibers with the dendritic processes of the supragranular dentate neurons is thought to contribute to the formation of aberrant excitatory connections between granule cells (Tauck, 1985; Cronin, 1988; Sutula, 1988; Sloviter, 1991, 1999; Wuarin, 2001). However, there is evidence that kainic acid induced SE may enhance dentate inhibition by reducing postsynaptic $GABA_B$ receptor function and lead thus to disinhibition and increased GABA release (Haas, 1996). Furthermore, phenotypic changes occur in both glial cells (Represa, 1993; Niquet, 1994) and neurons. These may include altered expression and function of excitatory or inhibitory neurotransmitter receptors (Schwarzer, 1997; Brooks-Kayal, 1998; Coulter, 1999) or morphological changes stemming from the birth of new neuronal progenitors (Parent, 1997; Covolan, 2000b; Sankar, 2000; Scharfman, 2000).

Proliferating neuronal progenitor cells are normally found within the subgranular layer of the dentate gyrus in adult brains (Kuhn, 1996). Seizures accelerate the birth of new granular cells (Parent, 1997; Covolan, 2000b; Sankar, 2000; Scharfman, 2000). The newborn granule cells migrate towards the hilar / CA3 border, integrate abnormally into the CA3 layer or appear ectopically in the inner molecular layer of the dentate gyrus (Parent, 1997; Scharfman, 2000), and project processes aberrantly towards both the CA3 pyramidal layer and the inner molecular layer of the dentate (Parent, 1997). The role of these newly born cells is not yet clear. It has been proposed that they may enhance the excitability of the epileptic hippocampus via creating aberrant connections with dentate granule cells (Parent, 1997). However blockade of neoneurogenesis via irradiation does not prevent mossy fiber synaptic reorganization (Parent, 1999). Furthermore, newborn neurons may contribute to the abnormal organizational pattern of the dentate gyrus, which is observed following prolonged seizures (Blumcke, 2002). Following SE, the rats may exhibit behavioral abnormalities. These include an elevation in nocturnal activity (Persinger, 1998), deficits in long-term spatial memory (Cook, 1998), working and reference memory deficits (Persinger, 1993), aggressive behavior (Desjardins, 1995), absence of maternal behavior (Peredery, 1992).

EFFECTS OF SE IN DEVELOPING RATS

The first attempts to evaluate the effects of limbic status epilepticus in developing rats were made in the '80s. Kainic acid (KA) was one of the first convulsant to be used, because of its well documented capability to induce prolonged limbic SE and extended hippocampal damage closely resembling human MTS, when administered in adult rats (Schwarcz, 1978; Pisa, 1980; Lothman, 1981a; Nadler, 1981a; Nadler, 1981b; Tanaka, 1982; Ben-Ari, 1985; Sperk, 1985; Nitecka, 1986). It was soon shown that systemic administration of kainic acid in rat pups induces a prolonged SE, the features of which are in some aspects behaviorally different from adult animals (Albala, 1984; Nitecka, 1984; Tremblay, 1984b; Holmes, 1988). Remarkably, if SE is induced prior to postnatal day 19 (PN19) there will be no MTS-like pathology, even in animals in which SE was very prolonged. Furthermore, immature rats do not develop mossy fiber sprouting, a typical chronic effect of KA-induced SE in adult rats (Sperber, 1991). It must be noted, however, that, employing detailed stereological counting, a 22% cell loss was detected in the CA3 area of PN16 rats subjected to KA-induced SE (Haas, 2001). This was however significantly smaller than the degree of cell loss (55%) observed in similarly treated adult rats (Haas, 2001). The small degree of cell loss observed in pups did not affect hippocampal paired-pulse inhibition, in the same study.

The resistance of the immature hippocampus to the effects of SE has also been shown using the pilocarpine model, which reproduces in adults hippocampal pathology similar to MTS and eventually results in epilepsy (Turski, 1986; Turski, 1989). In the study by Priel et al (Priel, 1996), PN12-PN24 rats had higher susceptibility to pilocarpine induced SE, as they required lower doses of the chemoconvulsant compared with rats older than PN25. None of the rats younger than PN18 developed hippocampal cell loss or any extra-hippocampal lesions, even if they were subjected to prolonged and intense episodes of SE. Most remarkably, even though this finding cannot be unequivocally attributed to the lack of acute pathological changes, rats subjected to SE prior to PN18 did not show spontaneous recurrent seizures, a *sine qua non* of the epileptic state (Priel, 1996).

Similar results were published by investigators who used the lithium-pilocarpine model (Clifford, 1987) and demonstrated that PN10 pups had no subsequent neuronal injury and did not develop epilepsy, whereas PN21 rats did (Dube, 2001). When however more detailed analysis of the age groups between PN10 and PN21 was attempted by Sankar and colleagues (Sankar, 1998) it became apparent that not only there was a gradual transition between the immature rats, that are highly resistant to subsequent neuronal injury and epilepsy, and the adult rats, which are highly vulnerable to the acute and long-term consequences of SE. Moreover, this transition was characterized by age-dependent regional differences in the vulnerability of hippocampal neurons to SE-induced injury. CA1 neuronal damage was maximal in the second and third week of life and declined thereafter. Hilar and CA3 neuronal loss was minimal early in life but gradually increased and in 3-week old animals the degree of neuronal loss was similar to adults. Following the 3rd week of life, damage was also visible at the amygdala and dentate gyrus. More importantly, 27% of the rats subjected to SE during the second week of life developed epilepsy, as opposed to 73% of rats that manifested SE during the 3rd and 4th weeks and 100% of those exposed to SE during adulthood.

In an elegant study, Roch and colleagues reported that certain MRI abnormalities can be used as surrogate markers to predict the development of subsequent epilepsy (Roch, 2002).

These investigators induced SE in PN21 rats, using the lithium-pilocarpine method, and performed longitudinal MRI follow up evaluations between 6h post-SE till 4 months after SE, to determine signal abnormalities in T2-weighted images and T2 relaxation time measurements. Similar to the study by Sankar et al (Sankar, 1998), 83% of these rats developed epilepsy after a latent period of 74 days. Three populations of rats were identified. Rats with no MRI abnormalities did not develop epilepsy. All the rats that showed a transient (24h - 72h post-SE) increase in T2 relaxation time, that was significant enough to appear as hyperdense signals in T2-weighted MRI images at the piriform and entorhinal cortices, developed epilepsy. An intermediate group was also identified, which had modest increases in T2 relaxation time measurements that could not be visible at the MRI images. All these rats however developed epilepsy. Interestingly, only a subpopulation of rats rendered epileptic following exposure to SE at PN21 had MTS. These findings are not only important because of their promise that MRI may be used as a tool to predict the development of epilepsy after the first prolonged seizure. They also underline the importance of extrahippocampal pathologies or functional changes that may be paramount in the establishment of the epileptic state in subjects that develop MTLE without overt MTS.

A variety of factors may contribute to the higher susceptibility to seizures but relative resistance to SE-induced damage of the naïve immature brain, which is also apparent in models of generalized epilepsy (Moshe, 1993; Sperber, 1999; Sanchez, 2001). The increased susceptibility of the immature brain to seizures may relate to enhanced excitability, due to the earlier maturation of the excitatory signaling pathways compared to the inhibitory mechanisms (Sanchez, 2001; Ben-Ari, 2002), immaturity of brain structures involved in seizure control (Veliskova, 2001), or resistance of the immature brain to metabolic stress (Vannucci, 2000; Sullivan, 2003). During the early postnatal days, the GABA-mediated inhibition is not yet fully functional, as the ionotropic $GABA_A$ receptors still mediate depolarizing responses, instead of the typical hyperpolarizing effects seen in mature neurons [reviewed in (Ben-Ari, 2002)]. Although the $GABA_A$ receptor mediated excitatory functions are crucial for neuronal differentiation and development, which are ongoing at these young ages, they create a relative deficit of inhibitory control under conditions that activate the already functionally enhanced glutamatergic excitatory signals [reviewed in (Ben-Ari, 2001; Sanchez, 2001; Ben-Ari, 2002)].

The immaturity of $GABA_A$ receptor mediated transmission in rat substantia nigra reticulata (SNR) (Galanopoulou, 2003a) may also explain the insufficient SNR-mediated seizure control in developing rats (Iadarola, 1982; Moshe, 1984; Veliskova, 2001). In addition, the NMDA-responsive seizure-suppressing function of the striatum is inactive in pups younger than 4 weeks old (Cavalheiro, 1992). The immaturity of these seizure controlling systems may result into heightened susceptibility of the immature rats to a variety of chemoconvulsant stimuli.

Developing rats, on the other hand, are more capable of coping with excitotoxic insults or metabolic stress related to seizures. Developmental changes in the expression and function of inhibitory or excitatory neurotransmitter systems may reduce the vulnerability to seizure-induced hippocampal injury early in life (Tremblay, 1988; Miller, 1990; Sperber, 1992; Brooks-Kayal, 1993; Marks, 1996; Raol, 2001). Another hypothesized mechanism explaining the resistance of the immature brain to seizures is its ability to maintain high expression of the GluR2 subunits of the AMPA (alpha-amino-3-hydroxy-5-methyl-4-isoxazole-propionic acid) receptors, even following seizures (Friedman, 1997). As a result, the permeability of AMPA receptors to calcium is reduced (Bennett, 1996) and thus neurons may survive this otherwise excitotoxic insult. Increased glycolysis is observed in both adult and immature rats during severe seizures (Sperber, 1992). In immature rats however lactate may be utilized as an alternative nutrient in the brain, especially during hypoglycemia (Vannucci, 2000), unlike adults in whom increased lactate levels may have detrimental effects. Finally, an important protective factor for developing rats undergoing SE is the high levels of the mitochondrial uncoupling protein (UCP2), attributed to the fat-rich diet of maternal milk (Sullivan, 2003). UCP2 is a mitochondrial protein that increases proton conductance across the inner mitochondrial membrane (uncoupling), reducing therefore the formation of reactive oxygen species during metabolic stress that would otherwise be harmful. As a result, increased levels of UCP2 have a neuroprotective role in seizures (Diano, 2003; Sullivan, 2003).

Long-Term Functional Consequences of SE

The idea that the naïve immature brain is relatively resistant to SE-induced pathological changes and epileptogenesis creates an obvious paradox with the epidemiological findings that support that early life prolonged seizures may predispose to the development of subsequent epilepsy and MTS. To reconcile these observations, several studies have investigated whether early life SE may have long-term functional consequences that albeit insufficient to establish epileptogenesis on their own, they may facilitate the development of epilepsy when given after, simultaneously or prior to specific independent "additional hits", that occur at specific vulnerable developmental ages. The experimental epilepsy models have been proven an important tool to study whether early life seizures or SE may cause delayed behavioral or neurocognitive abnormalities, even when no neuronal loss is apparent. Such studies have been particularly useful because retrospective epidemiological studies in epileptic patients do not allow to discern whether the frequently encountered cognitive impairment, is due to the epileptic state *per se*, rather than to the etiology of the epileptic syndrome or to the chronic antiepileptic drug therapy.

Adult rats subjected to SE typically develop learning and memory impairment (Stafstrom, 1993; Rice, 1998; Kelsey, 2000). Developing rats however show age-dependent differences in cognitive testing (Stafstrom, 1993). Adult rats exposed to KA-induced SE at PN5 or PN10 had no demonstrable deficits in visuospatial learning and memory, response to novelty or emotionality (Stafstrom, 1993). Rats that experienced SE at older ages had increasingly more cognitive and behavioral deficits compared to controls and those that had SE during adulthood were the most impaired (Stafstrom, 1993). Similar results were obtained by Koh et al (Koh, 1999). A similar trend was observed for the lithium-pilocarpine model, although the age at which SE induced long-lasting cognitive impairments was younger. Lithium-pilocarpine-induced SE in PN12 rats resulted in no detectable morphological or functional changes during adulthood (Cilio, 2003). When SE was induced at older ages (PN16, PN20), it resulted in cell loss, mossy fiber sprouting and impaired visuospatial learning and memory in adulthood (Cilio, 2003). Regardless of the age at first SE (PN12-20), adult rats with a history of SE during development had similar thresholds to flurothyl-induced myoclonic and generalized seizures compared to controls. Furthermore, adult rats that had experienced SE at PN20 were kindled faster than controls (Cilio, 2003). In contrast with these findings, Lynch et al (Lynch, 2000) reported impaired spatial learning, reduced susceptibility to kindling and enhanced paired pulse inhibition in the dentate in adulthood as a result of early life KA-induced SE (PN1 through PN14).

Delayed or long-lasting electrophysiological changes have also been reported as a result of prolonged seizures. Using paired-pulse inhibition, no significant changes were observed two weeks following KA- or flurothyl-induced SE at PN16 or in amygdala kindled immature rats (Sperber, 1999; Haas, 2001), whereas adults had enhanced dentate-mediated inhibition (Haas, 2001). A delayed effect of pentylenetetrazole induced seizures at PN18-20 on the excitability of CA3 neurons has been recently reported, in that acetylcholinergic stimulation generates interictal discharges, 40 days after the initial SE, but not 10 days post-SE (Meilleur, 2003). This effect was only transient in similarly treated adult rats.

Again these studies show an age-dependency of seizure aftermaths as well as a variability in the long-term outcome depending upon the etiology or severity of initial seizures. In addition, there is a notable dissociation between the morphological and functional consequences of prolonged seizures and epileptogenesis. These support that epileptogenesis is a multifactorial process that requires the interplay of different genetic, environmental and developmental factors that have to occur at specific vulnerable ages to allow the establishment of the epileptic state.

Conditions that Facilitate Seizure-Induced Hippocampal Changes in Immature Hippocampus

The resistance however of the immature hippocampus to seizures is not absolute. Repetitive episodes of prolonged seizures or SE in immature rats may trigger the appearance of hippocampal injury. Holmes' group evaluated the effects of recurrent seizures induced by flurothyl in neonatal rats, and reported that these induce mossy fiber sprouting in the hippocampus without evident cell loss (Holmes, 1998; Liu, 1999). There were no differences in paired pulse excitation or inhibition, or duration of afterdischarges in electrophysiological testing of intact hippocampal formations derived from these rats shortly after the period of repetitive seizures. Following maturation, however, the rats that had been exposed to these seizures had both morphological and functional abnormalities. They had greater numbers of dentate granule cells, and although no neuronal loss was noted, they had exacerbated neuronal injury in response to SE triggered by KA or perforant pathway stimulation (Schmid, 1999). Furthermore, they had decreased threshold to pentylenetetrazole seizures, impaired learning and hypoactivity (Holmes, 1998). Similarly, impaired functioning in spatial processing or auditory discrimination was found in adult rats that were exposed to repetitive flurothyl seizures between PN15-19 (Neill, 1996).

Underlying neurological abnormalities may also precipitate the seizure-induced injury in immature rats. Rats with perinatal ischemia or cortical dysplasias induced by fetal exposure to methylaxozymethanol are more prone to seizures and seizure-induced injury (Olson, 1985; Baraban, 1996; Germano, 1996). The combination of anoxia / aglycemia or hypoxia and seizures may increase the ensuing damage (Dzhala, 2000; Wirrell, 2001) as well as the long term increases in seizure susceptibility (Koh, 2001). The pyrogenic effects of infections may lead to the production of proconvulsant molecules, such as interleukin-1beta (IL-1β)(Dinarello, 1988; Vezzani, 1999), which are known to enhance the NMDA-mediated excitotoxicity (Viviani, 2003). Although febrile seizures *per se* have not been associated with increased production of IL-1β (Lahat, 1997), a high IL-1β producer allele has been linked with febrile seizures and MTLE (Kanemoto, 2000; Virta, 2002). This supports the thesis that febrile seizures do not normally lead to the development of MTLE. However, when the insult is severe or under a permissive genetic substrate, increased IL-1β production may ensue, promoting the development of epilepsy.

Conclusions

Epileptogenesis as a multifactorial process, resulting from the interplay of a permissive genetic substrate, initial precipitating event(s) occurring at a vulnerable age, and may perhaps be further sustained by the occurrence of seizures. When the initial precipitating event occurs at a vulnerable age in an individual that has a permissive genetic substrate, it will trigger functional or pathological changes, which will facilitate the manifestation of the first provoked or unprovoked seizure. Those patients, who are genetically predisposed towards epilepsy, and who experience the first seizure at a sensitive age, will further develop the characteristic structural (ie MTS) and functional changes associated with the specific epileptic syndrome (ie MTLE). The high incidence of intractable MTLE obviates the need for new therapies. The age-specific differences in the semiology, sensitivity to treatment, and function of brain structures implicated in seizure generation and control obviate the need to design age-specific antiepileptic therapies. The recent data suggesting that the available anticonvulsants may actually be harmful for the development of immature neurons (Bittigau, 2003) urges for more research aiming to elucidate the age-specific factors involved in epileptogenesis, in order to design novel and safe antiepileptic therapies. Genotyping of genes that are involved in epileptogenesis or increase the possibility that specific IPIs may trigger epilepsy needs to be implemented for the early detection of vulnerable individuals, allowing thus early intervention and prevention of epilepsy. Novel antiepileptic treatments may include vaccinations against or specific inhibitors of excitotoxic factors (Etzioni, 1991; During, 2000; Vezzani, 2000), viral gene delivery systems of proteins capable of suppressing seizures (Lin, 2003), deep brain electrical stimulation of structures involved in seizure control (Velisek, 2002; Lado, 2003). The rapid hormonal changes during development may also modify epilepsy and its consequences (Herzog, 1999). Gonadal hormones were recently shown to reduce seizure-induced hippocampal injury (Reibel, 2000; Veliskova, 2000), but this effect largely depends upon the hormonal milieu (Galanopoulou, 2003b). More studies are needed to determine whether and in what form hormonotherapy might be beneficial during development or adulthood and implemented with the least adverse effects for the development of the child or the reproductive health. Immunomodulatory agents may be proven beneficial in the selected population of children with prolonged febrile seizures, or early life meningitis, or excessive release of cytokines (Etzioni, 1991; During, 2000; Vezzani, 2000). Future treatments need not only target seizures but also the ensuing acute and long-term morphological and functional changes, as well as inhibit or reverse epileptogenesis.

ACKNOWLEDGEMENTS

This study was supported in part by grants NS-45243 (ASG) and NS-20253 (SLM) from NINDS and the Heffer Family Foundation of America. SLM is a Martin A and Emily L Fisher Fellow in Neurology and Neuroscience.

REFERENCES

Abou-Khalil B, Ge Q, Desai R, Ryther R, Bazyk A, Bailey R, Haines JL, Sutcliffe JS, & George AL, Jr. (2001). Partial and generalized epilepsy with febrile seizures plus and a novel SCN1A mutation. *Neurology, 57*(12), 2265-2272.

Adelson PD, Peacock WJ, Chugani HT, Comair YG, Vinters HV, Shields WD, & Shewmon DA. (1992). Temporal and extended temporal resections for the treatment of intractable seizures in early childhood. *Pediatr Neurosurg, 18*(4), 169-178.

Aguglia U, Gambardella A, Le Piane E, Messina D, Oliveri RL, Russo C, Zappia M, & Quattrone A. (1998). Mild non-lesional temporal lobe epilepsy. A common, unrecognized disorder with onset in adulthood. *Can J Neurol Sci, 25*(4), 282-286.

Albala BJ, Moshe SL, & Okada R. (1984). Kainic-acid-induced seizures: a developmental study. *Brain Res, 315*(1), 139-148.

Andersen P, Bliss TVP, & Skrede K. (1971). Lamellar organization of hippocampal excitatory pathways. *Exper Brain Res, 13*, 222-238.

Annegers JF, Grabow JD, Groover RV, Laws ER, Jr., Elveback LR, & Kurland LT. (1980). Seizures after head trauma: a population study. *Neurology, 30*(7 Pt 1), 683-689.

Annegers JF, Rocca WA, & Hauser WA. (1996). Causes of epilepsy: contributions of the Rochester epidemiology project. *Mayo Clin Proc, 71*(6), 570-575.

Arpino C, Domizio S, Carrieri MP, Brescianini DS, Sabatino MG, & Curatolo P. (2001). Prenatal and perinatal determinants of neonatal seizures occurring in the first week of life. *J Child Neurol, 16*(9), 651-656.

Babb TL, & Brown WJ. (1987). Pathological findings in epilepsy. In Press R (Ed.), *Surgical Treatment of the Epilepsies*. (pp. 511-540). NY: Raven Press.

Baraban SC, & Schwartzkroin PA. (1996). Flurothyl seizure susceptibility in rats following prenatal methylazoxymethanol treatment. *Epilepsy Res, 23*(3), 189-194.

Baulac S, Huberfeld G, Gourfinkel-An I, Mitropoulou G, Beranger A, Prud'homme JF, Baulac M, Brice A, Bruzzone R, & LeGuern E. (2001a). First genetic evidence of GABA(A) receptor dysfunction in epilepsy: a mutation in the gamma2-subunit gene. *Nat Genet, 28*(1), 46-48.

Baulac S, Picard F, Herman A, Feingold J, Genin E, Hirsch E, Prud'homme JF, Baulac M, Brice A, & LeGuern E. (2001b). Evidence for digenic inheritance in a family with both febrile convulsions and temporal lobe epilepsy implicating chromosomes 18qter and 1q25-q31. *Ann Neurol, 49*(6), 786-792.

Ben-Ari Y. (1985). Limbic seizure and brain damage produced by kainic acid: mechanisms and relevance to human temporal lobe epilepsy. *Neuroscience, 14*(2), 375-403.

Ben-Ari Y. (2001). Developing networks play a similar melody. *Trends Neurosci, 24*(6), 353-360.

Ben-Ari Y. (2002). Excitatory actions of gaba during development: the nature of the nurture. *Nat Rev Neurosci, 3*(9), 728-739.

Ben-Ari Y, Tremblay E, Ottersen OP, & Meldrum BS. (1980). The role of epileptic activity in hippocampal and "remote" cerebral lesions induced by kainic acid. *Brain Res, 191*(1), 79-97.

Benbadis SR, So NK, Antar MA, Barnett GH, & Morris HH. (1995). The value of PET scan (and MRI and Wada test) in patients with bitemporal epileptiform abnormalities. *Arch Neurol, 52*(11), 1062-1068.

Benbadis SR, Wallace J, & Reed Murtagh F. (2002). MRI evidence of mesial temporal sclerosis in subjects without seizures. *Seizure, 11*(5), 340-343.

Bennett MV, Pellegrini-Giampietro DE, Gorter JA, Aronica E, Connor JA, & Zukin RS. (1996). The GluR2 hypothesis: Ca(++)-permeable AMPA receptors in delayed neurodegeneration. *Cold Spring Harb Symp Quant Biol, 61*, 373-384.

Berg AT, Langfitt J, Shinnar S, Vickrey BG, Sperling MR, Walczak T, Bazil C, Pacia SV, & Spencer SS. (2003). How long does it take for partial epilepsy to become intractable? *Neurology, 60*(2), 186-190.

Berg AT, Levy SR, Novotny EJ, & Shinnar S. (1996). Predictors of intractable epilepsy in childhood: a case-control study. *Epilepsia, 37*(1), 24-30.

Berg AT, & Shinnar S. (1997). Do seizures beget seizures? An assessment of the clinical evidence in humans. *J Clin Neurophysiol, 14*(2), 102-110.

Berg AT, Shinnar S, Levy SR, & Testa FM. (1999). Childhood-onset epilepsy with and without preceding febrile seizures. *Neurology, 53*(8), 1742-1748.

Berg AT, Testa FM, Levy SR, & Shinnar S. (2000). Neuroimaging in children with newly diagnosed epilepsy: A community- based study. *Pediatrics, 106*(3), 527-532.

Bergamasco B, Benna P, Ferrero P, & Gavinelli R. (1984). Neonatal hypoxia and epileptic risk: a clinical prospective study. *Epilepsia, 25*(2), 131-136.

Berkovic SF, Andermann F, Olivier A, Ethier R, Melanson D, Robitaille Y, Kuzniecky R, Peters T, & Feindel W. (1991). Hippocampal sclerosis in temporal lobe epilepsy demonstrated by magnetic resonance imaging. *Ann Neurol, 29*(2), 175-182.

Berkovic SF, McIntosh A, Howell RA, Mitchell A, Sheffield LJ, & Hopper JL. (1996a). Familial temporal lobe epilepsy: a common disorder identified in twins. *Ann Neurol, 40*(2), 227-235.

Berkovic SF, McIntosh AM, Kalnins RM, Jackson GD, Fabinyi GC, Brazenor GA, Bladin PF, & Hopper JL. (1995). Preoperative MRI predicts outcome of temporal lobectomy: an actuarial analysis. *Neurology, 45*(7), 1358-1363.

Bernasconi A, Tasch E, Cendes F, Li LM, & Arnold DL. (2002). Proton magnetic resonance spectroscopic imaging suggests progressive neuronal damage in human temporal lobe epilepsy. *Prog Brain Res, 135*, 297-304.

Bittigau P, Sifringer M, & Ikonomidou C. (2003). Antiepileptic drugs and apoptosis in the developing brain. *Ann N Y Acad Sci, 993*, 103-114; discussion 123-104.

Blennow G, Brierley JB, Meldrum BS, & Siesjo BK. (1978). Epileptic brain damage: the role of systemic factors that modify cerebral energy metabolism. *Brain, 101*(4), 687-700.

Blumcke I, Thom M, & Wiestler OD. (2002). Ammon's horn sclerosis: a maldevelopmental disorder associated with temporal lobe epilepsy. *Brain Pathol, 12*(2), 199-211.

Blumcke I, Zuschratter W, Schewe JC, Suter B, Lie AA, Riederer BM, Meyer B, Schramm J, Elger CE, & Wiestler OD. (1999). Cellular pathology of hilar neurons in Ammon's horn sclerosis. *J Comp Neurol, 414*(4), 437-453.

Bocti C, Robitaille Y, Diadori P, Lortie A, Mercier C, Bouthillier A, & Carmant L. (2003). The pathological basis of temporal lobe epilepsy in childhood. *Neurology, 60*(2), 191-195.

Bourgeois BF. (1998). Temporal lobe epilepsy in infants and children. *Brain Dev, 20*(3), 135-141.

Bower SP, Kilpatrick CJ, Vogrin SJ, Morris K, & Cook MJ. (2000). Degree of hippocampal atrophy is not related to a history of febrile seizures in patients with proved hippocampal sclerosis. *J Neurol Neurosurg Psychiatry, 69*(6), 733-738.

Bratz E. (1899). Ammonshornbefunde bei epileptikern. *Arch Psychiatr Nervenkr, 32*, 820-835.

Briellmann RS, Berkovic SF, & Jackson GD. (2000a). Men may be more vulnerable to seizure-associated brain damage. *Neurology, 55*(10), 1479-1485.

Briellmann RS, Berkovic SF, Syngeniotis A, King MA, & Jackson GD. (2002a). Seizure-associated hippocampal volume loss: a longitudinal magnetic resonance study of temporal lobe epilepsy. *Ann Neurol, 51*(5), 641-644.

Briellmann RS, Kalnins RM, Berkovic SF, & Jackson GD. (2002b). Hippocampal pathology in refractory temporal lobe epilepsy: T2-weighted signal change reflects dentate gliosis. *Neurology, 58*(2), 265-271.

Briellmann RS, Torn-Broers Y, Busuttil BE, Major BJ, Kalnins RM, Olsen M, Jackson GD, Frauman AG, & Berkovic SF. (2000b). APOE epsilon4 genotype is associated with an earlier onset of chronic temporal lobe epilepsy. *Neurology, 55*(3), 435-437.

Briellmann RS, Torn-Broers Y, Jackson GD, & Berkovic SF. (2001). Seizures in family members of patients with hippocampal sclerosis. *Neurology, 57*(10), 1800-1804.

Brockhaus A, & Elger CE. (1995). Complex partial seizures of temporal lobe origin in children of different age groups. *Epilepsia, 36*(12), 1173-1181.

Brooks-Kayal AR, & Pritchett DB. (1993). Developmental changes in human gamma-aminobutyric acidA receptor subunit composition. *Ann Neurol, 34*(5), 687-693.

Brooks-Kayal AR, Shumate MD, Jin H, Rikhter TY, & Coulter DA. (1998). Selective changes in single cell GABA(A) receptor subunit expression and function in temporal lobe epilepsy. *Nat Med, 4*(10), 1166-1172.

Buono RJ, Ferraro TN, O'Connor MJ, Sperling MR, Ryan SG, Scattergood T, Mulholland N, Gilmore J, Lohoff FW, & Berrettini WH. (2001). Lack of association between an interleukin 1 beta (IL-1beta) gene variation and refractory temporal lobe epilepsy. *Epilepsia, 42*(6), 782-784.

Burnham WM. (1975). Primary and "transfer" seizure development in the kindled rat. *Can J Neurol Sci, 2*(4), 417-428.

Cascino GD, Jack CR, Jr., Parisi JE, Sharbrough FW, Hirschorn KA, Meyer FB, Marsh WR, & O'Brien PC. (1991). Magnetic resonance imaging-based volume studies in temporal lobe epilepsy: pathological correlations. *Ann Neurol, 30*(1), 31-36.

Cavalheiro EA, de Feo MR, Mecarelli O, & Ricci G. (1992). Age-related anticonvulsant activity of NMDA in the rat caudate-putamen. *Brain Res Dev Brain Res, 67*(2), 371-374.

Cavalheiro EA, Riche DA, & Le Gal La Salle G. (1982). Long-term effects of intrahippocampal kainic acid injection in rats: a method for inducing spontaneous recurrent seizures. *Electroencephalogr Clin Neurophysiol, 53*(6), 581-589.

Cavalheiro EA, Silva DF, Turski WA, Calderazzo-Filho LS, Bortolotto ZA, & Turski L. (1987). The susceptibility of rats to pilocarpine-induced seizures is age- dependent. *Brain Res, 465*(1-2), 43-58.

Cendes F, Andermann F, Gloor P, Lopes-Cendes I, Andermann E, Melanson D, Jones-Gotman M, Robitaille Y, Evans A, & Peters T. (1993a). Atrophy of mesial structures in patients with temporal lobe epilepsy: cause or consequence of repeated seizures? *Ann Neurol, 34*(6), 795-801.

Cendes F, Andermann F, Gloor P, Lopes-Cendes I, Andermann E, Melanson D, Jones-Gotman M, Robitaille Y, Evans A, & Peters T. (1993b). Atrophy of mesial structures in patients with temporal lobe epilepsy: cause or consequence of repeated seizures? *Ann Neurol, 34*(6), 795-801.

Cendes F, Caramanos Z, Andermann F, Dubeau F, & Arnold DL. (1997). Proton magnetic resonance spectroscopic imaging and magnetic resonance imaging volumetry in the lateralization of temporal lobe epilepsy: a series of 100 patients. *Ann Neurol, 42*(5), 737-746.

Cendes F, Cook MJ, Watson C, Andermann F, Fish DR, Shorvon SD, Bergin P, Free S, Dubeau F, & Arnold DL. (1995). Frequency and characteristics of dual pathology in patients with lesional epilepsy. *Neurology, 45*(11), 2058-2064.

Cendes F, Lopes-Cendes I, Andermann E, & Andermann F. (1998). Familial temporal lobe epilepsy: a clinically heterogeneous syndrome. *Neurology, 50*(2), 554-557.

Cilio MR, Sogawa Y, Cha BH, Liu X, Huang LT, & Holmes GL. (2003). Long-term effects of status epilepticus in the immature brain are specific for age and model. *Epilepsia, 44*(4), 518-528.

Clifford DB, Olney JW, Maniotis A, Collins RC, & Zorumski CF. (1987). The functional anatomy and pathology of lithium-pilocarpine and high- dose pilocarpine seizures. *Neuroscience, 23*(3), 953-968.

Connell J, Oozeer R, de Vries L, Dubowitz LM, & Dubowitz V. (1989). Clinical and EEG response to anticonvulsants in neonatal seizures. *Arch Dis Child, 64*(4), 459-464.

Cook LL, & Persinger MA. (1998). "Subclinical" dosages of lithium and pilocarpine that do not evoke overt seizures affect long-term spatial memory but not learning in rats. *Percept Mot Skills, 86*(3 Pt 2), 1288-1290.

Coulter DA. (1999). Chronic epileptogenic cellular alterations in the limbic system after status epilepticus. *Epilepsia, 40*(Suppl 1), S23-33; discussion S40-21.

Covolan L, & Mello LE. (2000a). Temporal profile of neuronal injury following pilocarpine or kainic acid-induced status epilepticus. *Epilepsy Res, 39*(2), 133-152.

Covolan L, Ribeiro LT, Longo BM, & Mello LE. (2000b). Cell damage and neurogenesis in the dentate granule cell layer of adult rats after pilocarpine- or kainate-induced status epilepticus. *Hippocampus, 10*(2), 169-180.

Cronin J, & Dudek FE. (1988). Chronic seizures and collateral sprouting of dentate mossy fibers after kainic acid treatment in rats. *Brain Res, 474*(1), 181-184.

Davies KG, Hermann BP, Dohan FC, Jr., Foley KT, Bush AJ, & Wyler AR. (1996a). Relationship of hippocampal sclerosis to duration and age of onset of epilepsy, and childhood febrile seizures in temporal lobectomy patients. *Epilepsy Res, 24*(2), 119-126.

Davies KG, Hermann BP, Dohan FC, Jr., & Wyler AR. (1996b). Intractable epilepsy due to meningitis: results of surgery and pathological findings. *Br J Neurosurg, 10*(6), 567-570.

Depondt C, Van Paesschen W, Matthijs G, Legius E, Martens K, Demaerel P, & Wilms G. (2002). Familial temporal lobe epilepsy with febrile seizures. *Neurology, 58*(9), 1429-1433.

Desjardins D, & Persinger MA. (1995). Association between intermale social aggression and cellular density within the central amygdaloid nucleus in rats with lithium/pilocarpine-induced seizures. *Percept Mot Skills, 81*(2), 635-641.

Diano S, Matthews RT, Patrylo P, Yang L, Beal MF, Barnstable CJ, & Horvath TL. (2003). Uncoupling protein 2 prevents neuronal death including that occurring during seizures: a mechanism for preconditioning. *Endocrinology, 144*(11), 5014-5021.

Diaz-Arrastia R, Agostini MA, Frol AB, Mickey B, Fleckenstein J, Bigio E, & Van Ness PC. (2000). Neurophysiologic and neuroradiologic features of intractable epilepsy after traumatic brain injury in adults. *Arch Neurol, 57*(11), 1611-1616.

Dinarello CA, Cannon JG, & Wolff SM. (1988). New concepts on the pathogenesis of fever. *Rev Infect Dis, 10*(1), 168-189.

Du F, Williamson J, Bertram E, Lothman E, Okuno E, & Schwarcz R. (1993). Kynurenine pathway enzymes in a rat model of chronic epilepsy: immunohistochemical study of activated glial cells. *Neuroscience, 55*(4), 975-989.

Dube C, da Silva Fernandes MJ, & Nehlig A. (2001). Age-dependent consequences of seizures and the development of temporal lobe epilepsy in the rat. *Dev Neurosci, 23*(3), 219-223.

Duc CO, Trabesinger AH, Weber OM, Meier D, Walder M, Wieser HG, & Boesiger P. (1998). Quantitative 1H MRS in the evaluation of mesial temporal lobe epilepsy in vivo. *Magn Reson Imaging, 16*(8), 969-979.

Duchowny M, Levin B, Jayakar P, Resnick T, Alvarez L, Morrison G, & Dean P. (1992). Temporal lobectomy in early childhood. *Epilepsia, 33*(2), 298-303.

Dudek FE, Hellier JL, Williams PA, Ferraro DJ, & Staley KJ. (2002). The course of cellular alterations associated with the development of spontaneous seizures after status epilepticus. *Prog Brain Res, 135*, 53-65.

During MJ, Symes CW, Lawlor PA, Lin J, Dunning J, Fitzsimons HL, Poulsen D, Leone P, Xu R, Dicker BL, Lipski J, & Young D. (2000). An oral vaccine against NMDAR1 with efficacy in experimental stroke and epilepsy. *Science, 287*(5457), 1453-1460.

Dzhala V, Ben-Ari Y, & Khazipov R. (2000). Seizures accelerate anoxia-induced neuronal death in the neonatal rat hippocampus. *Ann Neurol, 48*(4), 632-640.

Engel J, Jr. (1996). Introduction to temporal lobe epilepsy. *Epilepsy Res, 26*(1), 141-150.

Engel J, Jr., Wiebe S, French J, Sperling M, Williamson P, Spencer D, Gumnit R, Zahn C, Westbrook E, & Enos B. (2003). Practice parameter: Temporal lobe and localized neocortical resections for epilepsy: Report of the Quality Standards Subcommittee of the American Academy of Neurology, in Association with the American Epilepsy Society and the American Association of Neurological Surgeons. *Neurology, 60*(4), 538-547.

Etzioni A, Jaffe M, Pollack S, Zelnik N, Benderly A, & Tal Y. (1991). High dose intravenous gamma-globulin in intractable epilepsy of childhood. *Eur J Pediatr, 150*(9), 681-683.

Falconer MA, Serafetinides EA, & Corsellis JAN. (1964). Etiology and pathogenesis of temporal lobe epilepsy. *Arch Neurol, 10*, 233-248.

Fogarasi A, Jokeit H, Faveret E, Janszky J, & Tuxhorn I. (2002). The effect of age on seizure semiology in childhood temporal lobe epilepsy. *Epilepsia, 43*(6), 638-643.

Foldvary N, Lee N, Thwaites G, Mascha E, Hammel J, Kim H, Friedman AH, & Radtke RA. (1997). Clinical and electrographic manifestations of lesional neocortical temporal lobe epilepsy. *Neurology, 49*(3), 757-763.

French JA, Williamson PD, Thadani VM, Darcey TM, Mattson RH, Spencer SS, & Spencer DD. (1993). Characteristics of medial temporal lobe epilepsy: I. Results of history and physical examination. *Ann Neurol, 34*(6), 774-780.

Friedman LK, Sperber EF, Moshe SL, Bennett MV, & Zukin RS. (1997). Developmental regulation of glutamate and GABA(A) receptor gene expression in rat hippocampus following kainate-induced status epilepticus. *Dev Neurosci, 19*(6), 529-542.

Fuerst D, Shah J, Kupsky WJ, Johnson R, Shah A, Hayman-Abello B, Ergh T, Poore Q, Canady A, & Watson C. (2001). Volumetric MRI, pathological, and neuropsychological progression in hippocampal sclerosis. *Neurology, 57*(2), 184-188.

Fuerst D, Shah J, Shah A, & Watson C. (2003). Hippocampal sclerosis is a progressive disorder: a longitudinal volumetric MRI study. *Ann Neurol, 53*(3), 413-416.

Galanopoulou AS, Kyrozis A, Claudio OI, Stanton PK, & Moshé SL. (2003a). Sex-specific KCC2 expression and GABAA receptor function in rat substantia nigra. *Exp Neurol, 183*(2), 628-637.

Galanopoulou AS, Alm EM, Veliskova J. (2003b). Estradiol reduces seizure-induced hippocampal injury in ovariectomized female but not in male rats. *Neurosci Lett, 342*(3), 201-205.

Gambardella A, Manna I, Labate A, Chifari R, La Russa A, Serra P, Cittadella R, Bonavita S, Andreoli V, LePiane E, Sasanelli F, Di Costanzo A, Zappia M, Tedeschi G, Aguglia U, & Quattrone A. (2003). GABA(B) receptor 1 polymorphism (G1465A) is associated with temporal lobe epilepsy. *Neurology, 60*(4), 560-563.

Gambardella A, Messina D, Le Piane E, Oliveri RL, Annesi G, Zappia M, Andermann E, Quattrone A, & Aguglia U. (2000). Familial temporal lobe epilepsy autosomal dominant inheritance in a large pedigree from southern Italy. *Epilepsy Res, 38*(2-3), 127-132.

Garcia PA, Laxer KD, Barbaro NM, & Dillon WP. (1994). Prognostic value of qualitative magnetic resonance imaging hippocampal abnormalities in patients undergoing temporal lobectomy for medically refractory seizures. *Epilepsia, 35*(3), 520-524.

Germano IM, Zhang YF, Sperber EF, & Moshe SL. (1996). Neuronal migration disorders increase susceptibility to hyperthermia- induced seizures in developing rats. *Epilepsia, 37*(9), 902-910.

Gloor P. (1997). Chapter 5: The Hippocampal System. In Gloor P (Ed.), *The Temporal Lobe and Limbic System* (pp. 325-590). New York: Oxford University Press.

Grattan-Smith JD, Harvey AS, Desmond PM, & Chow CW. (1993). Hippocampal sclerosis in children with intractable temporal lobe epilepsy: detection with MR imaging. *AJR Am J Roentgenol, 161*(5), 1045-1048.

Green C, & Buchhalter JR. (1993). Ictal SPECT in a 16-day-old infant. *Clin Nucl Med, 18*(9), 768-770.

Haas KZ, Sperber EF, Moshe SL, & Stanton PK. (1996). Kainic acid-induced seizures enhance dentate gyrus inhibition by downregulation of GABA(B) receptors. *J Neurosci, 16*(13), 4250-4260.

Haas KZ, Sperber EF, Opanashuk LA, Stanton PK, & Moshe SL. (2001). Resistance of immature hippocampus to morphologic and physiologic alterations following status epilepticus or kindling. *Hippocampus, 11*(6), 615-625.

Hamani C, & Mello LE. (1997). Status epilepticus induced by pilocarpine and picrotoxin. *Epilepsy Res, 28*(1), 73-82.

Harvey AS, Berkovic SF, Wrennall JA, & Hopkins IJ. (1997). Temporal lobe epilepsy in childhood: clinical, EEG, and neuroimaging findings and syndrome classification in a cohort with new-onset seizures. *Neurology, 49*(4), 960-968.

Harvey AS, Grattan-Smith JD, Desmond PM, Chow CW, & Berkovic SF. (1995). Febrile seizures and hippocampal sclerosis: frequent and related findings in intractable temporal lobe epilepsy of childhood. *Pediatr Neurol, 12*(3), 201-206.

Hellier JL, Patrylo PR, Buckmaster PS, & Dudek FE. (1998). Recurrent spontaneous motor seizures after repeated low-dose systemic treatment with kainate: assessment of a rat model of temporal lobe epilepsy. *Epilepsy Res, 31*(1), 73-84.

Herzog AG. (1999). Psychoneuroendocrine aspects of temporolimbic epilepsy. Part II: Epilepsy and reproductive steroids. *Psychosomatics, 40*(2), 102-108.

Ho SS, Kuzniecky RI, Gilliam F, Faught E, & Morawetz R. (1998). Temporal lobe developmental malformations and epilepsy: dual pathology and bilateral hippocampal abnormalities. *Neurology, 50*(3), 748-754.

Ho SS, Newton MR, McIntosh AM, Kalnins RM, Fabinyi GC, Brazenor GA, McKay WJ, Bladin PF, & Berkovic SF. (1997). Perfusion patterns during temporal lobe seizures: relationship to surgical outcome. *Brain, 120 (Pt 11)*, 1921-1928.

Holden KR, Mellits ED, & Freeman JM. (1982). Neonatal seizures. I. Correlation of prenatal and perinatal events with outcomes. *Pediatrics, 70*(2), 165-176.

Holmes GL, Gairsa JL, Chevassus-Au-Louis N, & Ben-Ari Y. (1998). Consequences of neonatal seizures in the rat: morphological and behavioral effects. *Ann Neurol, 44*(6), 845-857.

Holmes GL, Thompson JL, Marchi T, & Feldman DS. (1988). Behavioral effects of kainic acid administration on the immature brain. *Epilepsia, 29*(6), 721-730.

Holmes MD, Born DE, Kutsy RL, Wilensky AJ, Ojemann GA, & Ojemann LM. (2000). Outcome after surgery in patients with refractory temporal lobe epilepsy and normal MRI. *Seizure, 9*(6), 407-411.

Honchar MP, Olney JW, & Sherman WR. (1983). Systemic cholinergic agents induce seizures and brain damage in lithium- treated rats. *Science, 220*(4594), 323-325.

Hopkins KJ, Wang G, & Schmued LC. (2000). Temporal progression of kainic acid induced neuronal and myelin degeneration in the rat forebrain. *Brain Res, 864*(1), 69-80.

Hosford DA, & McNamara JO. (1988). Microinjection of muscimol into entopeduncular nucleus suppresses pilocarpine but not maximal electroshock seizures in rats. *Brain Res, 462*(2), 205-210.

Iadarola MJ, & Gale K. (1982). Substantia nigra: site of anticonvulsant activity mediated by gamma- aminobutyric acid. *Science, 218*(4578), 1237-1240.

Ikeda A, Kunieda T, Miyamoto S, Fukuyama H, & Shibasaki H. (2000). Autosomal dominant temporal lobe epilepsy in a Japanese family. *J Neurol Sci, 176*(2), 162-165.

Jackson GD, Kuzniecky RI, & Cascino GD. (1994). Hippocampal sclerosis without detectable hippocampal atrophy. *Neurology, 44*(1), 42-46.

Jefferys JG. (1989). Chronic epileptic foci in vitro in hippocampal slices from rats with the tetanus toxin epileptic syndrome. *J Neurophysiol, 62*(2), 458-468.

Jope RS, & Morrisett RA. (1986). Neurochemical consequences of status epilepticus induced in rats by coadministration of lithium and pilocarpine. *Exp Neurol, 93*(2), 404-414.

Kalviainen R, & Salmenpera T. (2002). Do recurrent seizures cause neuronal damage? A series of studies with MRI volumetry in adults with partial epilepsy. *Prog Brain Res, 135*, 279-295.

Kalviainen R, Salmenpera T, Partanen K, Vainio P, Riekkinen P, & Pitkanen A. (1998). Recurrent seizures may cause hippocampal damage in temporal lobe epilepsy. *Neurology, 50*(5), 1377-1382.

Kanemoto K, Kawasaki J, Miyamoto T, Obayashi H, & Nishimura M. (2000). Interleukin (IL)1beta, IL-1alpha, and IL-1 receptor antagonist gene polymorphisms in patients with temporal lobe epilepsy. *Ann Neurol, 47*(5), 571-574.

Kanos CC, Davies KG, O'Brien T, & Dohan FC, Jr. (2000). Hippocampal sclerosis in a two-year-old with temporal lobe epilepsy: case report with pathological confirmation. *Pediatr Neurosurg, 32*(6), 316-320.

Keller SS, Wieshmann UC, Mackay CE, Denby CE, Webb J, & Roberts N. (2002). Voxel based morphometry of grey matter abnormalities in patients with medically intractable temporal lobe epilepsy: effects of side of seizure onset and epilepsy duration. *J Neurol Neurosurg Psychiatry, 73*(6), 648-655.

Kelsey JE, Sanderson KL, & Frye CA. (2000). Perforant path stimulation in rats produces seizures, loss of hippocampal neurons, and a deficit in spatial mapping which are reduced by prior MK-801. *Behav Brain Res, 107*(1-2), 59-69.

Kikuchi S, Kubota F, Hattori S, Oya N, & Mikuni M. (2001). A study of the relationship between metabolism using 1H-MRS and function using several neuropsychological tests in temporal lobe epilepsy. *Seizure, 10*(3), 188-193.

Kim R, & Spencer D. (2001). Surgery for mesial temporal lobe sclerosis. In Luders HO & Comair YG (Eds.), (Second ed., pp. 643- 652). Philadelphia, PA: Lippincott, Williams & Wilkins.

Kim WJ, Park SC, Lee SJ, Lee JH, Kim JY, Lee BI, & Kim DI. (1999). The prognosis for control of seizures with medications in patients with MRI evidence for mesial temporal sclerosis. *Epilepsia, 40*(3), 290-293.

Kobayashi E, D'Agostino MD, Lopes-Cendes I, Berkovic SF, Li ML, Andermann E, Andermann F, & Cendes F. (2003). Hippocampal atrophy and T2-weighted signal changes in familial mesial temporal lobe epilepsy. *Neurology, 60*(3), 405-409.

Kobayashi E, Li LM, Lopes-Cendes I, & Cendes F. (2002). Magnetic resonance imaging evidence of hippocampal sclerosis in asymptomatic, first-degree relatives of patients with familial mesial temporal lobe epilepsy. *Arch Neurol, 59*(12), 1891-1894.

Kobayashi E, Lopes-Cendes I, Guerreiro CA, Sousa SC, Guerreiro MM, & Cendes F. (2001). Seizure outcome and hippocampal atrophy in familial mesial temporal lobe epilepsy. *Neurology, 56*(2), 166-172.

Koc E, Serdaroglu A, Kapucu O, Atalay Y, Gucuyener K, & Atasever T. (1997). Ictal and interictal SPECT in a newborn infant with intractable seizure. *Acta Paediatr, 86*(12), 1379-1381.

Kodama K, Murakami A, Yamanouchi N, Koseki K, Iwasa H, Okada S, Sakamoto T, Noda S, Komatsu N, & Sato T. (1995). MR in temporal lobe epilepsy: early childhood onset versus later onset. *AJNR Am J Neuroradiol, 16*(3), 523-529.

Koh S, & Jensen FE. (2001). Topiramate blocks perinatal hypoxia-induced seizures in rat pups. *Ann Neurol, 50*(3), 366-372.

Koh S, Storey TW, Santos TC, Mian AY, & Cole AJ. (1999). Early-life seizures in rats increase susceptibility to seizure-induced brain injury in adulthood. *Neurology, 53*(5), 915-921.

Kotagal P. (2001). Neocortical temporal lobe epilepsy. In Luders HO & Comair YG (Eds.), *Epilepsy surgery* (Second ed., pp. 105-109). Philadelphia, PA: Lippincott, Williams & Wilkins.

Kuhn HG, Dickinson-Anson H, & Gage FH. (1996). Neurogenesis in the dentate gyrus of the adult rat: age-related decrease of neuronal progenitor proliferation. *J Neurosci, 16*(6), 2027-2033.

Kuks JB, Cook MJ, Fish DR, Stevens JM, & Shorvon SD. (1993). Hippocampal sclerosis in epilepsy and childhood febrile seizures. *Lancet, 342*(8884), 1391-1394.

Kuzniecky R, de la Sayette V, Ethier R, Melanson D, Andermann F, Berkovic S, Robitaille Y, Olivier A, Peters T, & Feindel W. (1987). Magnetic resonance imaging in temporal lobe epilepsy: pathological correlations. *Ann Neurol, 22*(3), 341-347.

Kuzniecky R, Murro A, King D, Morawetz R, Smith J, Powers R, Yaghmai F, Faught E, Gallagher B, & Snead OC. (1993). Magnetic resonance imaging in childhood intractable partial epilepsies: pathologic correlations. *Neurology, 43*(4), 681-687.

Lado FA, Velisek L, & Moshe SL. (2003). The effect of electrical stimulation of the subthalamic nucleus on seizures is frequency dependent. *Epilepsia, 44*(2), 157-164.

Lahat E, Livne M, Barr J, & Katz Y. (1997). Interleukin-1beta levels in serum and cerebrospinal fluid of children with febrile seizures. *Pediatr Neurol, 17*(1), 34-36.

Lancman ME, & Morris HH, 3rd. (1996). Epilepsy after central nervous system infection: clinical characteristics and outcome after epilepsy surgery. *Epilepsy Res, 25*(3), 285-290.

Lee CL, Hrachovy RA, Smith KL, Frost JD, Jr., & Swann JW. (1995). Tetanus toxin-induced seizures in infant rats and their effects on hippocampal excitability in adulthood. *Brain Res, 677*(1), 97-109.

Lee JH, Lee BI, Park SC, Kim WJ, Kim JY, Park SA, & Huh K. (1997). Experiences of epilepsy surgery in intractable seizures with past history of CNS infection. *Yonsei Med J, 38*(2), 73-78.

Lewis DV, Barboriak DP, MacFall JR, Provenzale JM, Mitchell TV, & VanLandingham KE. (2002). Do prolonged febrile seizures produce medial temporal sclerosis? Hypotheses, MRI evidence and unanswered questions. *Prog Brain Res, 135*, 263-278.

Li LM, Dubeau F, Andermann F, & Arnold DL. (2000). Proton magnetic resonance spectroscopic imaging studies in patients with newly diagnosed partial epilepsy. *Epilepsia, 41*(7), 825-831.

Lin EJ, Richichi C, Young D, Baer K, Vezzani A, & During MJ. (2003). Recombinant AAV-mediated expression of galanin in rat hippocampus suppresses seizure development. *Eur J Neurosci, 18*(7), 2087-2092.

Liu Z, Yang Y, Silveira DC, Sarkisian MR, Tandon P, Huang LT, Stafstrom CE, & Holmes GL. (1999). Consequences of recurrent seizures during early brain development. *Neuroscience, 92*(4), 1443-1454.

Lopes da Silva FH, Wadman WJ, Leung LS, & Van Hulten K. (1982). Common aspects of the development of a kindling epileptogenic focus in the prepyriform cortex of the dog and in the hippocampus of the rat: spontaneous interictal transients with changing polarities. *Electroencephalogr Clin Neurophysiol Suppl, 36*, 274-287.

Lothman EW, & Collins RC. (1981a). Kainic acid induced limbic seizures: metabolic, behavioral, electroencephalographic and neuropathological correlates. *Brain Res, 218*(1-2), 299-318.

Lothman EW, Collins RC, & Ferrendelli JA. (1981b). Kainic acid-induced limbic seizures: electrophysiologic studies. *Neurology, 31*(7), 806-812.

Lynch M, Sayin U, Bownds J, Janumpalli S, & Sutula T. (2000). Long-term consequences of early postnatal seizures on hippocampal learning and plasticity. *Eur J Neurosci, 12*(7), 2252-2264.

Margerison JH, & Corsellis JA. (1966). Epilepsy and the temporal lobes. A clinical, electroencephalographic and neuropathological study of the brain in epilepsy, with particular reference to the temporal lobes. *Brain, 89*(3), 499-530.

Marks DA, Kim J, Spencer DD, & Spencer SS. (1992). Characteristics of intractable seizures following meningitis and encephalitis. *Neurology, 42*(8), 1513-1518.

Marks JD, Friedman JE, & Haddad GG. (1996). Vulnerability of CA1 neurons to glutamate is developmentally regulated. *Brain Res Dev Brain Res, 97*(2), 194-206.

Mathern GW, Adelson PD, Cahan LD, & Leite JP. (2002). Hippocampal neuron damage in human epilepsy: Meyer's hypothesis revisited. *Prog Brain Res, 135*, 237-251.

Mathern GW, Babb TL, & Armstrong DL. (1997). Hippocampal sclerosis. In Engel JJ & Pedley TA (Eds.), *Epilepsy: A Comprehensive Textbook.* (pp. 133-155). Philadelphia: Lippincott-Raven.

Mathern GW, Babb TL, Pretorius JK, Melendez M, & Levesque MF. (1995a). The pathophysiologic relationships between lesion pathology, intracranial ictal EEG onsets, and hippocampal neuron losses in temporal lobe epilepsy. *Epilepsy Res, 21*(2), 133-147.

Mathern GW, Babb TL, Vickrey BG, Melendez M, & Pretorius JK. (1995b). The clinical-pathogenic mechanisms of hippocampal neuron loss and surgical outcomes in temporal lobe epilepsy. *Brain, 118*(Pt 1), 105-118.

Mathern GW, Pretorius JK, & Babb TL. (1995c). Influence of the type of initial precipitating injury and at what age it occurs on course and outcome in patients with temporal lobe seizures. *J Neurosurg, 82*(2), 220-227.

McCaughran JA, Jr., Corcoran ME, & Wada JA. (1977). Facilitation of secondary-site amygdaloid kindling following bisection of the corpus callosum and hippocampal commissure in rats. *Exp Neurol, 57*(1), 132-141.

McIntyre DC, Nathanson D, & Edson N. (1982). A new model of partial status epilepticus based on kindling. *Brain Res, 250*(1), 53-63.

McNamara JO, Byrne MC, Dasheiff RM, & Fitz JG. (1980a). The kindling model of epilepsy: a review. *Prog Neurobiol, 15*(2), 139-159.

McNamara JO, Peper AM, & Patrone V. (1980b). Repeated seizures induce long-term increase in hippocampal benzodiazepine receptors. *Proc Natl Acad Sci U S A, 77*(5), 3029-3032.

Meilleur S, Aznavour N, Descarries L, Carmant L, Mamer OA, & Psarropoulou C. (2003). Pentylenetetrazol-induced seizures in immature rats provoke long-term changes in adult hippocampal cholinergic excitability. *Epilepsia, 44*(4), 507-517.

Meldrum BS, & Brierley JB. (1973a). Prolonged epileptic seizures in primates. Ischemic cell change and its relation to ictal physiological events. *Arch Neurol, 28*(1), 10-17.

Meldrum BS, Vigouroux RA, & Brierley JB. (1973b). Systemic factors and epileptic brain damage. Prolonged seizures in paralyzed, artificially ventilated baboons. *Arch Neurol, 29*(2), 82-87.

Mellanby J, George G, Robinson A, & Thompson P. (1977). Epileptiform syndrome in rats produced by injecting tetanus toxin into the hippocampus. *J Neurol Neurosurg Psychiatry, 40*(4), 404-414.

Millan MH, Patel S, Mello LM, & Meldrum BS. (1986). Focal injection of 2-amino-7-phosphonoheptanoic acid into prepiriform cortex protects against pilocarpine-induced limbic seizures in rats. *Neurosci Lett, 70*(1), 69-74.

Miller LP, Johnson AE, Gelhard RE, & Insel TR. (1990). The ontogeny of excitatory amino acid receptors in the rat forebrain-- II. Kainic acid receptors. *Neuroscience, 35*(1), 45-51.

Miller SP, Li LM, Cendes F, Tasch E, Andermann F, Dubeau F, & Arnold DL. (2000). Medial temporal lobe neuronal damage in temporal and extratemporal lesional epilepsy. *Neurology, 54*(7), 1465-1470.

Mitchell J, Gatherer M, & Sundstrom LE. (1995). Loss of hilar somatostatin neurons following tetanus toxin-induced seizures. *Acta Neuropathol, 89*(5), 425-430.

Mizrahi EM, Kellaway P, Grossman RG, Rutecki PA, Armstrong D, Rettig G, & Loewen S. (1990). Anterior temporal lobectomy and medically refractory temporal lobe epilepsy of childhood. *Epilepsia, 31*(3), 302-312.

Molnar J, Gyorgy L, Pfeifer KA, & Nador K. (1967). Tremorigenic and convulsant actions of intracerebrally administered vegetative poisons in the mouse. *Acta Physiol Acad Sci Hung, 31*(3), 249-256.

Moshe SL. (1993). Seizures in the developing brain. *Neurology, 43*(11 Suppl 5), S3-7.

Moshe SL, & Albala BJ. (1984). Nigral muscimol infusions facilitate the development of seizures in immature rats. *Brain Res, 315*(2), 305-308.

Moshe SL, Albala BJ, Ackermann RF, & Engel J, Jr. (1983). Increased seizure susceptibility of the immature brain. *Brain Res, 283*(1), 81-85.

Murakami N, Ohno S, Oka E, & Tanaka A. (1996a). Mesial temporal lobe epilepsy in childhood. *Epilepsia, 37*(Suppl 3), 52-56.

Murakami N, Ohno S, Oka E, & Tanaka A. (1996b). Mesial temporal lobe epilepsy in childhood. *Epilepsia, 37 Suppl 3*, 52-56.

Nadler JV. (1981a). Minireview. Kainic acid as a tool for the study of temporal lobe epilepsy. *Life Sci, 29*(20), 2031-2042.

Nadler JV, Evenson DA, & Smith EM. (1981b). Evidence from lesion studies for epileptogenic and non-epileptogenic neurotoxic interactions between kainic acid and excitatory innervation. *Brain Res, 205*(2), 405-410.

Nadler JV, Perry BW, & Cotman CW. (1978). Intraventricular kainic acid preferentially destroys hippocampal pyramidal cells. *Nature, 271*(5646), 676-677.

Nahm IM, Babb TL, Mohamed A, Diehl B, Ng TC, Bingaman WE, & Luders HO. (2001). Mesial temporal lobe sclerosis. In Luders HO & Comair YG (Eds.), *Epilepsy Surgery* (pp. 95-103). Philadelphia, PA: Lippincott Wiliams & Wilkins.

Namer IJ, Bolo NR, Sellal F, Nguyen VH, Nedelec JF, Hirsch E, & Marescaux C. (1999). Combined measurements of hippocampal N-acetyl-aspartate and T2 relaxation time in the evaluation of mesial temporal lobe epilepsy: correlation with clinical severity and memory performances. *Epilepsia, 40*(10), 1424-1432.

Neill JC, Liu Z, Sarkisian M, Tandon P, Yang Y, Stafstrom CE, & Holmes GL. (1996). Recurrent seizures in immature rats: effect on auditory and visual discrimination. *Brain Res Dev Brain Res, 95*(2), 283-292.

Nelson GB, Olson DM, & Hahn JS. (2002). Short duration of benign partial epilepsy in infancy. *J Child Neurol, 17*(6), 440-445.

Nevo Y, Shinnar S, Samuel E, Kramer U, Leitner Y, Fatal A, Kutai M, & Harel S. (1995). Unprovoked seizures and developmental disabilities: clinical characteristics of children referred to a child development center. *Pediatr Neurol, 13*(3), 235-241.

Nickel J, Jokeit H, Wunderlich G, Ebner A, Witte OW, & Seitz RJ. (2003). Gender-specific Differences of Hypometabolism in mTLE: Implication for Cognitive Impairments. *Epilepsia, 44*(12), 1551-1561.

Niquet J, Ben-Ari Y, & Represa A. (1994). Glial reaction after seizure induced hippocampal lesion: immunohistochemical characterization of proliferating glial cells. *J Neurocytol, 23*(10), 641-656.

Nitecka L, & Tremblay E. (1986). Long term sequelae of parenteral administration of kainic acid. *Adv Exp Med Biol, 203*, 147-155.

Nitecka L, Tremblay E, Charton G, Bouillot JP, Berger ML, & Ben-Ari Y. (1984). Maturation of kainic acid seizure-brain damage syndrome in the rat. II. Histopathological sequelae. *Neuroscience, 13*(4), 1073-1094.

O'Brien TJ, So EL, Meyer FB, Parisi JE, & Jack CR. (1999). Progressive hippocampal atrophy in chronic intractable temporal lobe epilepsy. *Ann Neurol, 45*(4), 526-529.

Olson JE, Horne DS, Holtzman D, & Miller M. (1985). Hyperthermia-induced seizures in rat pups with preexisting ischemic brain injury. *Epilepsia, 26*(4), 360-364.

Ozkara C, Altintas A, Yilmaz E, Eskazan E, Erkol G, Ozyurt E, Erdogan E, & Kuday C. (2002). An association between mesial temporal lobe epilepsy with hippocampal sclerosis and human leukocyte antigens. *Epilepsia, 43*(3), 236-239.

Parent JM, Tada E, Fike JR, & Lowenstein DH. (1999). Inhibition of dentate granule cell neurogenesis with brain irradiation does not prevent seizure-induced mossy fiber synaptic reorganization in the rat. *J Neurosci, 19*(11), 4508-4519.

Parent JM, Yu TW, Leibowitz RT, Geschwind DH, Sloviter RS, & Lowenstein DH. (1997). Dentate granule cell neurogenesis is increased by seizures and contributes to aberrant network reorganization in the adult rat hippocampus. *J Neurosci, 17*(10), 3727-3738.

Pasquier B, Peoc HM, Fabre-Bocquentin B, Bensaadi L, Pasquier D, Hoffmann D, Kahane P, Tassi L, Le Bas JF, & Benabid AL. (2002). Surgical pathology of drug-resistant partial epilepsy. A 10-year-experience with a series of 327 consecutive resections. *Epileptic Disord, 4*(2), 99-119.

Patrizi S, Holmes GL, Orzalesi M, & Allemand F. (2003). Neonatal seizures: characteristics of EEG ictal activity in preterm and fullterm infants. *Brain Dev, 25*(6), 427-437.

Peredery O, Persinger MA, Blomme C, & Parker G. (1992). Absence of maternal behavior in rats with lithium/pilocarpine seizure- induced brain damage: support of MacLean's triune brain theory. *Physiol Behav, 52*(4), 665-671.

Persinger MA, Bureau YR, Kostakos M, Peredery O, & Falter H. (1993). Behaviors of rats with insidious, multifocal brain damage induced by seizures following single peripheral injections of lithium and pilocarpine. *Physiol Behav, 53*(5), 849-866.

Persinger MA, & Koren SA. (1998). Persistent elevation of nocturnal activity in rodents following apparent recovery from lithium/pilocarpine-induced limbic seizures. *Percept Mot Skills, 86*(3 Pt 2), 1243-1248.

Pinel JP, & Rovner LI. (1978). Experimental epileptogenesis: kindling-induced epilepsy in rats. *Exp Neurol, 58*(2), 190-202.

Pisa M, Sanberg PR, Corcoran ME, & Fibiger HC. (1980). Spontaneously recurrent seizures after intracerebral injections of kainic acid in rat: a possible model of human temporal lobe epilepsy. *Brain Res, 200*(2), 481-487.

Pohlmann-Eden B, & Bruckmeir J. (1997). Predictors and dynamics of posttraumatic epilepsy. *Acta Neurol Scand, 95*(5), 257-262.

Priel MR, dos Santos NF, & Cavalheiro EA. (1996). Developmental aspects of the pilocarpine model of epilepsy. *Epilepsy Res, 26*(1), 115-121.

Raol YH, Lynch DR, & Brooks-Kayal AR. (2001). Role of excitatory amino acids in developmental epilepsies. *Ment Retard Dev Disabil Res Rev, 7*(4), 254-260.

Raymond AA, Fish DR, Sisodiya SM, Alsanjari N, Stevens JM, & Shorvon SD. (1995). Abnormalities of gyration, heterotopias, tuberous sclerosis, focal cortical dysplasia, microdysgenesis, dysembryoplastic neuroepithelial tumour and dysgenesis of the archicortex in epilepsy. Clinical, EEG and neuroimaging features in 100 adult patients. *Brain, 118*(Pt 3), 629-660.

Regesta G, & Tanganelli P. (2002). Temporal lobe epilepsy of adult age of possible idiopathic nature. *Seizure, 11*(2), 131-135.

Reibel S, Andre V, Chassagnon S, Andre G, Marescaux C, Nehlig A, & Depaulis A. (2000). Neuroprotective effects of chronic estradiol benzoate treatment on hippocampal cell loss induced by status epilepticus in the female rat. *Neurosci Lett, 281*(2-3), 79-82.

Represa A, Niquet J, Charriaut-Marlangue C, & Ben-Ari Y. (1993). Reactive astrocytes in the kainic acid-damage hippocampus have the phenotypic features of type-2 astrocytes. *J Neurocytol, 22*(4), 299-310.

Riban V, Bouilleret V, Pham-Le BT, Fritschy JM, Marescaux C, & Depaulis A. (2002). Evolution of hippocampal epileptic activity during the development of hippocampal sclerosis in a mouse model of temporal lobe epilepsy. *Neuroscience, 112*(1), 101-111.

Rice AC, Floyd CL, Lyeth BG, Hamm RJ, & DeLorenzo RJ. (1998). Status epilepticus causes long-term NMDA receptor-dependent behavioral changes and cognitive deficits. *Epilepsia, 39*(11), 1148-1157.

Roch C, Leroy C, Nehlig A, & Namer IJ. (2002). Predictive value of cortical injury for the development of temporal lobe epilepsy in 21-day-old rats: an MRI approach using the lithium-pilocarpine model. *Epilepsia, 43*(10), 1129-1136.

Rose RP, Morell F, & Hoeppner TJ. (1979). Influences of pituitary-adrenal hormones on kindling. *Brain Res, 169*(2), 303-315.

Sagar HJ, & Oxbury JM. (1987). Hippocampal neuron loss in temporal lobe epilepsy: correlation with early childhood convulsions. *Ann Neurol, 22*(3), 334-340.

Salmenpera T, Kalviainen R, Partanen K, & Pitkanen A. (2001). Hippocampal and amygdaloid damage in partial epilepsy: a cross-sectional MRI study of 241 patients. *Epilepsy Res, 46*(1), 69-82.

Saltik S, Angay A, Ozkara C, Demirbilek V, & Dervant A. (2003). A retrospective analysis of patients with febrile seizures followed by epilepsy. *Seizure, 12*(4), 211-216.

Sanchez RM, & Jensen FE. (2001). Maturational aspects of epilepsy mechanisms and consequences for the immature brain. *Epilepsia, 42*(5), 577-585.

Sankar R, Shin D, Liu H, Katsumori H, & Wasterlain CG. (2000). Granule cell neurogenesis after status epilepticus in the immature rat brain. *Epilepsia, 41*(Suppl 6), S53-56.

Sankar R, Shin DH, Liu H, Mazarati A, Pereira de Vasconcelos A, & Wasterlain CG. (1998). Patterns of status epilepticus-induced neuronal injury during development and long-term consequences. *J Neurosci, 18*(20), 8382-8393.

Savic I, & Engel J, Jr. (1998). Sex differences in patients with mesial temporal lobe epilepsy. *J Neurol Neurosurg Psychiatry, 65*(6), 910-912.

Scharfman HE, Goodman JH, & Sollas AL. (2000). Granule-like neurons at the hilar/CA3 border after status epilepticus and their synchrony with area CA3 pyramidal cells: functional implications of seizure-induced neurogenesis. *J Neurosci, 20*(16), 6144-6158.

Schmid R, Tandon P, Stafstrom CE, & Holmes GL. (1999). Effects of neonatal seizures on subsequent seizure-induced brain injury. *Neurology, 53*(8), 1754-1761.

Schuh LA, Henry TR, Fromes G, Blaivas M, Ross DA, & Drury I. (1998). Influence of head trauma on outcome following anterior temporal lobectomy. *Arch Neurol, 55*(10), 1325-1328.

Schwarcz R, Zaczek R, & Coyle JT. (1978). Microinjection of kainic acid into the rat hippocampus. *Eur J Pharmacol, 50*(3), 209-220.

Schwarzer C, Tsunashima K, Wanzenbock C, Fuchs K, Sieghart W, & Sperk G. (1997). GABA(A) receptor subunits in the rat hippocampus II: altered distribution in kainic acid-induced temporal lobe epilepsy. *Neuroscience, 80*(4), 1001-1017.

Scott RC, Gadian DG, Cross JH, Wood SJ, Neville BG, & Connelly A. (2001). Quantitative magnetic resonance characterization of mesial temporal sclerosis in childhood. *Neurology, 56*(12), 1659-1665.

Shinnar S. (1998). Prolonged febrile seizures and mesial temporal sclerosis. *Ann Neurol, 43*(4), 411-412.

Shinnar S. (2003). Febrile seizures and mesial temporal sclerosis. *Epilepsy Currents, 3*(4), 115-118.

Shinnar S, O'Dell C, Mitnick R, Berg AT, & Moshe SL. (2001). Neuroimaging abnormalities in children with an apparent first unprovoked seizure. *Epilepsy Res, 43*(3), 261-269.

Sinclair DB, Wheatley M, Aronyk K, Hao C, Snyder T, Colmers W, & McKean JD. (2001). Pathology and neuroimaging in pediatric temporal lobectomy for intractable epilepsy. *Pediatr Neurosurg, 35*(5), 239-246.

Sirven JI, Malamut BL, Liporace JD, O'Connor MJ, & Sperling MR. (1997). Outcome after temporal lobectomy in bilateral temporal lobe epilepsy. *Ann Neurol, 42*(6), 873-878.

Sloviter RS. (1991). Permanently altered hippocampal structure, excitability, and inhibition after experimental status epilepticus in the rat: the "dormant basket cell" hypothesis and its possible relevance to temporal lobe epilepsy. *Hippocampus, 1*(1), 41-66.

Sloviter RS. (1999). Status epilepticus-induced neuronal injury and network reorganization. *Epilepsia, 40*(Suppl 1), S34-39; discussion S40-31.

Sommer W. (1880). Erkrankung des ammonshorns als aetiologisches moment der epilepsie. *Arch Psychiatr Nervenkr, 10*, 631-675.

Sperber EF, Haas KZ, Romero MT, & Stanton PK. (1999). Flurothyl status epilepticus in developing rats: behavioral, electrographic histological and electrophysiological studies. *Brain Res Dev Brain Res, 116*(1), 59-68.

Sperber EF, Haas KZ, Stanton PK, & Moshe SL. (1991). Resistance of the immature hippocampus to seizure-induced synaptic reorganization. *Brain Res Dev Brain Res, 60*(1), 88-93.

Sperber EF, Stanton PK, Haas K, Ackermann RF, & Moshe SL. (1992). Developmental differences in the neurobiology of epileptic brain damage. *Epilepsy Res Suppl, 9*, 67-80.

Sperk G, Lassmann H, Baran H, Seitelberger F, & Hornykiewicz O. (1985). Kainic acid-induced seizures: dose-relationship of behavioural, neurochemical and histopathological changes. *Brain Res, 338*(2), 289-295.

Stafstrom CE, Chronopoulos A, Thurber S, Thompson JL, & Holmes GL. (1993). Age-dependent cognitive and behavioral deficits after kainic acid seizures. *Epilepsia, 34*(3), 420-432.

Stogmann E, Zimprich A, Baumgartner C, Aull-Watschinger S, Hollt V, & Zimprich F. (2002). A functional polymorphism in the prodynorphin gene promotor is associated with temporal lobe epilepsy. *Ann Neurol, 51*(2), 260-263.

Strauss E, Hunter M, Hermann BP, Loring DW, Trenerry MR, Barr WB, Chelune GJ, Perrine K, Westerveld M, & Wada J. (1997). Differential rates of age of seizure onset between sexes and between hemispheres? *J Int Neuropsychol Soc, 3*(5), 428-434.

Strober JB, Bienkowski RS, & Maytal J. (1997). The incidence of acute and remote seizures in children with intraventricular hemorrhage. *Clin Pediatr (Phila), 36*(11), 643-647.

Sullivan PG, Dube C, Dorenbos K, Steward O, & Baram TZ. (2003). Mitochondrial uncoupling protein-2 protects the immature brain from excitotoxic neuronal death. *Ann Neurol, 53*(6), 711-717.

Sutula T, He XX, Cavazos J, & Scott G. (1988). Synaptic reorganization in the hippocampus induced by abnormal functional activity. *Science, 239*(4844), 1147-1150.

Sztriha L, Gururaj AK, Bener A, & Nork M. (2002). Temporal lobe epilepsy in children: etiology in a cohort with new-onset seizures. *Epilepsia, 43*(1), 75-80.

Tanaka T, Kaijima M, Daita G, Ohgami S, Yonemasu Y, & Riche D. (1982). Electroclinical features of kainic acid-induced status epilepticus in freely moving cats. Microinjection into the dorsal hippocampus. *Electroencephalogr Clin Neurophysiol, 54*(3), 288-300.

Tasch E, Cendes F, Li LM, Dubeau F, Andermann F, & Arnold DL. (1999). Neuroimaging evidence of progressive neuronal loss and dysfunction in temporal lobe epilepsy. *Ann Neurol, 45*(5), 568-576.

Tauck DL, & Nadler JV. (1985). Evidence of functional mossy fiber sprouting in hippocampal formation of kainic acid-treated rats. *J Neurosci, 5*(4), 1016-1022.

Temkin NR, Jarell AD, & Anderson GD. (2001). Antiepileptogenic agents: how close are we? *Drugs, 61*(8), 1045-1055.

Tharp BR. (2002). Neonatal seizures and syndromes. *Epilepsia, 43 Suppl 3*, 2-10.

Theodore WH, Bhatia S, Hatta J, Fazilat S, DeCarli C, Bookheimer SY, & Gaillard WD. (1999). Hippocampal atrophy, epilepsy duration, and febrile seizures in patients with partial seizures. *Neurology, 52*(1), 132-136.

Theodore WH, Sato S, Kufta CV, Gaillard WD, & Kelley K. (1997). FDG-positron emission tomography and invasive EEG: seizure focus detection and surgical outcome. *Epilepsia, 38*(1), 81-86.

Thom M, Sisodiya SM, Beckett A, Martinian L, Lin WR, Harkness W, Mitchell TN, Craig J, Duncan J, & Scaravilli F. (2002). Cytoarchitectural abnormalities in hippocampal sclerosis. *J Neuropathol Exp Neurol, 61*(6), 510-519.

Tremblay E, & Ben-Ari Y. (1984a). Usefulness of parenteral kainic acid as a model of temporal lobe epilepsy. *Rev Electroencephalogr Neurophysiol Clin, 14*(3), 241-246.

Tremblay E, Nitecka L, Berger ML, & Ben-Ari Y. (1984b). Maturation of kainic acid seizure-brain damage syndrome in the rat. I. Clinical, electrographic and metabolic observations. *Neuroscience, 13*(4), 1051-1072.

Tremblay E, Roisin MP, Represa A, Charriaut-Marlangue C, & Ben-Ari Y. (1988). Transient increased density of NMDA binding sites in the developing rat hippocampus. *Brain Res, 461*(2), 393-396.

Trenerry MR, Jack CR, Jr., Cascino GD, Sharbrough FW, & Ivnik RJ. (1995). Gender differences in post-temporal lobectomy verbal memory and relationships between MRI hippocampal volumes and preoperative verbal memory. *Epilepsy Res, 20*(1), 69-76.

Trenerry MR, Jack CR, Jr., Sharbrough FW, Cascino GD, Hirschorn KA, Marsh WR, Kelly PJ, & Meyer FB. (1993). Quantitative MRI hippocampal volumes: association with onset and duration of epilepsy, and febrile convulsions in temporal lobectomy patients. *Epilepsy Res, 15*(3), 247-252.

Trinka E, Unterrainer J, Haberlandt E, Luef G, Unterberger I, Niedermuller U, Haffner B, & Bauer G. (2002). Childhood febrile convulsions--which factors determine the subsequent epilepsy syndrome? A retrospective study. *Epilepsy Res, 50*(3), 283-292.

Turski L, Cavalheiro EA, Sieklucka-Dziuba M, Ikonomidou-Turski C, Czuczwar SJ, & Turski WA. (1986). Seizures produced by pilocarpine: neuropathological sequelae and activity of glutamate decarboxylase in the rat forebrain. *Brain Res, 398*(1), 37-48.

Turski L, Ikonomidou C, Turski WA, Bortolotto ZA, & Cavalheiro EA. (1989). Review: cholinergic mechanisms and epileptogenesis. The seizures induced by pilocarpine: a novel experimental model of intractable epilepsy. *Synapse, 3*(2), 154-171.

Turski WA, Cavalheiro EA, Bortolotto ZA, Mello LM, Schwarz M, & Turski L. (1984). Seizures produced by pilocarpine in mice: a behavioral, electroencephalographic and morphological analysis. *Brain Res, 321*(2), 237-253.

Turski WA, Cavalheiro EA, Schwarz M, Czuczwar SJ, Kleinrok Z, & Turski L. (1983a). Limbic seizures produced by pilocarpine in rats: behavioural, electroencephalographic and neuropathological study. *Behav Brain Res, 9*(3), 315-335.

Turski WA, Czuczwar SJ, Kleinrok Z, & Turski L. (1983b). Cholinomimetics produce seizures and brain damage in rats. *Experientia, 39*(12), 1408-1411.

Tuunanen J, Lukasiuk K, Halonen T, & Pitkanen A. (1999). Status epilepticus-induced neuronal damage in the rat amygdaloid complex: distribution, time-course and mechanisms. *Neuroscience, 94*(2), 473-495.

Van Paesschen W, Duncan JS, Stevens JM, & Connelly A. (1998). Longitudinal quantitative hippocampal magnetic resonance imaging study of adults with newly diagnosed partial seizures: one-year follow-up results. *Epilepsia, 39*(6), 633-639.

Van Paesschen W, Revesz T, Duncan JS, King MD, & Connelly A. (1997). Quantitative neuropathology and quantitative magnetic resonance imaging of the hippocampus in temporal lobe epilepsy. *Ann Neurol, 42*(5), 756-766.

VanLandingham KE, Heinz ER, Cavazos JE, & Lewis DV. (1998). Magnetic resonance imaging evidence of hippocampal injury after prolonged focal febrile convulsions. *Ann Neurol, 43*(4), 413-426.

Vannucci RC, & Vannucci SJ. (2000). Glucose metabolism in the developing brain. *Semin Perinatol, 24*(2), 107-115.

Velisek L, Veliskova J, & Moshe SL. (2002). Electrical stimulation of substantia nigra pars reticulata is anticonvulsant in adult and young male rats. *Exp Neurol, 173*(1), 145-152.

Veliskova J, & Moshe SL. (2001). Sexual dimorphism and developmental regulation of substantia nigra function. *Ann Neurol, 50*(5), 596-601.

Veliskova J, Velisek L, Galanopoulou AS, & Sperber EF. (2000). Neuroprotective effects of estrogens on hippocampal cells in adult female rats after status epilepticus. *Epilepsia, 41*(Suppl 6), S30-35.

Vezzani A, Conti M, De Luigi A, Ravizza T, Moneta D, Marchesi F, & De Simoni MG. (1999). Interleukin-1beta immunoreactivity and microglia are enhanced in the rat hippocampus by focal kainate application: functional evidence for enhancement of electrographic seizures. *J Neurosci, 19*(12), 5054-5065.

Vezzani A, Michalkiewicz M, Michalkiewicz T, Moneta D, Ravizza T, Richichi C, Aliprandi M, Mule F, Pirona L, Gobbi M, Schwarzer C, & Sperk G. (2002). Seizure susceptibility and epileptogenesis are decreased in transgenic rats overexpressing neuropeptide Y. *Neuroscience, 110*(2), 237-243.

Vezzani A, Moneta D, Conti M, Richichi C, Ravizza T, De Luigi A, De Simoni MG, Sperk G, Andell-Jonsson S, Lundkvist J, Iverfeldt K, & Bartfai T. (2000). Powerful anticonvulsant action of IL-1 receptor antagonist on intracerebral injection and astrocytic overexpression in mice. *Proc Natl Acad Sci U S A, 97*(21), 11534-11539.

Virta M, Hurme M, & Helminen M. (2002). Increased frequency of interleukin-1beta (-511) allele 2 in febrile seizures. *Pediatr Neurol, 26*(3), 192-195.

Viviani B, Bartesaghi S, Gardoni F, Vezzani A, Behrens MM, Bartfai T, Binaglia M, Corsini E, Di Luca M, Galli CL, & Marinovich M. (2003). Interleukin-1beta enhances NMDA receptor-mediated intracellular calcium increase through activation of the Src family of kinases. *J Neurosci, 23*(25), 8692-8700.

Wall CJ, Kendall EJ, & Obenaus A. (2000). Rapid alterations in diffusion-weighted images with anatomic correlates in a rodent model of status epilepticus. *AJNR Am J Neuroradiol, 21*(10), 1841-1852.

Walz R, Castro RM, Velasco TR, Alexandre V, Jr., Lopes MH, Leite JP, Santos AC, Assirati JA, Jr., Wichert-Ana L, Terra-Bustamante VC, Bianchin MM, Maciag PC, Ribeiro KB, Guarnieri R, Araujo D, Cabalero O, Moura R, Salim AC, Kindlmann K, Landemberger MC, Marques W, Jr., Fernandes RM, Serafini LN, Machado HR, Carlotti CG, Jr., Brentani RR, Sakamoto AC, & Martins VR. (2003). Surgical outcome in mesial temporal sclerosis correlates with prion protein gene variant. *Neurology, 61*(9), 1204-1210.

Wang PJ, Liu HM, Fan PC, Lee WT, Young C, Tseng CL, Huang KM, & Shen YZ. (1997). Magnetic resonance imaging in symptomatic/cryptogenic partial epilepsies of infants and children. *Zhonghua Min Guo Xiao Er Ke Yi Xue Hui Za Zhi, 38*(2), 127-136.

Ward N, Evanson J, & Cockerell OC. (2002). Idiopathic familial temporal lobe epilepsy with febrile convulsions. *Seizure, 11*(1), 16-19.

Watson C, Jack CR, Jr., & Cendes F. (1997). Volumetric magnetic resonance imaging. Clinical applications and contributions to the understanding of temporal lobe epilepsy. *Arch Neurol, 54*(12), 1521-1531.

Wiebe S, Blume WT, Girvin JP, & Eliasziw M. (2001). A randomized, controlled trial of surgery for temporal-lobe epilepsy. *N Engl J Med, 345*(5), 311-318.

Wieshmann UC, Woermann FG, Lemieux L, Free SL, Bartlett PA, Smith SJ, Duncan JS, Stevens JM, & Shorvon SD. (1997). Development of hippocampal atrophy: a serial magnetic resonance imaging study in a patient who developed epilepsy after generalized status epilepticus. *Epilepsia, 38*(11), 1238-1241.

Williamson PD, French JA, Thadani VM, Kim JH, Novelly RA, Spencer SS, Spencer DD, & Mattson RH. (1993). Characteristics of medial temporal lobe epilepsy: II. Interictal and ictal scalp electroencephalography, neuropsychological testing, neuroimaging, surgical results, and pathology. *Ann Neurol, 34*(6), 781-787.

Wirrell EC, Armstrong EA, Osman LD, & Yager JY. (2001). Prolonged seizures exacerbate perinatal hypoxic-ischemic brain damage. *Pediatr Res, 50*(4), 445-454.

Woo NS, Lu J, England R, McClellan R, Dufour S, Mount DB, Deutch AY, Lovinger DM, & Delpire E. (2002). Hyperexcitability and epilepsy associated with disruption of the mouse neuronal-specific K-Cl cotransporter gene. *Hippocampus, 12*(2), 258-268.

Woolley CS, & McEwen BS. (1992). Estradiol mediates fluctuation in hippocampal synapse density during the estrous cycle in the adult rat. *J Neurosci, 12*(7), 2549-2554.

Woolley CS, & McEwen BS. (1994). Estradiol regulates hippocampal dendritic spine density via an N-methyl- D-aspartate receptor-dependent mechanism. *J Neurosci, 14*(12), 7680-7687.

Worrell GA, Sencakova D, Jack CR, Flemming KD, Fulgham JR, & So EL. (2002). Rapidly progressive hippocampal atrophy: evidence for a seizure-induced mechanism. *Neurology, 58*(10), 1553-1556.

Wuarin JP, & Dudek FE. (2001). Excitatory synaptic input to granule cells increases with time after kainate treatment. *J Neurophysiol, 85*(3), 1067-1077.

Wyllie E, Comair YG, Kotagal P, Bulacio J, Bingaman W, & Ruggieri P. (1998). Seizure outcome after epilepsy surgery in children and adolescents. *Ann Neurol, 44*(5), 740-748.

In: Focus on Epilepsy Research
Editor: Shawn M. Benjamin, pp. 59-78
ISBN 1-59454-087-X

Chapter III

PHYSIOPATHOLOGY OF EPILEPSY: WHAT COULD THE PARTICIPATION OF GLIA BE IN THE CONSTITUTION OF HUMAN TEMPORAL LOBE EPILEPSY?

Arielle Crespel[1, 2,*], Michel Baldy-Moulinier[1, 2] and Mireille Lerner-Natoli[2]

[1]Service Explorations Neurologiques et Epileptologie, Hôpital Gui de Chauliac, 80 avenue Fliche 34295 Montpellier Cedex 05, France.

[2]Laboratoire de Génomique Fonctionnelle, CNRS UPR 2580, CCIPE rue de la Cardonille, 34090 Montpellier France.

ABSTRACT

Animal models help us to define the development of temporal lobe epilepsy after an early event. Some models exhibit a latent period in which many changes appear: neuronal loss, inflammatory reaction, dispersion of granular layer, neurogenesis, sprouting leading to hyperexcitability and hypersynchronism. Some of these alterations can be observed in surgically removed specimens of temporal lobe epilepsy from patients with early events such as febrile seizures. After general considerations, we focus in this paper on our interest in glial cells observed in human temporal epilepsies. Indeed, glial cells are represented in the epileptic hippocampus by activated microglia and reactive astrocytes in damaged areas, where inflammatory markers are overexpressed. Moreover, associated with the dispersion of the dentate gyrus, characteristic glial cells have been described, which constitute a kind of scaffold evoking the developmental radial glia. The presence of radial glia in a neurogenic region such as the granular and subgranular layers is particularly interesting.

* Corresponding author: Arielle Crespel, Service Explorations Neurologiques et Epileptologie, Hôpital Gui de Chauliac, 80 avenue Fliche 34295 Montpellier Cedex 05, France, a-crespel@chu-montpellier.fr

Therefore, we attempt to describe the possible participation of glial inflammatory reactions and of immature astrocytes in the development of epilepsy, taking into account the current opinions on the role of glia in controlling cell death, excitability, neurogenesis and neuronal circuitry.

Key words: temporal lobe epilepsy, epileptogenesis, gliosis, inflammation, radial glia, tissue remodelling.

INTRODUCTION

Epilepsy is a frequent and severe neurological disease, and still a source of many taboos. Its prevalence is estimated at 0.7% in population based studies and an incidence of 0.5/1000/year (Picot et al.). Temporal lobe epilepsy represents more than half of the partial epilepsies and is very frequently refractory, thus resulting in a public health problem. The development of temporal lobe epilepsy in humans can be traced. Indeed, in most cases an early initial event, usually a complicated febrile seizure, took place in early childhood, followed by a silent phase during several years without any specific clinical features, which constitutes the latent period. Then, spontaneous recurrent seizures appear leading to the chronic epilepsy disease. In more than 80% of the cases, patients with temporal lobe epilepsy and a history of an early event have a hippocampal sclerosis.

The physiopathology of epilepsy, already described by Jackson in the 19th century, has been observed accurately with experimental models of epilepsy developed in animals. All these models are relevant for one or more characteristic aspects of epileptogenesis. The kindling model established electrophysiological and metabolic characteristics of interictal and ictal epileptic discharges, and the propagation circuitry. The lesional models (by injection of various neurotoxic agents) led to the description of neuronal loss and its consequences in tissue reorganization, leading to secondary epileptogenesis. Patients suffering from refractory temporal lobe epilepsy can benefit from surgery, which is a highly efficient treatment for this kind of epilepsy. From human specimens, electrophysiological and morphological studies have confirmed most of the results obtained in animals. These findings explain interictal and ictal excitability, its propagation, and the main metabolic and morphological changes in tissue reorganization. A particularly dense glial network is observed in human and animal epileptic tissue. Although glial cells were regarded as uninteresting bystanders for decades, their participation in various brain functions and neuropathologies is currently highlighted. Furthermore, the growing understanding of signalling through cytokines and growth factors enables a better approach of the cross-talk that occurs between neurons, microglia, astroglia and vascular cells, in response to seizures or insults. Among others, the surprising reappearance of immature cell phenotypes seems to be associated with the dispersion of the dentate granular layer.

Here, the issue of how physiopathological processes reported to occur during the latent period in animal models can account for the chronic patterns observed in human tissue is addressed. The role of glial cells in inflammatory processes and tissue remodelling, both features described in temporal lobe epilepsy, are then focused on.

I. Physiopathological Aspects of Temporal Lobe Epilepsy

In animals, after induction of status epilepticus by neurotoxic agents or electric stimulation, (miming the initial event) a neuronal loss, rapidly followed by an inflammatory reaction, astrogliosis and microgliosis, an increase of neurogenesis, functional reorganization like axonal sprouting and synaptogenesis are observed during the latent period. All these modifications take place before the occurrence of spontaneous seizures, suggesting that an important tissue reorganization is involved in epileptogenesis. In humans, even if analysis during the latent period can not be observed for obvious reasons, comparable results have been found in surgically removed hippocampi, except for the evidence of neurogenesis, due to methodological limitations. In refractory mesial temporal lobe epilepsy, which is the most common refractory epilepsy, a specific association is reported between the age at the initial event (febrile seizure), the existence of hippocampal sclerosis and a dispersion of the dentate granular layer. Nowadays, very few models enable us to understand the relationship between these features.

I.1 Neuronal Loss

Nearly 80% of patients with temporal lobe epilepsy and a history of febrile seizure have hippocampal sclerosis. Hippocampal sclerosis was described in 1825 by Bouchet and Cazauvieilh, then with microscopy by Sommer in 1880. The areas affected by neuronal loss presented shrinkage, hardness and gliosis. The histological procedures revealed a neuronal necrosis and an astroglial proliferation. In humans, elective lesions of the hippocampal sclerosis correspond to the loss of pyramidal cells in the CA1 area, the prosubiculum and the CA4 area, and, to a lesser extent, of hilar neurons (Bratz 1899, Houser 1999). A loss of granular cells is sometimes reported whereas the CA2 area appears to be spared. Such a neuronal loss is also observed in animal studies in response to sustained seizures. This selective damage is mainly due to immediate excitotoxic processes and to a delayed apoptosis. The first areas affected by neuronal loss in animal models are the CA3 pyramidal layer and the hilus, in which some somatostatin and neuropeptide Y interneurons degenerate (Ben Ari 1985, see for reviews Chevassus-with-Louis et al. 1999, and Dalby et al. 2001). In 1991, Sloviter evoked the "dormant basket cells" hypothesis, suggesting that the loss of somatostatin neurons suppressed the excitation of GABAergic interneurons, leading to a desinhibition that takes part in the development of epileptogenesis, but today, this theory is rejected. The cellular death observed in the CA3 area is due to the propagation of paroxystic activity from the granular cells through the glutamatergic mossy fibers. Moreover, mossy fibers in the epileptic hippocampus develop a particular axonal sprouting that reinforces the excitation in the dentate granular and in the CA3 pyramidal layers. In fonction of the animal models, one can observe an extension of neuronal loss in the CA1 pyramidal layer (see Chevassus-au-Louis et al. 1999, and Dalby et al. 2001). The extent of neuronal loss is correlated with the intensity and duration of the status epilepticus (Covolan and Mello 2000), but not with the later recurrent seizures (Gorter et al. 2003). The administration of NMDA receptor antagonists attenuates lesions in CA1, CA3, the amygdala and the piriform cortex to a significant degree, but not in the hilus, where neuronal loss is not prevented but does not progress. However, the significant reduction of neuronal damage in the hippocampus does not prevent the development of recurrent seizures, suggesting that cell death is not the only decisive element in the development of chronic epilepsy. On the other hand, the persistant neuronal loss in the hilus and the reorganization of the dentate gyrus occurring after status epilepticus may account for the development of epileptogenesis under these conditions (Brandt et al. 2003).

I.2 Neurogenesis

In various experimental models of temporal lobe epilepsy, an increase of neurogenesis was described in the subgranular layer of the dentate gyrus (Parent et al. 1997; Scott et al. 1998; Parent et al. 1998; Gray and Sundstrom 1998; Nakagawa et al. 2000; Covolan et al. 2000). Under physiological conditions, this neurogenesis leads to the formation of new granule cells. The significance of increased neurogenesis has not been elucidated yet. The main assumptions are either a compensatory mechanism, or a reorganization related to the seizures, such as mossy fiber sprouting (Parent 2002). In animal or human epilepsy, the newborn neurons integrate the granular layer of the dentate gyrus or adopt an ectopic localization in the hilus and in the molecular layer of the dentate gyrus (Houser 1990). The newborn neurons that integrate the granular layer may behave like additional "normal" granule cells, but those which have an ectopic migration in the molecular layer of the dentate gyrus or in the hilus may constitute an aberrant network (Parent et al. 1997) The newborn neurons located in the hilus project axonal processes onto the CA3 area and display morphological and electrophysiological characteristics of granule cells, but exhibit an abnormal spontaneous activity of bursts that are synchronous with the CA3 area (Scharfmann 2000, 2002). This abnormal integration in the network of the CA3 area may be involved in abnormal excitability. Moreover, ectopic neurons have more dendritic excitatory synapses than granular cells (Ribak et al. 2000). Whatever the epilepsy model studied, no other localization of newborn neurons was reported, even in lesioned areas. On the contrary, in experimental ischemia, newborn neurons originating from the posterior periventricular area, another proliferative zone, replace pyramidal neurons in the damaged CA1 area (Nakatomi H, et al. 2002). Therefore, in epilepsy, the increased neurogenesis cannot be regarded as a self-repair mechanism, unlike what is proposed in cases of ischemia.

Unexpectedly, neurogenesis and mossy fiber sprouting, both affecting the dentate granule cells, seem to be two independent phenomena. Indeed, synaptic reorganization of mossy fiber was observed even when the process of neurogenesis was prevented by irradiation (Parent et al. 1999) and, conversely, neurogenesis persists when mossy fiber sprouting is prevented by cycloheximide (Covolan et al. 2000). Finally, it should be pointed out that the increased neurogenesis described in response to seizures is followed by an intense apoptosis, considerably reducing survival of the newborn neurons. Indeed, Ekdahl et al. (2001) describe a better survival of newborn neurons if apoptosis is suppressed by caspase inhibitors.

I.3 Synaptogenesis

A morphological and functional remodeling gradually appears following status epilepticus, probably due to an increase in neuronal transcription, dependent on the c-jun/c-fos factors, which are activated by seizures. The first highlighted element is mossy fiber sprouting. The glutamatergic axons of the granule cells, which usually project onto the pyramidal neurons of the CA3 area but also onto interneurons and onto the mossy cells of the hilus, emit collateral processes. These collateral processes form synapses with dendrites of granular cells, but also with CA3 pyramidal cell dendrites, (Sutula et al. 1988, Sutula et al. 1989, Represa et al. 1989, Lynch et Sutula 2000) Pitkanen et Sutula 2002). The mossy cells, highly excitable, are connected in a bidirectional way to the granule cells, and their fate after intense seizures remains unclear. For a long time, they were considered vulnerable cells (a kind of fuse which, when dying, decreases the dentate excitability but triggers sprouting). But, according to recent literature (Ratzliff et al. 2002), they appear to survive and increase excitability. There is a similar sprouting in the CA1 area, where pyramidal neurons emit collateral processes which project onto the pyramidal layer and the stratum radiatum (Esclapez et al. 1999)

These morphological changes are accompanied by adaptative modifications in the neurotransmitter functions. Glutamate tranporters GLT1 and GLAST are decreased in experimental temporal lobe epilepsy, taking part in neuronal hyperexcitability (Tanaka et al. 1997, Watanabe et al. 1999). Mossy fiber sprouting is accompanied by an overexpression of both ionotropic and metabotropic glutamate receptors (Dalby et Mody 2001). Concurrent to this reorganization of the glutamatergic function, partly responsible for hyperexcitability and synchronism, a reorganization of the ionotropic $GABA_A$ receptors has been described. Thus, in epileptic patients with hippocampal sclerosis, an increased expression of $\alpha 1$ and $\alpha 2$ $GABA_A$ receptor subunits was noted in the dentate gyrus. In the CA2 area, a spared zone, there was a different arrangement of the $\alpha 3$ subunit. This redistribution could reflect a compensatory phenomenon, in response to recurrent excitability induced by mossy fiber sprouting (Loup et al. 2000). Many of the interneurons expressing $\alpha 1$ subunit disappear in the injured areas; those which survive present significant morphological modifications (shorter dendrites, more abundant, or radial in all hippocampal areas). After status epilepticus induced by kainate injection in mice, the parvalbumin and calbindin interneurons and GAT1 (GABA tranporter) disappear in the CA1 area and in the dentate gyrus (Bouilleret et al. 2000). In animals, an increase in the number of the $GABA_A$ receptors is noted, accompanied by changes in their properties (Fritschy et al. 1999). Lastly, $GABA_B$ metabotropic receptors could also participate in epileptogenesis since the knock-out of the $GABA_{B1}$ subunit is epileptogenic in mice (Prosser et al. 2001). Recently, the specific excitability of the subiculum of human epileptic hippocampus has been demonstrated: some interneurons and pyramidal cells of this area displayed a rhythmic and spontaneous activity that could correspond to the interictal discharges (Cohen et al. 2002) Interestingly, these events were mediated by both glutamate and GABA, suggesting that in this chronic focus, GABA is an excitatory neurotransmitter, as during the immature stages of development (Ben Ari et al. 2002).

In human epileptic tissue, it seems likely that extra-hippocampal areas are also reorganized and display specific activities: groups of neurons in the entorhinal cortex, with aberrant interconnexions, have synchronous electrical activities represented by high frequency oscillations called fast ripples, which would take part in the hypersynchronism of the dentate gyrus (Bragin et al. 2002). Therefore, modifications of synaptic function and tissue remodeling facilitate hyperexcitability and hypersynchronism, and we can hypothesize that recurrent seizures maintain, or even worsen, these processes. All of these elements constitute the secondary epileptogenesis phenomenon.

I.4 Dispersion of the Dentate Granular Layer

In 1990, Houser described a morphological abnormality in the dentate gyrus of patients suffering from a temporal lobe epilepsy associated with a hippocampal sclerosis and an antecedent of complicated febrile seizure: dispersion of the granule cells. Dispersion of the granule cells associates an increase in the width of this layer (> 120 μm), a loss of contacts between the granular cells and loss of the precise boundary between the granular and molecular layer of the dentate gyrus. Lurton et al. (1997) showed that cell density in the granular layer is inversely proportional to its width. In this study, all the patients presenting a dispersion of the granular layer have a history of early risk factors in early childhood (anoxia, febrile convulsion, meningitis) compared to the patients without dispersion of the granular layer. On the other hand, they did not observe other significant differences in the history of patients with epilepsy, with or without dispersion of the granular layer. Mathern et al. (1997) and Lurton et al. (1998) showed that a granular cell dispersion of the dentate gyrus is solely observed in cases with a risk factor appearing prior to the 4th year of life. In animals, a significant dispersion of the granular layer is described in induced models in the rat (Mello et al. 1993) and mouse (Bouilleret et al. 1999), but also in transgenic models associating abnormalities of migration and spontaneous seizures (Wenzel et al. 2001). Granule cell dispersion is particularly evident in the mouse model with an intrahippocampal injection of kainate, and seems to be the most relevant model to reproduce the clinical and morphological characteristics of human temporal lobe epilepsy (Suzuki et al. 1995, Bouilleret et al. 1999, Riban et al. 2002).

The mutant mouse for Reelin, a protein of the extracellular matrix released by the Cajal-Retzius cells in the molecular layer of the dentate gyrus (Reeler mouse), presents a dispersion of the granular layer and an epilepsy (Rakic and Caviness 1995). During development, the physiological role of this protein is a stop signal that indicates to neurons the end of their migration and that acts on the scaffold of radial glia which is necessary for neuronal migration (Frotscher et al. 2003). One can hypothesize that in pathological conditions, a loss of this tonic inhibition could induce an abnormal migration in the adult brain. It is noteworthy that in human temporal epileptic focus, in correlation with the increase of the granular layer width, both a reduction of reelin expression (Haas et al. 2002), and the existence of a radial glia scaffold in the granular layer were observed (Crespel et al. 2002a).

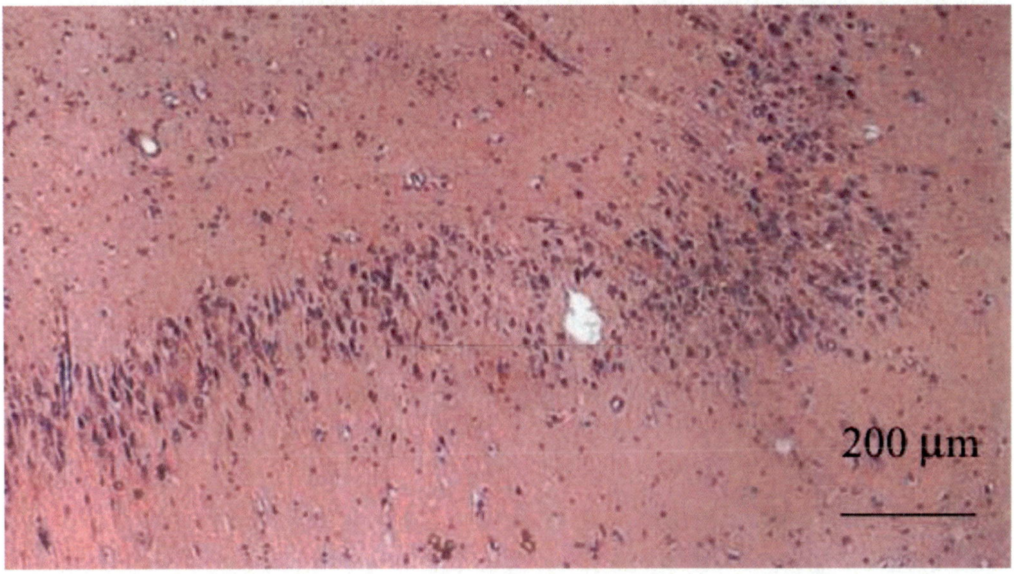

A

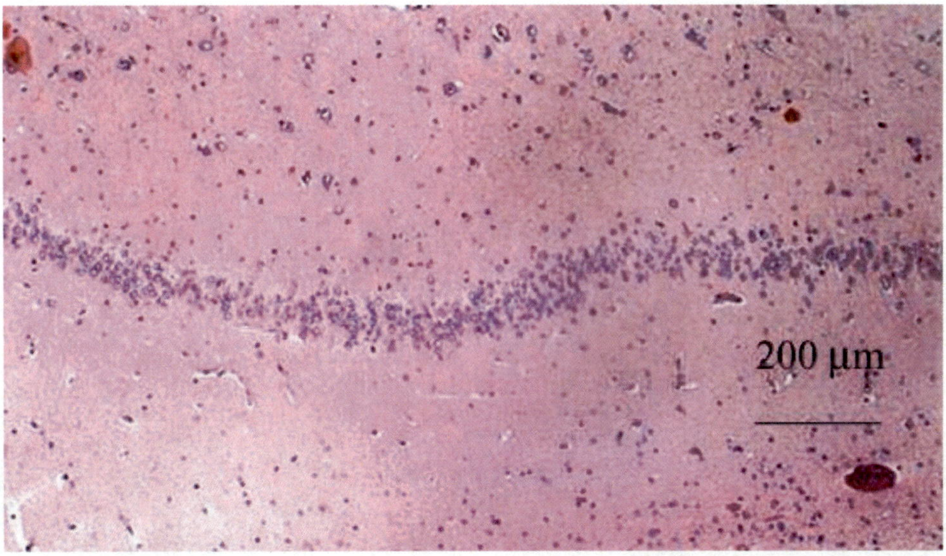

B

Figure 1: Granule cell dispersion in epileptic patients, Nissl staining. A. Granular layer of a patient with temporal lobe epilepsy associated with hippocampal sclerosis and history of febrile seizure: a dispersion of granule cells is observed all along the layer. B. Granular layer of a patient with temporal lobe epilepsy without hippocampal sclerosis or history of febrile seizure: no granule cell dispersion.

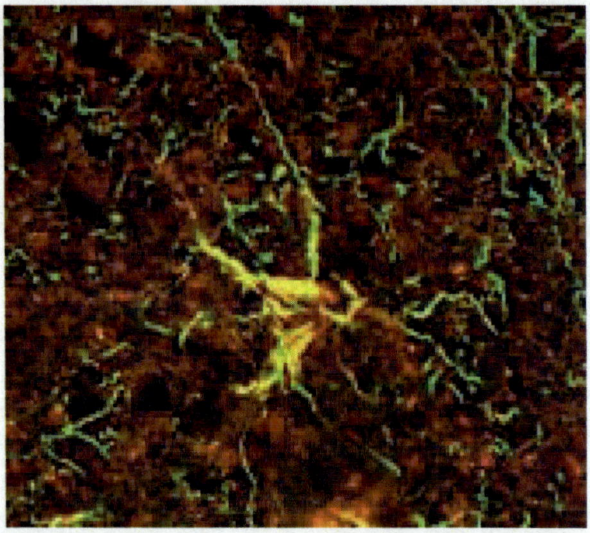

25 µm.

Figure 2: Reactive astrocyte in CA1 area of a patient with hippocampal sclerosis and history of febrile seizure. GFAP is labelled in green, NFkB in red, confocal microscopy

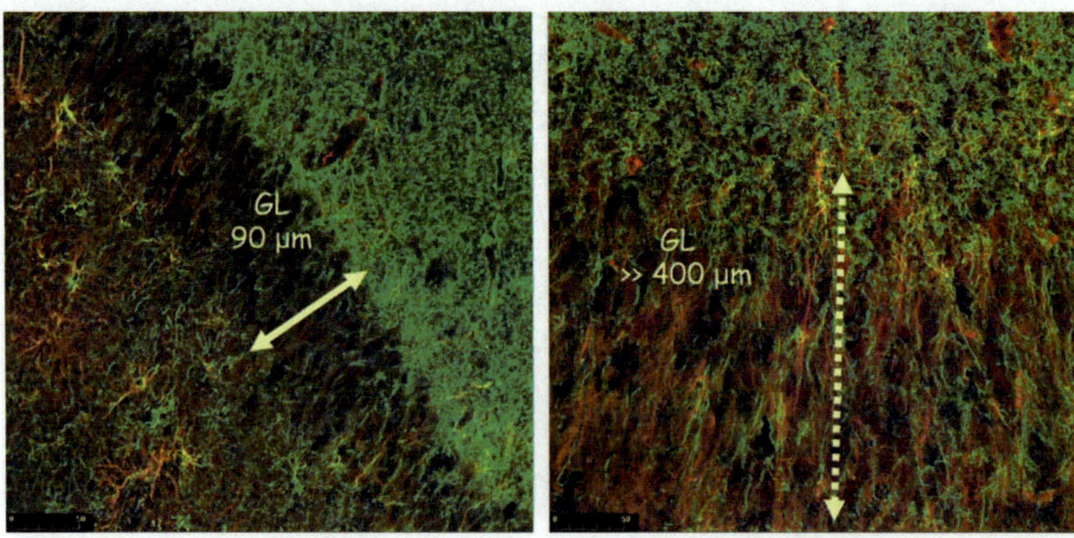

A B

Figure 3: Glial staining in the granular layer of epileptic patients. (GFAP labelled in green, vimentin labelled in red, confocal microscopy). A: Granular layer of an epileptic patient without hippocampal sclerosis. Normal granular layer width (90 µ□) containing GFPA-positive processes. No radial glia is highlighted in the granular layer. In subgranular and molecular layers few reactive astrocytes (vimentin plus GFAP positive) are observed. B: Granular layer of an epileptic patient with hippocampal sclerosis and history of febrile seizure. The granular layer is enlarged (>> 400 µ□). The granular layer contains both GFAP-positive processes and cells with long processes that are vimentin positive but do not co-express GFAP, evoking the immature radial glia (see higher mag in fig.4).

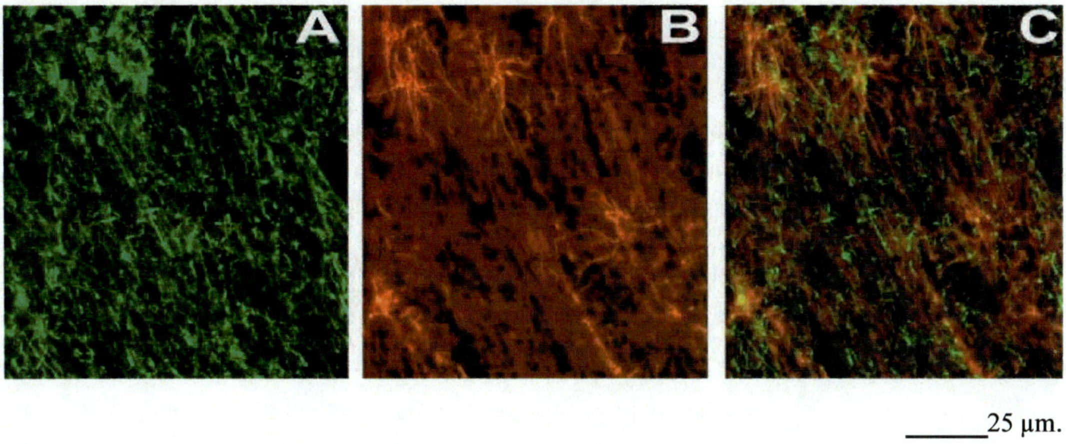

Figure 4: Radial glia in granular layer of patients with hippocampal sclerosis and history of febrile seizure. A: GFAP positive processes. B: Vimentin staining of large cell bodies and long bipolar processes. C. Images superposition (A+B): radial glia is only vimentin positive.

II. Glia: A Main Actor in the Constitution of Temporal Focus?

For a long time, epileptogenesis was limited to the concept of an imbalance between excitatotory and inhibitory systems while glia was regarded as a simple buffering system during seizures. Nowadays, glia is regarded as being of great importance in primary epileptogenesis and in tissue remodeling responsible for secondary epileptogenesis.

II.1 New Insights into Glial Function: Possible Involvement in Epilepsy?

In physiological conditions, in vitro and in vivo, astrocytes play a significant role in synaptic modulation (Newman 2003). Neurotransmitters released in the synaptic cleft interact with glial receptors and mediate an increase of intracellular Ca^{2+}, which propagates to surrounding astrocytes via an ATP release. These astrocytic Ca^{2+} waves lead to blood vessel dilation via a prostaglandin dependant mechanism. Indeed, astrocytes can release transmitters called "gliotransmitters" which can bind presynaptic neuronal receptors, modulating the release of neurotransmitters. They can also bind post-synaptic neuronal receptors, having an inhibitory or excitatory action. Thus, astrocytes can modulate synaptic transmission and regulate local blood flow. Moreover, astrocytes also release trophic factors and act on survival and neuronal growth. Finally, astrocytes participate in synaptogenesis and in mediating synaptic activity (Newman 2003, Nedergaard et al. 2003, Slezak et Pfrieger 2003, Ullian et al. 2001). In pathological conditions, the normal properties of the astrocytes, in particular the maintenance of hyperpolarisation and neurotransmitter recapture, are altered. Finally and above all, astrocytes and microglia communicate via a complex network of intercellular messengers, the cytokines. Their activation triggers the secretion of various factors having short and long term effects, which can be trophic, excitatory or toxic for the neurons.

II.2 Gliosis and Inflammation in Temporal Lobe Epilepsy

Glial Reaction

A few days after experimental status epilepticus, the astrocytes become reactive and proliferate, whereas the microglial cells proliferate and pass from a resting state (ramified shape) to an activated state (amiboïd state). Considering data from lesional and non lesional models, the astrocytes react to the seizures by a hypertrophy of the cell body and processes and by an overexpression of the glial fibrillary acidic protein (GFAP), the main intermediate filament of the mature astrocyte cytoskeleton.

Control by Astrocytes of Ionic Balance and Neurotransmitter Function

This control is modified in animal and in human temporal lobe epilepsy: a reorganization of membrane ionic channel distribution in astrocytes is noted with a predominance of Na+ channel representation (Bordey et Sontheimer 1998). K+ channels return to an immature state with a decrease in inward rectifying conductance; the loss of the inwardly rectifying currents that usually control the extracellular K+ concentration decreases their buffering potential, contributing to neuronal excitability (Bordey et Sontheimer 1998, Hinterkeuser et al. 2000). The expression of glutamate transporters is decreased, reinforcing hyperexcitability (Dalby et Mody 2001). A reorganization of glutamate receptors at the astrocyte membrane is also observed in epileptic focus. In a model of temporal lobe epilepsy, Aronica et al. 2000, showed a strong overexpression of the glutamate metabotropic receptors, mGluR2/3 and mGluR5, in the CA3 area and the hilus region, noticeable at one week and continuing more than third months after status epilepticus. An increase in the mGluR5 expression in astrocytes was also reported in other models (Ulas et al. 2000). In 1997, Ciccarelli et al. showed that mGluR5 participates in astrocyte proliferation. In vitro, mGluR5 expression is induced by trophic factors (Miller et al. 1995). It is noteworthy that Group 1 metabotropic receptors contribute to synaptogenesis, synaptic plasticity, neuro-glial interactions and glial proliferation (see for review Ramson 2003), all these functions being involved in the development of a chronic epileptic focus. In patients suffering from temporal lobe epilepsy with a hippocampal sclerosis, Seifert et al. 2002 showed a modification of glial AMPA receptors: the flip AMPA isoform was overexpressed (its desensitization is lower and more incomplete), leading to an increase of receptor activity with a prolonged depolarisation. These particularities could maintain the hyperexcitability with an increase of extracellular glutamate and K+ concentration. In the chronic epileptic focus, the glial AMPA receptors seem to modulate inwardly rectifying K+ channels, another element that contributes to hyperexcitability (Schroder et Steinhauser 1998).

Microglia, Actor of the Immune and Inflammatory Response

Like astrocytes, microglia is reactive in animal and human epileptic focus. Microglial cells have characteristic properties, acting as macrophagic cells in the brain (they derive from the same embryonic lineage) in immunitary and inflammatory processes. After an injury, they migrate to the affected area, proliferate, present leukocyte antigen and phagocyte foreign microorganisms and dead or injured cells (Altman 1994). Microglia, activated by excitoxic or inflammatory processes, releases various cytokines involved in inflammation, glial proliferation, apoptosis, which could modulate the response to pathologic processes (For review see Chevassus-au-Louis et al. 1999, and Dalby et al. 2001). An excessive microglial activation could be deleterious if its toxicity affects healthy neurons. This seems to be the case in several neurological diseases (Alzheimer's disease, multiple sclerosis, ischemia, dementia) and it may play also an important role in the constitution of hippocampal sclerosis (Tsirka et al. 1995).

Cytokines and Growth Factors, A Complex Orchestra of Intercellular Communication

Cytokines are small soluble peptides that form a complex network of intercellular messengers between astrocytes, microglia and neurons. They activate numerous receptors inducing metabolic cascades (activation of kinases, phosphatases and transcription factors) that lead to excitatory, trophic, mitotic or apoptotic effects on neurons and glia. Interleukin-1β, TNFα and Interleukin 6 are mainly released by activated microglia, and, according to some authors, TNFα could be secreted by neurons. Interleukine-1β, Interleukine-2, Interferon γ and TNFα have a direct pro-epileptic effect in animals, by facilitating the occurrence of discharges and the severity of the seizures (Vezzani et al. 1999). A direct implication in epileptogenesis and cell death of interleukine-1β, released by activated microglia, was shown to occur through the facilitation of NMDA receptor activation in models of cerebral lesions and epilepsy (Vezzani et al. 2000).The proconvulsivant effect of cytokines was highlighted in experimental models but also in humans in an indirect way. Indeed, epileptic seizures can be observed during treatments using cytokines (interleukin-1 for chemotherapy, or interferon for viral hepatitis, multiple sclerosis, or degenerative pathologies).

Numerous reports show that cytokines are secreted at the same time as growth factors in response to a seizure, suggesting a similar participation of these agents in the regulation of the various post-ictal events as fast and polyvalent intercellular messengers (Jankowsky and Patterson 2001, Minami et al. 1991, Sheng et al. 1994, Peltola et al. 1998, De Bock et al. 1996). Cytokines and growth factors (mainly BDNF and NGF) are expressed throughout the latent period, thereby participating in the morphological reorganization of epileptic focus, for example by stimulating axonal mossy fiber sprouting. This role was highlighted in particular for NGF in the kindling model (For review see Jankowsky and Patterson 2001). Lastly, when excessive neurogenesis occurs, the various growth factors and cytokines are still present at a high rate in particular: NGF, known to stimulate the proliferation and the migration of the neuronal precursors, is at its peak of expression (Temple and Alvarez-Buylla 1999). An upregulation of NGF and BDNF after seizures suggest they are involved in sequellae or in secondary epileptogenesis. This increase seems to be more significant in the dentate gyrus than in the CA1 and CA3 areas and was also described in human epileptic focus (Mathern et al. 1997).

NFκB, the Conductor of the Orchestra

This transcription factor is of particular interest as it seems to be deteminant in the cascade of events that occur during the silent period: it activates genes implied in inflammation (pro- and anti-inflammatory cytokines), in the immune response (MHC molecules), and in tissue remodelling (growth factors and cell adhesion molecules) (Blank et al. 1992, Miyamoto et Verma 1995, for review Mattson and Camandola 2001). For example, in a rat model of temporal lobe epilepsy, a precise sequence of inflammatory processes organized by NFκB was observed after status epilepticus, involving successively neurons, microglia, then astrocytes in surviving neurons and in reactive astrocytes. An overexpression of the p65 subunit (active monomer) of NFκB as well as an increase in its transcriptional activity, persisted at least for 2 weeks after status epilepticus (Lerner-Natoli et al. 2000). In human chronic focus, compared to control tissue, an overexpression of NFκB-p65 was detected in cell bodies, nuclei and processes of all reactive astrocytes in damaged areas as well as in some surviving neurons (Crespel et al. 2002b). Activation of NFκB in neurons and astrocytes in chronic and acute pathologies can, depending on its level, the duration of its expression and the cellular type, lead either to the secretion of neurotoxic factors or to the synthesis of beneficial molecules.

Consequences of NFkB Activation in Astrocytes

The reactive astrocytes in the injured areas constitute the main cellular population which expresses NFκB. In astrocytes, the function of NFκB is controversial (Mattson et al. 2000, Mattson et Camandola 2001). Indeed, it activates the transcription of many coding genes for proteins which have a deleterious effect on neurons, like iNOS or proinflammatory cytokines, but also an anti-inflammatory cytokines, protective enzymes, growth factors and adhesion molecules or cytoskeleton proteins that participate in glial scar formation and axonal sprouting, therefore in secondary epileptogenesis (Represa et al. 1995, Babb et al 1991). It is noteworthy that, in human epileptic hippocampi, many reactive astrocytes which overexpressed the p65 subunit were also observed on each side of the granular layer, in the area where neuronal dispersion and sprouting is also observed (Crespel et al. 2002b).

Consequences of Microglial Activation

Microglial activation is characterized by the neo-expression of leukocyte and macrophage antigens but these markers are also markers of infiltrating leukocytes and are difficult to distinguish in chronic epileptic focus. In neuro-inflammation, activated microglial cells normally respond by activating the NFκB transcriptional pathway. However, in chronic epileptic tissue, NFκB was never detected, suggesting it is transiently expressed after a seizure. The involvement of other microglial transcription factors cannot be excluded, in particular the "stat" (signal transducer and transcription factors) that are activated rapidly and persistent in ischemia or in experimental excitoxicity (Planas et al. 1996). Activated microglia expresses cyclooxygenase-2, and the inducible synthesis enzyme of nitric oxide (iNOS) releases various toxic factors such NO and free radicals leading to oxydative stress, quinolinate which is a potent agonist of glutamate receptors, tissue plasminogen activator (tPA) which triggers a proteolytic cascade, pro-inflammatory cytokines and colony stimulating factor, increasing astro- and micro-glial recruitment (Rogove et al. 2002, Nakamura 2002).

II.3 Immature-like Glia in Temporal Lobe Epilepsy

Immature Glial Phenotypes

Reactive astrocytes in the epileptic focus express several proteins which are normally described during development. For example, astrocytes in injured areas express the embryonic form of adherence molecule PSA-NCAM and secrete neurotrophic factors rapidly and in a persistent manner after the induction of status epilepticus,. In parallel to the overexpression of the cytoskeleton protein GFAP, reactive astrocytes of the injured area express vimentin, an intermediate filament of immature neuroglial lineage (Aronica et al. 2000). The reexpression of vimentin in mature astrocytes is reported in various models of temporal lobe epilepsy (Stringer 1996), including kindling, a non lesional model (Khurgel et al. 1995, Khurgel et Ivy 1996) and in human epilepsy (Crespel et al. 2002a). Reactive astrocytes also re-express nestin, another immature intermediate filament of neural precursors (Umeoka et al. in 2001). Thus, these reactive processes seem to be related to the intensity and duration of seizures and not directly to neuronal damage. Moreover, it is noteworthy that the promoter of the gene coding for vimentin is controlled by AP-1 and NFκB (Lilienbaum et al. 1990), two transcription factors rapidly activated by single seizures.

However, in human chronic epileptic foci, two populations of astrocytes that re-express vimentin can be distinguished (Crespel et al. 2002a). The first population of reactive astrocytes, located in the CA1, CA3 and CA4 areas, co-expressed the two intermediate filaments vimentin/GFAP regardless of the degree of neuronal loss. The second population was observed only in case of dispersion of the dentate gyrus: numerous cells with a morphology of astrocytes located in the molecular and subgranular layers, with many long and strongly intermingled processes that cross the granular layer with a radial orientation. These cells expressed vimentin but rarely co-expressed vimentin and GFAP. Inside the granular layer, some small cell bodies with short stellate processes and very long radial processes, exclusively immunoreactive for vimentin, seem to migrate radially from the subgranular layer to the molecular layer of dentate gyrus. They respond completely to the descriptive criteria of radial glia. In control tissue and in epileptic tissue without granular layer dispersion, no radial oriented vimentin-positive cells were observed.

Significance of Radial Glia in Adult Epileptic Focus

Granular layer dispersion is only associated with an immature glial phenotype in patients with a history of febrile seizures and hippocampal sclerosis. This glial phenotype evokes the radial glia which supports the neuronal migration during development. We can hypothesize that, in these pathological conditions as well, the expression of vimentin is transitory during dispersion and ceases when neurons achieve their abnormal migration. Indeed, there were fewer vimentin-positive radial cells in some cases of intense dispersion than in cases of moderate dispersion.

What could the origin, evolution and role of the radial glia be in the adult pathological brain? During the developmental stage of neuronal migration, immature astrocytes migrate from the subgranular layer to the molecular layer of dentate gyrus, building a radial scaffold which supports and guides the neurons. Vimentin expression by immature astrocytes appears to be limited to this developmental period. According to standard theories, when neuronal migration is achieved, radial glia is differentiated into mature astrocytes in which GFAP replaces vimentin. This pattern was described during the embryonic development of the neocortex and hippocampus (Rakic 1972, Cameron et al. 1993, Seki and Arai 1999, Eckenhoff and Rakic 1988, Alvarez-Buylla 1987). However, it has recently been demonstrated that radial glia (the first element to appear) is the primary precursor of both neurons or astrocytes (Alvarez Buylla et al. 2001, Seri et al. 2001, Rose and Konnerth 2001, Gould and Gross 2002, Misson et al. 1988, Alvarez Buylla et al. 1990). Although many experimental studies suggest a neuronal phenotype of the newborn cells, this estimation by specific markers remains difficult (Rakic 2002) and it seems likely that the newborn cells are undifferentiated precursors. Therefore, the observation of significant radial glia in human epileptic focus could be related to the increased proliferative activity of the subgranular layer, one of the two germinal zones in the adult brain in mammals. Radial glia, now regarded as a true neural stem cell during development (Goetz et al. 2002) could, in the adult pathological hippocampus, give rise either to neurons or to astrocytes ("neuronogenesis" vs "gliogenesis"). It is very likely that environmental elements such as cytokines or growth factors control cell fate at this crucial differentiation stage.

Conclusion

Diverse phenomena observed in chronic temporal lobe epilepsy associated with hippocampal sclerosis provide evidence of an inflammatory reaction, even though the assumed triggering event had occurred many years earlier. Whether inflammatory processes in chronic foci are related to the initial febrile seizure, to the hippocampal sclerosis *per se* or to the occurrence of recurrent seizures still remains unexplained.

We can hypothesize that inflammation is initiated by the febrile seizure itself, particularly through the secretion of cytokines, such as interleukine, or by delayed degenerative processes induced by febrile seizure. Inflammation could be self-maintained during a certain period of time by redundant cascades of neuro-glial interactions mediated by pro-inflammatory cytokines and stimulating factors. However, it is very likely that, at the chronic stage of pathology, each recurrent seizure easily re-activates these cascades, since NFκB, the main actor of inflammatory reaction, is persistently overexpressed in astrocytes and neurons during the interictal period.

The acute deleterious or protective effects of NFκB activation, depending on the concerned type of cell, are still a matter of controversy. It is tempting to speculate that both cytokines and growth factors are involved in epileptic tissue remodelling, particularly by modulating birth, differentiation, migration and death of neurons. The existence of radial glia, in association with granule cell dispersion and hippocampal sclerosis, illustrates the complexity and plasticity of neuro-glial interactions in adult chronic epilepsy. Animal epilepsies provide evidence of an increased neurogenesis in the chronic focus. Furthermore, experimental models reproducing other degenerative hippocampal pathologies such as ischemia, give interesting results that promise new approaches to stimulate brain self-repair. Moreover, in human temporal lobe epilepsy, the proliferation of progenitors appears to constitute a source of immature glia, which participates in hyperexcitability or synchronism, builds a scaffold for granule cell dispersion and can be transformed into ectopic neurons or increase the pool of astrocytes.

While numerous convincing articles currently rehabilitate astrocytes as the main partners of neurons in brain functions, this review attempted to collect evidence that glial cells and their complex network of intercellular signalling are determinant factors at each stage of the constitution of chronic epilepsy.

References

Altman J. (1994). Microglia emerge from the fog", *Trends Neurosci*, **17**: 47-49.

Alvarez-Buylla A, Buskirk DR, Nottebohm F. (1987). Monoclonal antibody reveals radial glia in adult avian brain. *J Comp Neurol*, **8** 264(2):159-170.

Alvarez Buylla A, Theelen M, Nottebhom F. (1990). Proliferation « hot spots » in adult avian ventricular zone reveal radial cell division. *Neuron,* **5**: 101-109.

Alvarez-Buylla A, Garcia-Verdugo JM, Tramontin AD. (2001). A unified hypothesis on the lineage of neural stem cells. *Nat Rev Neurosci*, **2**: 287-293.

Aronica E, van Vliet EA, Mayboroda OA, Troost D, da Silva FH, Gorter JA. (2000). Upregulation of metabotropic glutamate receptor subtype mGluR3 and mGluR5 in reactive astrocytes in a rat model of mesial temporal lobe epilepsy. *Eur J Neurosci,* **12**: 2333-2344.

Babb TL, Kupfer WR, Pretorius JK, Crandall PH, Levesque MF. (1991). Synaptic reorganization by mossy fibers in human epileptic fascia dentate. *Neuroscience*, **42**: 351-363.

Ben Ari Y. (2002). Excitatory actions of GABA during development: the nature of the nurture, *Nature Neuroscience Reviews*, **3**: 728-739.

Ben Ari Y. 1985. Limbic seizue and brain damage produced by kainic acid: mechanism and relevance to human temporal lobe epilepsy. *Neuroscience*, **14**: 475-503.

Blank V, Kourilsky P, Israel A. (1992). NFkB and related proteins: Rel/dorsal homologies meet ankyrin-like repeats. *Trends Biochem. Sci*, 17: 135-140.

Bordey A, Sontheimer H. (1998). Properties of human glial cells associated with epileptic seizure foci. *Epilepsy Res,* **32***:* 286-303.

Bouchet C, Cazauvielh Y. (1825). De l'épilepsie considérée dans ses rapports avec l'aliénation mentale. *Arch Gen Med Paris*, **9**: 510–542.

Bouilleret V, Ridoux V, Depaulis A, Marescaux C, Nehlig A, Le Gal La Salle G. (1999). Recurrent seizures and hippocampal sclerosis following intrahippocampal kainate injection in adult mice: electroencephalography, histopathology and synaptic reorganization similar to mesial temporal lobe epilepsy, *Neuroscience*, **89**: 717-729.

Bouilleret V, Loup F, Kiener T, Marescaux C, Fritschy JM. (2000). Early loss of interneurons and delayed subunit-specific changes in $GABAs_A$-receptor expression in a mouse model of mesial temporal lobe epilepsy. *Hippocampus*, **10**: 305-324.

Bragin A, Wilson CL, Staba RJ, Reddick M, Fried I, Engel J Jr. (2002). Interictal high-frequency oscillations (80-500 Hz) in the human epileptic brain: entorhinal cortex. *Ann Neurol.* **52**(4): 407-415.

Brandt C, Potschka H, Loscher W, Ebert U. (2003). N-methyl-D-aspartate receptor blockade after status epilepticus protects against limbic brain damage but not against epilepsy in the kainate model of temporal lobe epilepsy. *Neuroscience*, **118**: 727-740.

Bratz E. (1899). Ammonshornbefunde bei epileptikern. *Arch Psychiatr Nervenkr*, **32**: 820–835.

Cameron HA, Woolley CS, McEven BS, Gould E. (1993). Differentiation of newly born neurons and glia in the dentate gyrus of the adult rat. *Neuroscience,* **56**: 337-344.

Chevassus-au-Louis N, Niquet J, Ben Ari Y, Represa A. (1999). *Cellular plasticity in temporal lobe epilepsy*", In Engel J and Pedley TA (eds). Lippincott Williams & Wilkins, 387-396.

Covolan L, Mello LE. (2000). Temporal profile of neuronal injury following pilocapine or kainic acid-induced status epilepticus. *Epilepsy Res*, **39**: 133-152.

Ciccarelli R, Sureda FX, Casabona G, Di Ioro P, Caruso A, Spinella F, Condorelli DF, Nicolletti F, Caciagli F. (1997). Opposite influence of the metabotropic glutamate receptor subtypes mGlu3 and –5 on astrocytes proliferation in culture. *Glia*, **21**: 390-398.

Cohen I, Navarro V, Clemenceau S, Baulac M, Miles R. (2002). On the Origin of Interictal Activity in Human Temporal Lobe Epilepsy in Vitro. *Science,* **298**: 1418-1421.

Covolan L, Ribeiro LT, Longo BM, Mello LE. (2000). Cell damage and neurogenesis in the dentate granule cell layer of adult rats after pilocarpine- or kainate-induced status epilepticus. *Hippocampus,* **10**: 169-180.

Crespel A, Coubes P, Rousset MC, Alonso G, Bockaert J, Baldy-Moulinier M, Lerner-Natoli M. (2002a). Immature-like astrocytes are associated with dentate granule cell migration in human temporal lobe epilepsy. *Neurosci Lett*, **13**:114-118.

Crespel A, Coubes P, Rousset MC, Brana C, Rougier A, Rondouin G, Bockaert J, Baldy-Moulinier M, Lerner-Natoli M. (2002b). Inflammatory reactions in human medial temporal lobe epilepsy with hippocampal sclerosis. *Brain Res.* **18** 952(2): 159-169.

Dalby NO, Mody I. (2001). The process of epileptogenesis: a pathophysiological approach. *Curr Opin Neurol*, **14**: 187-192.

De Bock F, Dornand J, Bockaert J, Rondouin G. (1996). Release of TNFa in the rat hippocampus following epileptic seizures and excitotoxic neuronal damage, *NeuroReport*, **7**: 1125-1129.

Eckenhoff MF, Rakic P. (1989). Radial organization of the hippocampal dentate gyrus: a golgi ultrastructural and immunocitochemichal analysis in the developping rhesus monkey. *J Comport Neurol,* **223**: 1-21.

Ekdahl C, Mohapel P, Elmer E, Lindvall O. (2001). Caspase inhibitors increase short-term survival of progenitor-cell progeny in the adult rat dentate gyrus following status epilepticus. *Eur J Neurosci,* **14**: 937-945.

Esclapez M, Hirsch JC, Ben-Ari Y, Bernard C. (1999). Newly formed excitatory pathways provide a substrate for hyperexcitability in experimental temporal lobe epilepsy. *J Comp Neurol,* **14** 408(4): 449-460.

Fritschy JM, Kiener T, Bouilleret V, Loup F. (1999). GABAergic neurons and $GABA_A$-receptors in temporal lobe epilepsy. *Neurochem int*, **34**: 435-445.

Frotscher M, Haas CA, Forster E. (2003). Reelin controls granule cell migration in the dentate gyrus by acting on the radial glial scaffold. *Cerebral Cortex*, **13**: 634-640.

Gorter JA, Gonçalves Pereira PM, van Vliet EA, Aronica E, Lopes da Silva FH, Lucassen PJ. (2003). Neuronal cell death in a rat model for mesial temporal lobe epilepsy is induced by the initial status epilepticus and not by later repeated spontaneous seizures. *Epilepsia*, **44**: 647-658.

Gotz M, Hartfuss Eva, Malatesta P. (2002). Radial glia cells as neuronal precursors: anew perspective on the correlation of morphology and lineage restriction in the developing cerebral cortex of mice. *Brain Res*, **57**: 777-788.

Gould E, Gross CG. (2002). Neurogenesis in adults mammals: some progress and problems. *J Neurosience,* **22**: 619-623.

Gray WP, Sundstrom LE. (1998). Kainic acid increases the proliferation of granule cell progenitors in the dentate gyrus of the adult rat, *Brain Res,* **790**: 52-59.

Haas CA, Dudeck O, Kirsch M, Huszka C, Kann G, Pollak S. (2002). Role for reelin in the development of granule cell dispersion in temporal lobe Epilepsy. *J Neuroscience*; **22**: 5797-5802.

Hinterkeuser S, Schroder W, Hager G, Seifert G, Blumcke I, Elger CE, Schramm J, Steinhauser C. (2000). Astrocytes in the hippocampus of patients with temporal lobe epilepsy display changes in potassium conductances. *E J Neuroscience*, **12**: 2087-2096.

Houser CR. (1999). Neuronal loss and synaptic reorganization in temporal lobe epilepsy. *Adv Neurol*, **79**: 743-761.

Houser CR. (1990). Granule cell dispersion in the dentate gurus of humans with temporal lobe epilepsy. *Brain Res*, **535**: 192-204.

Jankowsky JL, Patterson PH. (2001). The role of cytokines and growth factors in seizures and their sequelae. *Progress in Neurobiology*, **63**: 125-149.

Khurgel M, Ivy GO (1996). Astrocytes in kindling: relevance to epileptogenesis. *Epilepsy Res*, **26**: 163-175.

Khurgel M, Switzer RC 3rd, Teskey GC, Spiller AE, Racine RJ, Ivy GO. (1995). Activation of astrocytes during epileptogenesis in the absence of neuronal degeneration. *Neurobiol Dis*, **2**: 23-35.

Lerner-Natoli M, Montpied P, Rousset MC, Bockaert J, Rondouin G. (2000). Sequential expression of surface antigens and transcription factor NFkB by hippocampal cells in excitotoxicity and experimental epilepsy. *Epilepsy Res*, **41**: 141-154.

Lilienbaum A, Duc Dodon M, Alexandre C, Gazzolo L, Paulin D. (1990). Effect of human T-cell leukemia virus type I tax protein on activation of the human vimentin gene. *J. Virol*, **64**: 256-263.

Loup F, Wieser HG, Yonekawa Y, Aguzzi A, Fritschy JM. (2000). Selective alterations in $GABA_A$ receptor subtypes in human temporal lobe epilepsy. *J Neuroscience*, **20**: 5401-5419.

Lurton D, El Bahh B, Sundstrom L, Rougier A. (1998). Granule cell dispersion is correlated with early epileptic events in human temporal lobe epilepsy. *J Neurol Sci*, **154**: 133-136.

Lurton D, Sundstrom L, Brana C, Bloch B, Rougier A. (1997). Possible mechanisms inducing granule cell dispersion in humans with temporal lobe epilepsy. *Epilepsy Res*, **26**: 351-361.

Lynch M, Sutula T. (2000). Recurrent excitatory connectivity in the dentate gyrus of kindled and kainicacid-treated rats. *J Neurophysiol*. **83**(2): 693-704.

Mathern GW, Babb TL, Mycevych PE, Blanco CE, Pretorius JK. (1997a). Granule cell mRNA levels for BDNF, NGF, and NT3 correlate with neuron losses or supragranular mossy fiber sprouting in the chronically damaged and epileptic human hippocampus. *Mol Chem Neuropathol*, **30**: 53-76.

Mathern GW, Kuhlman PA, Mendoza D, Pretorius JK. (1997b). Human fascia dentata anatomy and hippocampal neuron densities differ depending on the epileptic syndrome and age at first seizure. *J Neuropathol Exp Neurol*, **56**: 199-212.

Mattson MP, Camandola S. (2001). NFkB in neuronal plasticity and neurodegerative disorders. *J Clin Invest*, **107**: 247-254.

Mattson MP, Cumsee C, Yu Z, Camandola S. (2000). Roles of nuclear Factor κ B in neuronal survival and plasticity. *J. Neurochem*, **74**: 443-456.

Mello LE, Cavalheiro EA, Tan AM, Kupfer WR, Pretorius JK, Babb TL, Finch DM. (1993). Circuit mechanisms of seizures in the pilocarpine model of chronic epilepsy: cell loss and mossy fiber sprouting. *Epilepsia*, **34**: 985-995.

Miller S, Romano C, Cotman CW (1995). Growth factor upregulation of a phosphoinositide coupled metabotropic glutamate receptor in cortical astrocytes. *J Neuroscience,* **15**: 6103-6109.

Minami M, Kuraishi Y, Satoh M. (1991). Effects of kainic acid on messenger RNA levels of IL-1beta, IL-6, TNFalpha and LIF in the rat brain. *Biochem. Biophys. Res. Commun*, **176**: 593-598.

Misson JP, Edwards MA, Yamamoto M, Caviness VS Jr. (1988). Identification of radial glia cells within the developing murine central nervous system: studies based upon a new immunohistochemical marker. *Dev Brain Res,* **44**: 95-108.

Miyamoto S, Verma IM. (1995). Rel/ NFkB / IkB story. *Adv. Cancer Res*, **66**: 255-292.

Nakagawa E, Aimi Y, Yasuhara O, Tooyama I, Shimada M, McGeer PL, Kimura H. (2000). Enhancement of progenitor cell division in the dentate gyrus triggered by initial limbic seizures in rat models of epilepsy. *Epilepsia,* **41**: 10-18.

Nakamura Y. (2002). Regulating factors for microglial activation. *Biol Pharm Bull*, **25**: 945-953.

Nakatomi H, Kuriu T, Okabe S, Yamamoto S, Hatano O, Kawahara N, Tamura A, Kirino T, Nakafuku M. (2002). Regeneration of Hippocampal Pyramidal Neurons after Ischemic Brain Injury by Recruitment of Endogenous Neural Progenitors. *Cell*, **110**: 429–441.

Nedergaard M, Ransom B, Goldman SA. (2003). New roles for astrocytes: redefining the functional architecture of the brain. *Trends Neurosci*, **26**: 523-530.

Newman EA. (2003). New role for astrocytes: Regulation of synaptic transmission. *Trends in Neuroscience*, **26**: 536-542.

Parent JM, Janumpalli S, McNamara JO, Lowenstein DH. (1998). Increased dentate granule cell neurogenesis following amygdala kindling in the adult rat. *Neurosci Lett*, **247**: 9-12.

Parent JM, Tada E, Fike JR, Lowenstein DH. (1999). Inhibition of dentate granule cell neurogenesis with brain irradiation does not prevent seizure-induced mossy fiber synaptic reorganization in the rat. *J Neuroscience,* **19**: 4508-4519.

Parent JM, Yu TW Leibowittz RT, Geschwind DH, Sloviter RS, Lowenstein DH. (1997). Dentate granule cell neurogenesis is increased by seizures and contributes to aberrant network reorganization in the adult rat hippocampus, *J Neuroscience,* **17**: 3727-3738.

Parent JM. (2002). The role of seizure-induced neurogenesis in epileptogenesis and brain repair. *Epilepsy Res*, **50**: 179-189.

Peltola J, Hurme M, Miettinen A, Keranen T. (1998). Elevated levels of interleukine-6 may occur in cerebrospinal fluid from patients with recent epileptic seizures. *Epilepsy Res*, **31**: 129-133.

Pitkanen A, Sutula TP. (2002). Is epilepsy a progressive disorder? Prospects for new therapeutic approaches in temporal-lobe epilepsy. *Lancet Neurol.* **1**(3): 173-181.

Planas AM, Soriano MA, Berruezo M, Justicia C, Estrada A, Pitarch S, Ferrer I. (1996). Induction of Stat3, a signal transducer and transcription factor, in reactive microglia following transient focal cerebral ischaemia. *Eur J Neurosci*, **8**: 2612-2618.

Prosser HM, Gill CH, Hirst WD, Grau E, Robbins M, Calver A, Soffin EM, Farmer CE, Lanneau Cc, Gray J, Schenk E, Warmerdam, BS, Clapham C, Reavill, Rogers DC, Stean T, Upton N, Humphreys K, Randall A, Geppert M, Davies CH, Pangalos MN. (2001). Epileptogenesis and enhanced preepulse inhibition in $GABA_{B1}$-deficient mice. *Molecular and Cellular Neuroscience*, **17**: 1059-1070.

Rakic P. (1972). Mode of cell migration to the superficial layers of fetal monkey neocortex. *J Compot Neurol,* **145**: 61-84.

Rakic P, Caviness VS Jr. (1995). Cortical development: view from neurological mutants two decades later. *Neuron,* **14**: 1101-1104.

Rakic P. (2002). Adult neurogenesis in mammals: an identity crisis. *J Neuroscience*, **22**: 614-618. Review.

Ramson B, Behar T, Nedergaard M. (2003). New roles for astrocytes (stars at last). *Trends Neurosci.*, **26**: 520-522.

Ratzliff AH, Santhakumar V, Howard A, Soltesz I. (2002). Mossy cells in epilepsy: rigor mortis or vigor mortis?. *Trends Neurosci.*, **25**: 140-144.

Represa A, Niquet J, Pollard H, Ben Ari Y. (1995). Cell death, gliosis and synaptic remodeling in the hippocampus of epileptic rats. *J. Neurobiol*, **26**: 413-425.

Represa A, Le Gall La Salle G, Ben-Ari Y. (1999). Hippocampal plasticity in the kindling model of epilepsy in rats. *Neurosci Lett*, **99**(3): 345-350.

Ribak CE, Tran PH, Spigelman I, Okazaki MM, Nadler JV. (2000). Status epilepticus-induced hilar basal dendrites on rodent granule cells contribute to recurrent excitatory circuitry. *J Comp Neurol*, **248**: 240-253.

Riban V, Bouilleret V, Pham-Lè BT, Fritschy JM, Marescaux C, Depaulis A. (2002). Evolution of hippocampal epileptic activity during the development of hippocampal sclerosis in a mouse model of temporal lobe epilepsy. *Neurosci*, **112**, 101-111.

Rogove AD, Lu W, Tsirka SE. (2002). Microglial activation and recruitment, but not proliferation, suffice to mediate neurodegeneration. *Cell death and Differentiation*, **9**: 801-806.

Rose CR, Konnerth A. (2001). Exciting glial oscillations. *Nat Neurosci,* **4**: 773-774.

Seki T, Arai Y. (1999). Temporal and spacial relationships between PSA-NCAM-expressing, newly generated granule cells, and radial glia-like cells in the adult dentate gyrus. *J Comp Neurol,* **410**: 503-513.

Scharfman HE, Goodman Jh, Sollas AL. (2000). Granule-Like Neurons at the hilar/CA3 border after status epilepticus and their synchrony with area CA3 pyramidal cells: functional implications of seizure-induced neurogenesis. *J. Neuroscience*, **20**: 6144-6158.

Scharfman HE, Sollas AL, Goodman JH. (2002) Spontaneous recurrent seizures after pilocarpine-induced status epilepticus activate calbindin-immunoreactive hilar cells of the rat dentate gyrus. *Neuroscience*, **111**: 71-81.

Schroder W, Steinhauser C. (1998). AMPA receptor mediated modulation of inward rectifier K+ channels in immature astrocytes of mouse hippocampus. *Eur J Neuroscience*, **S10**: 114.

Scott BW, Wang S, Burnham WM, De Boni U, Wojtowicz JM. (1998). Kindling-induced neurogenesis in the dentate gyrus of the rat, *Neurosci Lett,* **248**: 73-76.

Seifert G, Schroder W, Hinterkeuser S, Schumacher T, Scramm J, Steinhauser C. (2003). Chqmges in Flip/flop splicing of astroglial AMPA receptors in human temporal lobe epilepsy. *Trends Neurosci*, **26**: 162-167.

Seri B, Garcia-Verdugo JM, McEwens BS, Alvarez-Buylla A. (2001). Astrocytes give rise to new neurons in the adult mammalian hippocampus. *J Neuroscience,* **21**: 7153-7160.

Sheng JG, Boop FA, Mrak RE, Griffin WST. (1994). Increased neuronal beta amyloid precursor protein expression in human temporal lobe epilepsy: association with interleukine-1alpha immunoreactivity. *J. Neurochem*, **63**: 1872-1879.

Slezak M. Pfieger FW. (2003). New roles fo astrocytes: regulation of CNS synaptogenesis. *Trends Neurosci*, **26**: 531-535.

Sloviter RS. (1991). Permanently altered hippocampal structure, excitability and inhibition after experimental status epilepticus in the rat: the "dormant basket cell" hypothesis and its possible relevance to temporal lobe epilepsy. *Hippocampus*, **1**: 41-66.

Sommer W. (1880). Erkrankung des Ammonshorns als Aetiologisches Moment der Epilepsie. *Arch Psychiatr* 10: 631-675.

Stringer JL. (1996). Repeated seizures increase GFAP and vimentin in the hippocampus. *Brain Res*, **717**: 147-153.

Sutula T, Xiao-Xian H, Cavazos J, Scott G. (1988). Synaptic reorganization induced in the hippocampus by abnormal functional activity. *Science*, **230**: 1147-1150.

Sutula T, Cascino G, Cavazos J. (1989). Mossy fiber synaptic reorganization in the epileptic human temporal lobe. *Ann Neurol*, **26**: 321-330.

Suzuki F, Junier MP, Guilhem D, Sorensen JC, Onteniente B. (1995). Morphogenetic effect of kainate on adult hippocampal neurons associated with a prolonged expression of brain-derived neurotrophic factor. *Neuroscience*, **64**(3):665-674.

Tanaka K, Watase K, Manabe T, Yamada K, Watanabe M, Takahashi K, Iwama H, Nishikawa T, Ichihara N, Kikuchi T, Okuyama S, Kawashima N, Hori S, Takimoto M, Wada K. (1997). Epilepsy and exacerbation of brain injury in mice lacking the glutamate transporter GLT-1. *Science,* **13** 276(5319): 1699-1702.

Temple S, Alvarez Buylla A. (1999). Stem cells in the adult mammalian central nervous system. *Curr Opin Neurobiol*, **9**: 135-141.

Tsirka SE, Gualandris A, Amaral DG, Strickland S. (1995). Excitotoxin-induced neuronal degeneration and seizure are mediated by tissue plasminogen activator. *Nature*, **377**: 340-344.

Ulas J, Satou T, Ivins KJ, Kesslak JP, cotman CW, Balazs R. (2000). Expression of metabotropic glutamate receptor 5 is increased in astrocytes after kainate induced epileptic seizures. *Glia*, **30**: 352-361.

Ullian EM, Sapperstein SK, Christopherson KS, Barres BA. (2001). Control of synapse number by glia. *Science*, **291**: 657-661.

Umeoka S, Miyamoto O, Nakagawa T, Janjua NA, Nagao S, Itano T. (2001). Expression of an embryonic intermediate filament protein in amygdaloid kindled rats. *Epilepsy Res*, **43**: 249-253.

Vezzani A, Conti M, De Luigi A. (1999). Interleukine1b immunoreactivity and microglia are enhanced in the rat hippocampus by focal kainate application: functional evidence for enhancement of electrographic seizures. *J Neuroscience*, **19**: 5054-5065.

Vezzani A, Moneta D, Conti M, Richichi C, Ravizza T, De Luigi A, De Simoni MG, Sperk G, Andell-Jonsson S, Lundkvist J, Iverfeldt K, Bartfai T. (2000). Powerful anticonvulsant action of IL-1 receptor antagonist on intracerebral injection and astrocytic overexpression in mice. *Proc Natl Acad Sci USA*, **97**: 11534-11539.

Watanabe T, Morimoto K, Hirao T, Suwaki H, Watase K, Tanaka K. (1999). Amygdala-kindled and pentylenetetrazole-induced seizures in glutamate transporter GLAST-deficient mice. *Brain Res*. **16** 845(1): 92-96.

Wenzel HJ, Robbins CA, Tsai LH, Schwartzkroin PA. (2001). Abnormal morphological and functional organization of the hippocampus in a p35 mutant model of cortical dysplasia associated with spontaneous seizures. *J Neuroscience*, **21**: 983-998.

In: Focus on Epilepsy Research
Editor: Shawn M. Benjamin, pp. 79-104

ISBN 1-59454-087-X

Chapter IV

PATHOPHYSIOLOGY OF WEST SYNDROME – CONSIDERATION FROM SLEEP STUDIES

Jun Kohyama*
Division of Human Ontogeny and Childhood Development, Graduate School,
Tokyo Medical and Dental University, Tokyo, Japan

ABSTRACT

The brainstem is closely involved in the generation of rapid-eye-movement (REM) sleep, and a reduction of the amount of REM sleep is a commonly reported sleep character of West syndrome (WS). Function of the brainstem might closely be correlated with the pathophysiology of WS. This review tried to verify this possibility. A reduction of REM sleep is a too nonspecific finding seen in various types of brain impairment. In addition, this finding did not correlate with clinical features of WS. In 1976, Fukuyama's group reported the prolongation of the period of muscle atonia during the slow wave sleep stage in WS. In 1996, the weakness of rapid eye movement-related phasic loss of muscle activity in REM sleep of WS was reported by our group. The degree of this weakness reflected a patient's prognosis as to convulsions. These findings are both implicated in muscle tone activity during sleep. Then, basic studies involved in the muscle tone control during sleep were reviewed. The following tentative conclusions were obtained; 1) dorsolateral pontine tegmentum is a key site to produce rapid eye movement-related phasic muscle activity loss, 2) prolongation of the period of muscle atonia during non-REM sleep is produced by the decrease of monoaminergic activity and/or the increase of cholinergic activity in the brainstem. The period of muscle atonia during non-REM sleep was examined in my series of WS patients, and found to show no significance difference from the controls.

Based on the weakness of rapid eye movement-related phasic loss of muscle activity in REM sleep of WS, instability of the rostral pontine tegmentum is assumed to be indispensable for the development of WS. This instability could lead to the occurrence of WS by itself, but a cortical influence on this region might also promote WS. ACTH is

* Corresponding author: Jun Kohyama, Tokyo Kita Shakai Hoken Hospital, 4-17-56 Akabanedai, Tokyo 115-0053, Japan, TEL: +81 3 5963 3311, FAX: +81 3 5963 6678, E mail: j-kohyama@tokyokita-jadecom.jp

hypothesized to suppress the spasms in WS patients not only through corticosteroids, but also through a direct action on the pontine tegmentum. Since phasic inhibition index has been reported to be elevated in patients with an autistic tendency, the appearance of an autistic tendency is also hypothesized to be involved in the functional disturbance of the pontine tegmentum.

I. Introduction

Although West syndrome (WS) (infantile spasms) was originally reported in 1841 [1], the neuroanatomical substrates responsible for the occurrence of spasms remain unknown. Moreover, no one knows the mechanisms that generate hypsarythmia, which is a representative electroencephalographic (EEG) finding of WS. Since the spasms tend to occur in clusters, particularly upon awakening or on falling asleep [2], their pathophysiology is suggested to be involved in neuronal mechanisms that regulate sleep. Similarly, a typical hypsarythmia appears during wakefulness, and as patients fall into sleep, EEG features of hypsarythmia are altered. It is obvious that neuronal mechanisms that produce hypsarythmia is affected by sleep.

Although the role of sleep remains unknown, everybody knows that the loss of sleep leads to death. Although a sleep state is looked like a passive condition, sleep is produced not by the cessation of neuronal activities, but by the active process of neuronal networks. Although mechanisms of sleep remain to be determined, recent advances in neuroscience have clarified the neuronal connections and substrates involved in the generation, maintenance and cessation of sleep. The brainstem structure is closely involved in the generation of rapid-eye-movement (REM) sleep. Interestingly, a significant role of subcortical structures including brainstem for the occurrence of WS has also been hypothesized [3]. In this review, pathophysiology of WS will be considered with special references with sleep, subcortical structures, and muscle tone control during sleep which is affected by the brainstem.

II. REM Sleep, Subcortical Structures, and WS

II.1 Previous Sleep Studies on WS

The first sleep study on WS was reported in 1976, although in Japanese [4]. In that study, polysomnography was performed for nine WS patients before the beginning of ACTH therapy. The nine patients comprised five who responded well to ACTH (good responders) and four who did not (poor responders). They found 1) a reduction of REM sleep stage and the slow wave sleep stage in poor responders, 2) prolongation of the period of muscle atonia during the slow wave sleep stage in both poor and good responders, and 3) a decrease in the frequency of body movements in poor responders. The same authors published these results in English in 1979 [5]. In 1978, Hashimoto et al. [6] described a reduction of the amount of REM sleep in nine WS patients compared with that in nine controls. They also reported a decrease in the localized phasic muscle activity (twitching) in the right palm. In 1979, Horita reported a reduction of REM sleep in four WS patients before the beginning of ACTH treatment in a Japanese paper with an English abstract [7]. He also described a reduction of the number of muscle twitches in WS patients. In 1981, two papers on sleep recordings in WS patients before and after ACTH administration appeared. Hrachovy et al. [8] reported an increase in the amount of REM sleep after ACTH treatment in good responders, while Hashimoto et al. [9] pointed out a reduction of REM sleep after the administration of ACTH. All of these studies, including that of Hrachovy et al. [8], commonly revealed that the amount of REM sleep was reduced in WS patients who had not yet been under treatment. However, this is a too nonspecific finding seen in various types of brain impairment for specifying brain lesions [10].

In addition to the reduction of REM sleep in WS, we found the weakness of rapid eye movement (rem) -related phasic loss of muscle activity in REM sleep of WS patients before treatment [11]. The degree of this weakness is quantified by the phasic inhibition index (PII), which has been found to reflect a patient's prognosis as to convulsions [11, 12]. In the following session, further explanation for the rem-related phasic loss of muscle activity in REM sleep, and the presumable structures involved in the production of this phenomena would be made. We also reported that PII decreased significantly in all WS patients examined after ACTH treatment [13]. According to this finding, we hypothesized that ACTH suppresses the spasms in WS patients not only through corticosteroids, but also through a direct action on the pontine tegmentum.

II.2 Subcortical Structures and WS

The occurrence of WS has been reported in a patient without cerebral hemispheric structures [14], and the symmetrical nature of the spasms in WS predominantly involving proximal muscles suggests the participation of the reticulospinal tract rather than the corticospinal tract as an executive system for spasms [15, 16]. Studies of brainstem auditory-evoked potentials in WS patients found abnormal subcortical function in up to half of patients evaluated [17-19]. Chugani et al. [20] used positron emission tomography (PET) to assess cerebral metabolic rates for glucose in 44 WS infants. They found a symmetrical increase in metabolic rate in the lenticular nuclei. In addition, although not statistically significant, the brainstem appeared to be visually more prominent in 21 children. According to these findings, they presumed that focal lesions, through abnormal functional interactions with raphe nuclei in the brainstem, produce abnormalities in projections of serotonergic fibers to the cortex.

Haginoya et al. reported a patient of porencephaly and hydrocephalus with focal hypsarrhythmia [21]. The left hemisphere of the patient was virtually completely defective and continuous hypsarrhythmia was only seen in the residual right frontal cortex, where an interictal single photon emission computed tomography (SPECT) showed hyperperfusion. Despite a focal epileptic pattern, the tonic spasms were quite symmetrical. This author performed ictal and interictal SPECT on 26 WS patients [22], and found that 12 patients showed definite focal cortical ictal hyperperfusion, indicating that these patients can be classified as infantile localization-related epilepsy. Interestingly, of these 12 patients, 9 patients showed symmetrical spasms. According to these findings, they assumed that spasms in some WS patients might not require the sensorimotor cortex, but the brainstem containing the descending pathways that control spinal reflexes and other infratentorial structures seem to be essential for the occurrence of spasms.

Some studies emphasized pathological changes in the pontine tegmentum of WS patients [23-26]. Although WS could be occurred with variable etiologies such as brain malformations, perinatal and postnatal insults, Sato et al. found the common pathological changes in the brainstem of WS patients, such the small size of the tegmentum, the spongy state in the central tegmental tract and the localized peri-aqueductal fibrillary gliosis [24]. Hayashi et al. [26] analyzed autopsy cases of WS with various etiologies immunohistochemically, and found the decreased parvalbumin-immunoreactivity in the brainstem auditory tract without an apparent neuropathological lesion on routine staining regardless of the etiology. They also found that the dissociative expression of methionine-enkephalin (vanished) and substance P (preserved) in the spinal trigeminal nucleus irrespective of etiologies. Subcortical structures are likely to be involved in the occurrence of WS.

II.3 Subcortical Structures and REM Sleep

The significant role of the pons in the generation of animal REM sleep has long been known [15, 27]. Animal experiments used transections established that structures caudal to the midbrain and rostral to the spinal cord are necessary for the occurrence of REM sleep. Midbrain transections produced animals in which the forebrain spontaneously alternated between synchronization of fast and slow rhythms, whereas the brainstem caudal to the transection exhibited REM sleep signs. A specific group of nuclei in the pontomesencephalon appears essential for the brainstem control of sleep-wake states. The main brainstem cell groups identified as participating in this modulation are the cholinergic pedunculopontine (PPN) and laterodorsal nuclei, the noradrenergic locus coeruleus (LC), and the serotonergic raphe nuclei (RN).

Significant increases in glucose metabolism occur in the thalamus, the limbic system, and the pontine reticular formation during REM sleep in comparison to during quiet wakefulness in the cat [28]. Recent studies using PET have found that there is a significant decrease in cerebral blood flow during slow-wave sleep compared to waking in the brainstem, thalamus, hypothalamus, basal forebrain, basal ganglia, and in the cortex of the human [29]. Contrarily, cerebral blood flow is increased during REM sleep in the human brainstem and limbic areas, but decreased in frontal cortex [30]. Hobson et al. also showed a preferential activation of the pontine brain stem and of limbic and paralimbic cortical structures in human REM sleep by means of PET [31]. It is obvious that subcortical brain structures including the pons are activated during human REM sleep [32].

II.4 REM Sleep, Subcortical Structures, and WS

We now know that 1) the amount of REM sleep is decreased in WS patients before treatment, 2) subcortical structures are likely to be involved in the occurrence of WS, and. 3) the pontine structure plays a significant role in the generation of human REM sleep These findings raised the possibility that the function of subcortical structures might be closely correlated with the pathophysiology of WS. However, not only the amount of REM sleep but also other REM sleep components such as the rate of phasic chin muscle activity (PCMA), gross movements, and bursts of rems, exhibited no significant correlation with the clinical features of WS patients [11].

In addition to our recent finding –the weakness of rem-related phasic loss of muscle activity in REM sleep-, Shionaga et al. described prolongation of the period of muscle atonia during the slow wave sleep stage of WS patients in 1976 [4]. The brainstem is activated during REM sleep when muscle activity is completely abolished. Brainstem is considered to play significant roles on the regulation of muscle tone during sleep. In the next section, I will explain neuronal background for the control of muscle tone during sleep, and introduce pathological conditions including WS in which muscle tone control during sleep is disturbed.

III. Muscle Tone Suppression during Sleep

In physiological conditions, muscle activity during REM sleep is abolished, while that in non-REM sleep is sustained. Brainstem inhibitory/facilitatory centers are considered to have a great contribution to this muscle activity alteration [15, 16, 33].

The brainstem inhibitory centers consist of 3 major sites; the midbrain, pontine and medial medullary reticular formations. The midbrain inhibitory centers include the retrorubral nucleus, ventral paralemniscal tegmental field and the PPN [34]. The pontine inhibitory centers are located in the rostral part of the pontine reticular formation, and the medullary inhibitory centers are distributed in the nucleus reticularis gigantocellularis, nucleus reticularis magnocellularis and nucleus reticularis paramedianus [15, 35, 36]. Chemical stimulation of these areas suppresses muscle activity [35, 37-39], which indicates that cellular components in these brainstem regions are responsible for the suppression of muscle activity. The pontine inhibitory centers are activated by cholinomimetic agents [39], glutamate [38] as well as GABA A antagonist [40]. The neurons in the nucleus reticularis magnocellularis are activated by the non N-methyl-D-aspartate agonist [38], and those in the nucleus reticularis paramedianus are sensitive to the cholinergic stimulation [35], resulting in the production of muscle tone reduction.

In freely moving, awake cats, electrical stimulation of the descending fibers from the pontine to medullary inhibitory centers produces natural postural suppression with termination of ongoing locomotor movements [41]. Also, neurons in the pontine inhibitory centers intervene in the control of the postural adjustments induced by cortical stimulation [42]. Some cells in feline brainstem inhibitory centers exhibit increased firing not only in REM sleep but also in postural relaxation during wakefulness [43, 44]. Recently, the medullary reticular formation has been found to produce a motor inhibition by acting on alpha- and gamma-motoneurons, and on interneurons in reflex pathways in the spinal cord [45]. These findings demonstrate an important contribution of the medullary reticular formation to suppressing muscle activity not only during REM sleep but also during wakefulness.

Serotonin [46] and noradrenalin [47] exert an excitatory effect on motoneurons. The brainstem sources of these neurotransmitters (RN for serotonin and the LC for noradrenalin) could be a part of brainstem facilitatory centers. The midbrain locomotor region (MLR), the PPN, the caudal half of the cuneiform nucleus and the caudal part of the pontine reticular formation (the nucleus reticularis pontis caudalis, NRPc) could also be included in these functional centers. Firing of the neurons in the association cortex exhibits little correlation with phasic muscle activity [48], while unit discharges correlated with phasic muscle activity (twitches) during REM sleep are recorded in the NRPc [49] and in the dorsal RN [50]. The firing rate of neurons in the RN and the LC is highest during wakefulness, decreases during non-REMS, and completely ceases during REM sleep [51]. Several other evidences revealed that disfacilitatory mechanisms of the serotonergic system play significant roles on diminishing muscle activity during REM sleep [52, 53]. An activation of the oral part of the pontine reticular formation, a part of the former mentioned brainstem inhibitory centers, evoked bilateral suppression of muscle activity as well as the inhibition of unit activity in the MLR and LC [54]. Orexin, a recently identified excitatory neuropeptide, is reported to enhance the firing rate of neurons in the LC, resulting in the suppression of REM sleep and in the increase of wakefulness [55]. In addition, during cataplexy, a sudden loss of muscle tone seen in canine narcoleptics, discharge rates of neurons in the LC are as low as or lower than these seen during REM sleep [56]. Disfacilitatory mechanisms are considered to be involved in the loss of muscle tone in cataplexy [56] and REM sleep [57]. It is difficult to deny that this disfacilitatory mechanisms involved in the brainstem facilitatory centers are not implicated in muscle activity reduction during wakefulness.

During REM sleep, antigravity muscle activity is completely abolished [15, 16]. Upon this tonic muscle atonia, additional phasic suppression of muscle activity occurs in association with rems during REM sleep [58]. López-Rodríguez et al. proposed that the phasic inhibition that occurs in association with ponto-geniculo-occipital (PGO) wave or rem in REM sleep is produced through phasic enhancement of the activity of an inhibitory system that tonically inhibits motoneurons during REM sleep [59]. On the contrary, Ornitz et al. [60] proposed that the phasic inhibition that occurs with the ocular activity during REM sleep is mediated through a different system from the system that produces tonic inhibition in REM sleep. Slow conducting reticulospinal cells (6-8 m/s), that fire specifically during REM sleep, have been identified in the feline ventral medulla [61]. On the other hand, fast conducting neurons (80-100 m/s) that inhibit motoneuronal excitability have been found in the dorsal medulla in decerebrate cats [36]. By stimulating the brainstem reticular formation in the decerebrate cat, the fast (22.8 m/s $\leq$) and slow (<22.8 m/s) conducting systems that mediate muscle tone suppression have been identified [62]. Unilateral stimulation of trigeminal sensory fibers reduces the activities of the masseter and temporal muscles bilaterally with short and long latencies (two successive exteroceptive suppressions) [63]. Each component of muscle activity reduction is considered to be relayed by independent circuits [64]. On inhibition of the masseteric reflex, the involvement of glycine in the early phase suppression and that of GABA in the late phase were suggested [65, 66]. All these findings support the idea that more than a single supraspinal system mediates the suppression of muscle activity.

By comparing the results in two papers on PGO wave-related phasic inhibitory postsynaptic potentials [59, 67], it can be calculated that it took 20 to 30 ms for volleys mediating this phasic suppression of motoneuronal activity to be conducted from the brainstem to the lumbar segment of the spinal cord [62]. Taking into account the distance between these two sites (in general, it would be 200 to 300 mm), PGO wave-related phasic inhibitory postsynaptic potentials are likely to be mediated primarily by the slow conducting system [62].

In this section, the following four issues regarding muscle tone suppression during sleep were summarized. 1) Brainstem structures are involved in the control of muscle activity during sleep. 2) Cholinergic agents microinjected into the specific sites of the brainstem elicit muscle tone suppression. 3) Disfacilitation of monoaminergic systems is implicated in the decrease of excitability of motoneurons. 4) Not a single descending pathway is involved in the suppression of muscle tone.

IV. Quantification of Muscle Tone Suppression during Sleep

We designated two indices (the tonic inhibition index, TII [68]; the phasic inhibition index, PII [20]) which could quantify muscle activity loss during REM sleep on the routine polysomnographic recording [15, 16, 33]. Interestingly, however, muscle activity level could decrease even during non-REM sleep. Quantification of the level of muscle activity during non-REM sleep might also be useful for assessing functional activity of the brainstem involved in the control of muscle activity. In this content, we paid a great attention on an index that was proposed more than 30 years before; the percentage of chin muscle atonia during non-REM sleep (%ATNR) [69]. Taken together with background mechanisms that regulate muscle tone during sleep described above, %ATNR is expected to be elevated in cases when the activity of serotonergic and/or noradrenergic systems is disturbed and/or when the activity of cholinergic system is increased.

IV.1 Phasic Inhibition Index (PII) and Tonic Inhibition Index (TII)

IV.1.1 PII

A rem-related phasic loss of muscle activity during REM sleep has been identified in decerebrate cats [70] as well as in infants who had no cerebral hemispheric structures [58]. Therefore, the brainstem appears to be a sufficient structure for the generation of this type of muscle activity suppression. Dorsolateral pontine lesions are reported to abolish the brief pauses in the feline diaphragm [71]. These brief pauses normally occur most frequently in association with rems [72]. The pontine tegmentum is considered to be a key site as to production of the rem-related phasic muscle activity loss.

To quantify rem-related phasic muscle activity reduction, we proposed PII [11]. PII is a geometric mean of the following two values; 1) the percentage of PCMAs that occur with rems bursts (RBs) in relation to the total number of PCMAs, and 2) the percentage of RBs that appear with PCMAs in relation to the total number of RBs. PII standardizes the rate of simultaneous occurrence of a PCMA and a RB. A rem was defined as having a 75 μV or greater amplitude, with calibration at 50 μV/ mm (or 50 μV/2.5 mm), a time constant of 2.0 (or 1.5 when the calibration was 50 μV/2.5 mm), and a 50° (70° when the calibration was 50 μV/2.5 mm) or greater angle of rise. A RB was defined as 2 or more consecutive rems occurring at intervals of less than 0.5 sec. PCMA was taken as chin muscle activity lasting less than 2 seconds, with a peak amplitude of at least 50 % above the baseline amplitude (calibration, 50 μV/5 mm; time constant, 0.003). The minimum inter-PCMA duration was 0.25 sec. When a part of a PCMA was observed between the onsets of the first and last rems that formed a RB, we took the PCMA and RB as occurring simultaneously. This interrelationship was judged by visual inspection.

IV.1.2 TII

TII is the rate of short PCMA during REM sleep against the total number of PCMA during REM sleep [15, 68]. PCMA is defined as chin muscle activity lasting less than 2 seconds, with a peak amplitude of at least 50 % above the baseline amplitude (calibration at 50uV/5 mm; time constant, 0.003). If the peak interval of two PCMAs is 0.25 sec. or more, they are defined as different PCMA. We took the cutoff between long PCMA and short PCMA as the duration of 0.5 sec. TII expresses the shortness of PCMA in REM sleep regardless of the difference in the definition of the short PCMA (e.g., 0.2 sec [73]). Similar to in the study of Fish et al. [74], shortening of PCMA (= elevation of TII with age) is assumed to be produced through relative elevation of inhibitory drives against excitatory ones to the trigeminal motoneurons which control chin muscles [68]. Since both drives originate in the brainstem, TII is taken to be determined by the brainstem structure.

IV.1.3 Age-related Changes of PII and TII

PII (Fig. 1) and TII (Fig. 2) were calculated in 135 polysomnographical recordings obtained for healthy humans, from premature babies to a 77-year-old man [75]. PII and TII showed marked decremental and incremental age variation, respectively, particularly in infancy and childhood [16]. Both indices showed small interindividual variations [68, 76] and are known to be unaffected by the first night effect [77]. These characters are convenient for clinical usage.

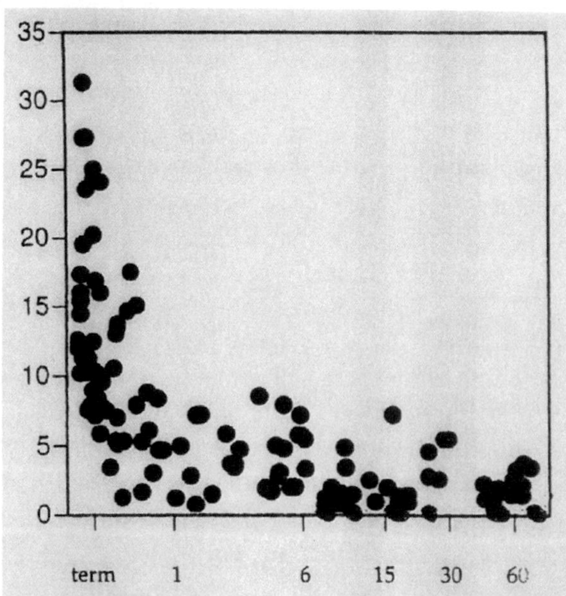

Figure 1 Chronological change of PII.

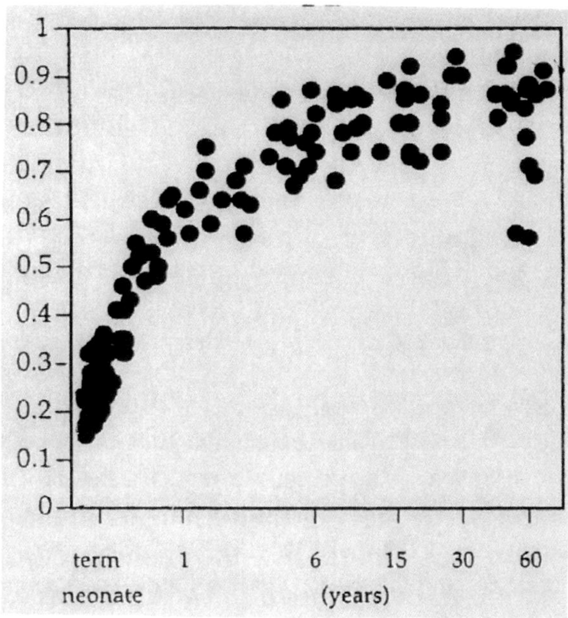

Figure 2 Chronological change of TII

The chronological changes in PII and TII have been concluded to indicate that the activity of the human nervous systems involved in both tonic and phasic inhibition in REM sleep increases with age [75]. The normal upper (PII) and lower (TII) levels in each age group obtained by calculating mean + 2 standard deviations (SDs) for PII and the mean-2SDs for TII are presented in Table 1 [75].

Table 1 Normal upper (PII) and lower (TII) levels in each age group.

Age group (n)	PII	TII
Preterm babies (11)	**32.3**	**0.10**
Term babies (25)	**31.6**	**0.16**
< 6 months (15)	**26.2**	**0.25**
< 1 year (8)	**12.3**	**0.44**
< 6 yeras (23)	**10.2**	**0.55**
< 15 years (17)	**8.3**	**0.69**
< 30 years (14)	**9.2**	**0.68**
< 60 years (10)	**6.3**	**0.79 (n=9)**
60 years ≤ (12)	**4.9**	**0.68 (n=11)**

In two normal elder subjects, with ages of 56 and 64 years, the TII values were low, being equivalent to the 1-year-old level. The neuronal systems that determine TII might lose their activities with the normal aging which produces undetectable minor lesions or physiological cell losses [78]. In addition to these 2 subjects, the mean PII and TII values in the eldest age group (60 years ≤) (PII, 2.0;TII, 0.83) were higher for PII and lower for TII than those in the second eldest age group (30-60 years) (PII, 1.5;TII, 0.88) [75]. The normal aging might also affect these indices. Consistently, disturbance of REM sleep atonia has been reported in healthy elderly subjects [78].

By calculating the age when each regression line ($\ln(PII + 2) = -1.05\ln[\ln(x-30)] + 3.44$, $TII = 0.47\ln[\ln(x-30)] - 0.09$, x: postconceptional weeks of age (in term neonates, it is usually 40) [75]) crossed the upper (PII; mean+2SDs) or lower (TII; mean-2SDs) range of the adult group aged between 30 and 60, PII was found to reach the adult level (6.3) in early infancy (0.4-year-old), while TII reached it (0.79) in preadolescence (12.3-year-old) [75]. According to this difference, PII and TII are suggested to be determined by different systems, respectively. Thus, the human nervous systems involved in the suppression of muscle activity during REM sleep were hypothesized to comprise at least 2 independent systems [75].

IV.1.4 PII/TII and the Basal Ganglia

As described above, PII and TII are considered to be affected by the activity of the brainstem. The outflow from the basal ganglia is requisite for movement control, and has recently been recognized to travel to the brainstem [79, 80]. PII and TII are likely to be influenced also by the activity of the basal ganglia. Regarding the functional maturation of neuronal systems in the basal ganglia, several findings have been accumulated. Then, PII and TII might be altered by these factors, as well.

From the striatum to the substantia nigra pars reticularis/globus pallidus interna, two functional pathways are postulated; direct pathway and indirect one. The ventral part of the striatum had D1 dopamine receptors and send direct fibers to the substantia nigra pars reticularis/globus pallidus interna (direct pathway), while the dorsal part of the striatum has D2 dopamine receptors, and has indirect connections with the substantia nigra pars reticularis/globus pallidus interna through the globus pallidus externs and the subthalamic nucleus. The direct pathway is known to develop functionally during early stage of life, while the indirect pathway is functionally immature in childhood [81]. The latencies of both visually- and memory-guided saccades during wakefulness reach the adult levels at around 12 years [82]. For the initiation of both types of saccades, the basal ganglia, especially tonic inhibitory influences from the substantia nigra pars reticulata over the superior colliculus, plays a crucial role [83]. However, for the completion of saccades, sensory systems, as well as the interconnection between sensory and motor systems are needed to act properly. It is obscure which components are essential for determinating the maturation of the latencies of saccades during wakefulness.

We found that TII reached the adult level at 12.3 years of age, while PII decreased to the adult value at 0.4 years. If PII were affected by the basal ganglia activity, neuronal systems that are involved in the determination of the PII value are likely to complete their maturation before 0.4 years of age. Further evidences are needed to obtain definitive conclusion.

IV.1.5 PII/TII in Various Clinical Conditions

IV.1.5.1 WS

TII in WS showed no significant difference with age-matched controls [84]. However, PII was markedly disturbed in WS patients. The following three observations were found in both cryptogenic and symptomatic WS patients on PII. 1) PII was higher in patients who had a recurrence of convulsions than in patients who were free from convulsions [11] (Table 2). 2) Patients who did not respond to conventional antiepileptic drugs and needed ACTH to stop the spasms had higher PII values than patients whose spasms were controlled by conventional antiepileptic drugs [12] (Table 3). 3) PII decreased markedly after ACTH treatment [13] (Table 4). Although the data is not shown, REM sleep components showed no significant differences between WS patients with cryptogenic and symptomatic types.

Table 2 Comparison of REM sleep components between the controls and WS patients

	Weeks of age	%SREM	GM/h	PCMA	RB	PII
Control n=22	63.6, 13.2, 48-96	35.5, 7.0, 25.0-48.2	18.5, 6.6, 9.0-31.6	3.1, 1.4, 0.9-6.6	1.0, 0.8, 0.2-3.8	7.8, 4.8, 1.2-17.6
WS n=17	64.0, 8.8, 51-83	23.9, 5.1, 14.7-31.8	19.2, 8.6 3.1-33.8	3.6, 2.7, 0.9-12.1	0.8, 0.3, 0.3-1.3	13.4, 3.5, 8.1-19.1
Significance (Control vs WS)	NS	p<0.001	NS	NS	NS	p<0.001
WS with good prognosis on convulsion (n=10)	67.1, 9.9 51-83	22.5, 5.3, 14.7-31.8	17.2, 6.4, 9.6-29.7	4.7, 3.0, 2.1-12.1	0.7, 0.3, 0.4-1.3	12.0, 2.5, 8.1-15.9
WS with poor prognosis on convulsion (n=7)	59.6, 4.4 51-63	26.0, 5.0, 17.1-31.3	21.9, 11.0, 9.6-33.8	2.1, 1.1, 0.9-3.9	0.8, 0.3, 0.3-1.3	15.5, 3.9, 9.5-19.1
Significance (good vs poor)	NS	NS	NS	NS	NS	P<0.05

Mean, SD, range, NS; not significant

Table 3 Comparison of REM sleep components among the controls, good responders in WS patients, and poor responders in WS patients

	Weeks of age	%SREM	PCMA	RB	PII
Control n=26	69.0, 19.8, 48-118	34.8, 7.1 24.0-48.2	3.2, 1.5, 0.9-6.6	1.0, 0.8, 0.2-3.8	7.2, 4.9, 0.7-17.6
Good responders n=6	63.2, 2.6, 60-68	23.5, 8.6, 15.0-35.4	3.1, 2.0, 0.4-5.0	1.4, 1.2, 0.4-3.5	6.1, 1.7, 4.6-8.8
Poor responders n=9	67.6, 13.8, 55-96	29.2, 2.5, 24.1-32.0	2.5, 1.0, 1.3-4.3	0.8, 0.3, 0.4-1.3	12.6, 3.4, 7.2-4.9
F test value (significance)	0.18 (NS)	6.02 (p<0.01)	0.71 (NS)	1.05 (NS)	5.77 (p<0.01)

Mean, SD, range, NS; not significant

Table 4 Comparison of REM sleep components between the controls and WS patients before and after ACTH treatment

	Weeks of age	%SREM	PCMA	RB	PII
Control n=26	69.0, 19.8, 48-118	34.8, 7.1 24.0-48.2	3.2, 1.5, 0.9-6.6	10.4/0.8/1.7 0.2-3.8	7.2, 4.9, 0.7-17.6
WS Pre-treatment	67.4, 10.4, 55-96	23.8, 5.3, 14.7-32.9	3.9, 2.4, 1.5-12.1	0.5,0.8/1.0, 0.4-1.3	12.7, 3.1, 8.1-19.1
WS Post-treatment	74.4, 11.2, 59-102	29.1, 6.8, 22.4-46.3	3.1, 2.3, 0.4-10.8	0.1/0.6/1.3, 0.02-2.9	4.2, 1.8, 1.3-8.5
significance control vs pre	NS	p<0.001	NS	NS	p<0.001
significance control vs post	NS	p<0.005	NS	NS	p<0.003
significance pre vs post		p<0.02	p=0.005	NS	p<0.0001

Mean, SD, range; RB (mean-SD/mean/mean+SD); NS, not significant

IV.1.5.2 Disturbance of PII/TII

In addition to WS, disturbance of rem-related phasic inhibition with a normal TII value was reported in patients with nocturnal enuresis [85], severe myoclonic epilepsy in infancy [86], autisms [87], and Parkinson disease (PD) [75]. On the contrary, disturbance of TII without an affect on phasic inhibition was found in a patient who subsequently died of suspected sudden infant death syndrome (SIDS) [84], in infants who experienced an apparent life-threatening event [84], in newborn patients with congenital hypothyroidism [88], and in patients with Down syndrome (DS) [87]. In patients with group A xeroderma pigmentosum (XP) [89], both PII and TII were affected. In infants who had breath-holding spells, phasic REM sleep components were disturbed [90]. In these infant patients with breath-holding spell, PII and TII were also impaired. [33] So far, corresponding to these findings, pathological changes in the brainstem have been reported in patients with SIDS [91], and functional brainstem disturbance has been suggested in patients with nocturnal enuresis [92].

In PD patients, the occurrence of disturbed REM sleep atonia is well known [93]. Disturbance of rem-related phasic suppression of muscle activity (= an elevation of PII) is observed in a patient with PD of pure akinesia [94], in an idiopathic PD patient [75], and also in PD patients with REM sleep without atonia (personal communication; Miyamoto M. and Miyamoto T.), although the degree of disturbance varied among patients. PD patients are suggested to have reduced reticulospinal activity [95-97], and also impaired inhibitory inputs to motoneurons [98]. For the occurrence of REM sleep behavior disorder in patients with PD, degeneration of brainstem neurons that promote REM sleep with atonia is hypothesized [99]. Consistently, taken together with the abnormal response of the late component in exteroceptive suppression in PD patients [100], the brainstem reticular formation, which is involved in the suppression of muscle activity, might be impaired in PD.

The TII value in the baby exposed to methamphetamine was low, while that in the baby exposed to haloperidol was high [15]. Methamphetamine exposure results in exaggeration of monoaminergic action, and haloperidol blocks its transmission. In the production of REM sleep atonia, activity of cholinergic system is profoundly involved. Then, TII is hypothesized to be elevated by the relative increase of the cholinergic tone against the monoaminergic tone [15]. Interestingly, in these babies, PII values were unaffected. The above-mention haloperidol baby showed jitteriness (JT). JT is a rhythmic tremor of equal amplitude around a fixed axis, and is one of the most common involuntary movements observed in the neonatal period. Its prevalence reaches 41-44% during the first hours of life [101]. Although JT has been found to be associated with a variety of pathologic conditions (e.g., hypoglycemia, hypocalcemia, drug withdrawal syndrome, hypoxic ischemic encephalopathy, etc.), its pathogenesis remains unclear [102]. Including the above-mentioned haloperidol baby, infants with JT were found to show abnormally higher TII values than in the controls [103] without an affection of PII [15]. The elevation of TII in infants with JT is the first neurophysiological finding commonly seen in jittery infants. This finding is considered to reflect the accelerated maturation of nervous systems involved in atonia during REM sleep. It is obscure as to whether the acceleration of maturation is favorable for the developing brain or not. Relative elevation of the cholinergic systems against the monoaminergic systems is hypothesized to produce this condition [15, 16].

IV.1.5.3 Conditions with Unaffected PII/TII

So far, in the following conditions, both PII and TII have been known to be unaffected; the non-group A XP patients, the patients with epilepsy without brainstem involvement (absence epilepsy, frontal lobe epilepsy [104], localization-related epilepsy, and generalized tonic-clonic seizures without exhibiting a focal abnormality on brain imaging or electroencephalography), neurologically unaffected children who had a cerebral structural anomaly (a double cortex or a subependymal heterotopia, both of which were found by chance) [16], and patients with rhythmic movement disorder [105].

IV.2 The Percentage of Chin Muscle Atonia during non-REM Sleep (%ATNR)

Petre-Quadens [69] reported that %ATNR in ten normal children aged less than 5 years old was 14.7%. The same author also found that this value was 9.0% in four normal children aged between five and fifteen years, 2.4% between fifteen and twenty-five years, and 0.9% in a 62-year-old person. According to Werth et al. [106], chin muscle atonia during non-REM sleep appears at a constant rate of 10-15% throughout the night in healthy young adults. We found that the average %ATNR value in 25 children aged 0.3-12.0 years (Fig. 3) was 14.2% (range; 3.4-29.4, standard deviation; 8.4), and the correlation coefficient between the age and %ATNR was low (0.06, not significant). Chin muscle atonia is supposed to appear in a constant rate during non-REM sleep in neurologically unaffected children. Regarding the chronological changes of %ATNR, our data did not support the observation made by Petre-Quadens [69], although our subjects were limited to children.

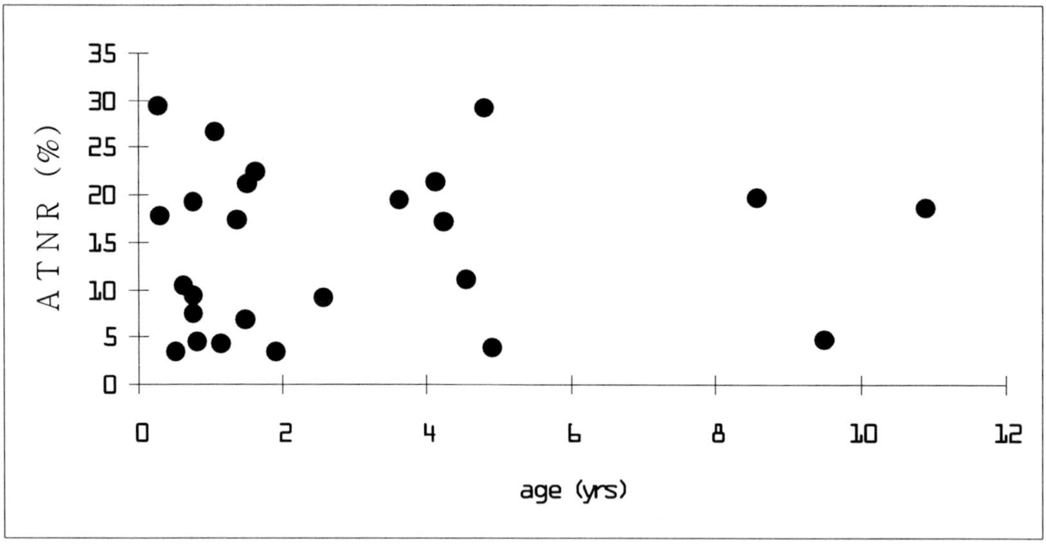

Fig. 3 Chronological change of % ATNR.

Taken together with neuronal background of muscle tone control, an elevation of %ATNR is supposed to be produced by the decrease of monoaminergic activity and/or the increase of cholinergic activity in the brainstem.

Since the elevation of %ATNR was reported in WS patients [4], we calculated %ATNR in twelve WS patients, who had not previously been treated (Table 5). Nine out of twelve patients had a good prognosis on convulsion. The result was compared with age-matched neurologically unaffected control. The mean %ATNR in WS patients was higher than that in the controls, although no significant difference was obtained.

Table 5 %ATNR in WS patients

	Age (postconceptional weeks)	%SREM	%ATNR
Control (n=7)	70.4, 11.2, 55-81	29.3, 5.6, 25.0-39.4	13.8, 8.9, 3.4-29.4
WS (n=12)	62.1, 6.8, 53-83	22.5, 8.5, 10.9-38.3	21.2, 10.1, 5.5-33.4
WS with poor prognosis (n=3)	60.0, 6.1, 53-64	21.3, 4.7, 16.4-25.7	22.4, 8.3, 14.3-30.9
WS with good prognosis (n=9)	65.4, 6.7, 60-83	20.9, 9.7, 10.9-38.3	17.9, 10.9, 5.5-33.4
p value (WS vs Control)	NS	0.03	NS
p value (poor vs good)	NS	NS	NS

Mean, SD, range

%SREM; percent of rapid-eye-movement sleep against total sleep time, %ATNR, percentage of chin muscle atonia during non-REM sleep; NS, not significant.

In 7 children aged between two and ten years old with sleep disordered breathing (SDB), %ATNR reduced significantly after the treatment (adenotonsillectomy) (Table 6), although %ATNR value was increased after the treatment in one patient. In addition, the mean pretreatment %ATNR value tended to be higher than that of age-matched control, whereas the average posttreatment %ATNR value showed no statistically significant difference with that of age-matched control. According to the observation in adults, Werth et al. [106] assumed that muscle tone suppression during non-REM sleep contributes to the compensation of an REM sleep deficit. In child SDB, sleep structures were reported to be less affected in comparison with adult cases [107], whereas various deficits in the central nervous system reflected in performance [108] or behaviors [109] have been reported in child SDB patients. Indeed, the amount of REM sleep of our patients showed no significance difference with that of the controls. However, %ATNR was obviously elevated in our child SDB patients. Although it is obvious that the amount of REM sleep determined by the classic but currently used standard [110-112] is not affected by SDB, SDB might substantially affect central nervous system that modulate the fundamental mechanisms involved in the occurrence of REM sleep.

Table 6 Summary of polysomnographic data in sleep disordered breathing children with non-Down syndrome.

	Age (months)	%SREM	DT	SaO_2nadir	OAI	%ATNR
Control	60.2, 13.4, 50-83	23.5, 4.8, 18.8-30.1	0.1, 0.1, 0-0.1	89.6, 2.6, 86.3-92.4	0.6, 1.0, 0-2.3	18.1, 9.2, 3.7-29.0
SDB pretreatment	57.9, 30.5, 33-123	23.8, 2.8, 18.2-26.8	31.5, 33.4, 0.9-94.3	62.4, 21.6, 30.5-89.4	52.5, 47.5, 2.8-115.5	28.2, 8.5, 13.4-38.2
SDB posttreatment	64.1, 30.1, 38-129	22.7, 1.9, 20.0-25.5	0.9, 1.9, 0-5.2	85.1, 9.8, 65.0-92.4	1.5, 3.3, 0-8.9	13.5, 8.6, 1.2-27.2
P value (pre vs post)	0.014	NS	0.048	0.095	0.025	0.043
P value (pre vs Control)	NS	NS	0.065	0.022	0.037	0.077
p value (post vs Control)	NS	NS	NS	NS	NS	NS

Mean, SD, range

%SREM; percent of rapid-eye-movement sleep against total sleep time, DT; desaturation time, OAI; obstructive apnea index, %ATNR, percentage of chin muscle atonia during non-REM sleep, NS, not significant.

In 5 DS patients (Table 7) who were referred to our institution for evaluation of suspected SDB, one all-night polysomnography was performed. All of these patients showed SDB, but were free from cardiac, renal, or other diseases, and were taking no medication. Patient 3 (12-year-od female), who showed worst polysomnographic data on SBD, has suffered from SDB for more than 8years, and was undertaken adenoidectomy, pharyngeal tonsillectomy as well as lingual tonsillectomy. The minimum %ATNR value among DS/SDB patients was 29.4%, and the %ATNR values did not show significant correlations with any of polysomnographic data obtained. The mean %ATNR in these 5 DS patients (average, 64.9 (range; 29.4-93.6, standard deviation; 27.8)) was extremely higher than that of both normal children (average, 14.2, $p<0.001$) and non-DS child patients with SDB (average, 28.2, $p<0.001$) shown in the former part of this discussion. %ATNR in DS patients with SDB was found to show a markedly high value. As described in a former session, %ATNR is elevated in SDB. However, the mean %ATNR value in SDB patients with DS was significantly higher than that in SDB patients without DS. %ATNR is likely to be elevated in DS patients. So far, several studies have pointed out the existence of the disturbance of the serotonergic system in DS patients [113]. An association of a loss of serotonin has been reported postmortem brain [114, 115], cerebrospinal fluid [116], and blood [117, 118] of DS patients. Treatments for DS have long included serotonergic agents and recent studies suggest that these may be particularly helpful in self-injurious behaviors and in unprovoked aggression [119, 120] as well as in improving cognition and depression in the elderly [121].

Table 7 Summary of polysomnographic data in Down syndrome patients with sleep disordered breathing.

Patient No.	age, gender	%SREM	DT	SaO_2 nadir	OAI	%ATNR
1	2 yrs, F	29.4	13.9	55%	33.2	29.4
2	12 yrs, F	23.0	1.0	81%	1.5	45.0
3	12 yrs, F	17.7	29.6	59%	55.7	89.3
4	17 yrs, F	17.0	1.2	87%	2.9	93.6
5	26 yrs, M	15.7	1.3	81%	13.0	67.3

%SREM; percent of rapid-eye-movement sleep against total sleep time, DT; desaturation time, OAI; obstructive apnea index, %ATNR, percentage of chin muscle atonia during non-REM sleep.

Petre-Quadens [69] pointed out the elevation of the percentage of chin muscle atonia during non-REM sleep in patients with metal retardation. Although anecdotal, we observed marked elevation of %ATNR in a boy patient with autism who also had restless legs syndrome. In addition to the balance of activity between monoaminergic and cholinergic systems, another mechanism that determines %ATNR remains unknown.

IV.3 Correlation between %ATNR and Phasic REM Sleep Components

To know the relationship between %ATNR and phasic REM sleep components including PII and TII, we calculated correlation coefficients (r) between %ATNR and phasic REM sleep indices in 25 neurologically unaffected children aged 0.3-12.0 years. No significant correlation were obtained, although PCMA tended to show negative correlation with %ATNR ($r=-0.38$, $0.05<p<0.1$). The occurrence of phasic muscle twitches during REM sleep (PCMA) is correlated with unit discharges of the RN where serotonergic neurons are located [50]. Hypoactivity of serotonergic neurons might contribute to the elevation of %ATNR values. Since no significance correlation was obtained between %ATNR and both PII and TII, these 3 indices are likely to reflect different aspects of muscle tone control during sleep, although they are all designated to quantify the degree of muscle tone control during sleep.

V. PATHOPHYSIOLOGY OF WS

To sum up findings on muscle tone control in WS, three issues were obvious; elevated PII, and normal TII and %ATNR. Taken these together, a specific deficit in the process of mediation of phasic inhibition from phasic event generator [70, 122, 123] presumably located in the rostral pontine tegmentum to various peripheral effectors can be speculated.

An elevation of PII means disturbance of the phasic muscle activity suppression in REM sleep. Both the cholinergic and cholinoceptive descending pathways originating in the rostral pontine tegmentum are implicated in the muscle activity suppression during REM sleep [15, 16]. Anticholinesterase, which increases the cholinergic activity in the central nervous system, is also reported to have a favorable effect on WS [124]. Presumable hypofunction of cholinergic system is considered to exist in WS.

As mentioned earlier, the pontine tegmentum is involved in the production of the rem-related phasic loss of muscle activity in REM sleep [15, 16]. Thus, the elevation of PII in WS patients is likely to indicate functional instability of the pontine tegmentum. Patients with WS are hypothesized to have an instability of the pontine tegmentum [11]. This hypothesis is consistent with the possibility raised before that the brainstem might be correlated with the pathophysiology of WS. Furthermore, neuropathological changes have been reported in the brainstem tegmentum of WS patients [23-26]. In rats, dorsal tegmentum kindling has been reported [125]. Chugani et al. proposed the role of lenticular and raphe nuclei in the occurrence of WS [20]. Baram proposed the corticotropin releasing hormone excess theory and that the brainstem is one of its action sites [126]. These reports also suggested the involvement of the brainstem in the occurrence of WS.

Instability of the rostral pontine tegmentum is assumed to be indispensable for the development of WS [11]. This instability could lead to the occurrence of WS by itself, but a cortical influence on this region might also promote WS [11]. PII was found to decrease rapidly during early infancy, reaching the adult level (6.3) at 0.4-years-old [16, 74, 75], when WS most commonly develops. This chronological change is taken as reflecting maturation, and the maturational process is proposed to be easily affected [11]. Around the age when PII decreases to the adult level (0.4 years), one of the primitive responses -the Moro reflex- disappears. The symmetrical extension and abduction of the upper extremities in this reflex suggest the participation of the reticulospinal tract as an executive system for the Moro reflex. In WS patients, similar movements predominantly involving bilateral proximal muscles occur. It was described in a Japanese classic textbook that WS was sometimes mistaken for the Moro reflex [127]. Rem-related phasic suppression of muscle activity is produced through excitement of the putative phasic event generator in the brainstem [70, 122, 123]. This excitement was found not only to suppress muscle activity but also to facilitate muscle activity at the same time [70, 122, 123]. Extrinsic stimuli such as auditory ones can induce the Moro reflex as well as the excitement of the phasic event generator [122]. In patients with WS, unknown intrinsic stimulation might affect the phasic event generator. However, WS patients have a deficit in the mediation of phasic inhibition shown by the elevation of the PII. Insufficient phasic inhibition may produce a relative increase in facilitatory drives from the brainstem (phasic event generator/brainstem facilitatory centers) to motoneurons. This imbalance might produce the Moro reflex in normal infants aged 5 months (0.4 years) or less [75], and spasms in WS patients who have instability of the rostral pontine tegmentum [16].

On adequate electrical stimulation of one side of the mesopontine locomotor region (MLR) of the decerebrate cat, the cat shows locomotor activity on a treadmill [128]. By increasing the intensity of the stimulation, the stepping interval of the locomotion becomes shorter, resulting in a trot, and finally the locomotion changes into a gallop [128, 129]. The gallop involves bilateral proximal muscles symmetrically. The MLR is now known as a structure very close to the PPN, which is located in the rostral part of the pontine tegmentum. The PPN is known to be rich in cholinergic neurons [130]. The MLR-PPN complex is an interesting structure when considering the pathogenesis of the interval of each spasm seen in a series of WS patients (frequency of the spasms in a series).

VI. Action Sites of ACTH

After ACTH treatment, high PII, which reflects the instability of the rostral pontine tegmentum, decreased significantly in all WS patients examined [13]. Konishi et al. observed a reduction of the volume of the pons on magnetic resonance imaging in WS patients after ACTH treatment [131]. The pontine tegmentum could be the action site of ACTH. Indeed, immunoreactive ACTH fibers have been identified in the human pontine tegmentum [132]. ACTH is hypothesized to act on the pontine tegmentum and to elicit phasic inhibition, resulting in reduction of PII and in suppression of the spasms in WS patients [13]. In patients with Lennox Gastaut syndrome, we experienced a favorable effect of ACTH on convulsions in patients with elevation of PII, but its unfavorable effect in patients who had normal PII values [133]. Functional instability or prematurity of the pontine tegmentum might be needed for ACTH to exert an antiepileptic effect.

In newborn patients with congenital adrenal hyperplasia, physiological doses of corticosteroids corrected (= decreased) the increased intrinsic ACTH level and increased PII [13]. Corticosteroids at therapeutic doses elicit no constant PII change in patients with nephrotic syndrome, but decrease the incidence of PCMA [13]. PII in WS was decreased by ACTH, and PII in the pre-treatment records of patients with congenital adrenal hyperplasia might have been suppressed by the intrinsically elevated ACTH. ACTH is suggested to decrease PII not through corticosteroids but through a direct action. PCMA was decreased both by ACTH in WS patients and by corticosteroids in patients with nephritic syndrome. Thus, the decrease in PCMA is likely to be mediated by therapeutic doses of corticosteroids. This corticosteroid-induced suppression of PCMA might be involved in the suppression of convulsions in WS. The therapeutic superiority of ACTH over corticosteroids in WS has been demonstrated [134]. Here, ACTH was found to suppress PCMA through corticosteroids, and to reduce PII directly. ACTH was hypothesized to eliminate the spasms in WS through these dual modes of action [13].

VII. Autistic Tendency and Subcortical Structures

Diomedi et al. reported the elevation of PII without affecting TII in autistic patients [135]. They speculated the involvement of a particular brainstem system in autistic subjects. WS patients often develop mental retardation or behavioral difficulties including autistic tendency in addition to convulsions [136], showing an elevation of PII without affecting TII.

It is interesting that patients with autistic behavior and those with WS share the same polysomnographical finding. In addition, both conditions could be combined. According to the MRI findings, Hashimoto et al. suggested a small decrease in each region of the brainstem with normal volumes for all other brain regions viewed on the midline [137]. Rodier et al. reported a short brainstem in a patient with autism [138], and speculated that disturbances in communication and social behavior might be mediated by more basic deficits in sensory and motor function in which the brainstem is involved [139]. These reports supported the hypothesis that the appearance of an autistic tendency might be involved in the functional disturbance of the pontine tegmentum.

VIII. Summary

In addition to the previously known finding -the amount of REM sleep is reduced in WS patients-, weakness of the phasic suppression of chin muscle activity has recently been found in WS patients. The degree of this weakness, which is expressed as PII, reflects a patient's prognosis as to convulsions. PII is proposed to be a useful parameter for assessing the prognosis of WS. However, previously reported finding that WS patients have a prolongation of the period of muscle atonia during non-REM sleep could not be confirmed.

Since the pontine tegmentum is involved in the production of the rapid eye movement-related phasic loss of muscle activity in REM sleep, WS patients are hypothesized to have functional instability of the pontine tegmentum. ACTH is hypothesized to suppress the spasms in WS patients not only through corticosteroids, but also through a direct action on the pontine tegmentum. Since PII has been reported to be elevated in patients with an autistic tendency, the appearance of an autistic tendency is hypothesized to be involved in the functional disturbance of the pontine tegmentum.

References

[1] West WJ. On a peculiar form of infantile convulsions. *Lancet* 1984;i:724-725.

[2] Appleton RE. Infantile spasms. *Arch Dis Child* 1993; 69: 614-618.

[3] Lado FA, Moshé SL. Role of subcortical structures in the pathogenesis of infantile spasms: what are possible subcortical mediators. *Int Rev Neurobiol* 2002:49;115-140.

[4] Shionaga A, Iida Y, Fukuyama Y. Polygraphical all night EEG in infantile spasms (in Japanese). *Shouni-Geka·Naika* 1976; 8: 1415-1423.

[5] Fukuyama Y, Shionaga A, Iida Y. Polygraphic study during whole night sleep in infantile spasms. *Eur Neurol* 1979; 18: 302-311.

[6] Hashimoto T, Ohara K, Hiura K, Suzue J, Kawano N, Kobayashi Y, et al. Sleep polygraphic studies on infantile spasms. *Acta Paediatr Jpn* 1978;20:1-7.

[7] Horita H. Overnight polygraphic studies of age-dependent epilepsy in infancy: part 1. Sleep states and changes in pulse, respiration and seizure activities during sleep states (in Japanese). *No To Hattatsu* 1979;11:229-246.

[8] Hrachovy RA, Frost JD Jr, Kellaway P. Sleep characteristics in infantile spasms. *Neurology* 1981; 31: 688-694.

[9] Hashimoto T, Hiura K, Suzue J, Kokawa T, Fukuda K, Endo S, et al. Influence of ACTH therapy on overnight sleep polygrams in infantile spasms. *Brain Dev* 1981; 3: 51-56.

[10] Okawa M, Sasaki H. Sleep disorders in mentally retarded and brain-impaired children. In: Guilleminault C, ed. *Sleep and its disorders in children*. New York: Raven Press; 1987, 269-290.

[11] Kohyama J, Ohsawa Y, Shimohira M, Iwakawa Y. Phasic motor activity reduction occurring with horizontal rapid eye movements during REM sleep is disturbed in infantile spasms. *J Neurol Sci* 1996; 138:82-87.

[12] Kohyama J, Sugimoto J, Itoh M, Sakuma H, Shimohira M, Hasegawa T, et al. REM sleep components predict the response to initial treatment of infantile spasms. *Epilepsia* 1999;40:992-996.

[13] Kohyama J, Shimohira M, Tanuma N, Hasegawa T, Iwakawa Y. ACTH activates rapid eye movement-related phasic inhibition during REM sleep in patients with infantile spasms. *Acta Neurol Scand* 2000;101:145-152.

[14] Neville BGR. The origin of infantile spasms: evidence from a case of hydranencephaly. *Dev Med Child Neurol* 1972; 14: 644-656.

[15] Kohyama J. Sleep as a window on the developing brain. *Curr Probl Pediatr* 1998; 28: 73-92.

[16] Kohyama J. REM sleep atonia: responsible brain regions, quantification, and clinical implication. *Brain Dev* 2000;22:S136-S142.

[17] Kaga M, Marsh RR, Fukuyama Y. Auditory brain stem responses in infantile spasms. *Int J Paediatr Otorhinolaryngol* 1982;4:57-67.

[18] Miyazaki M, Hashimoto T, Tayama M, Kuroda Y. Brainstem involvement in infantile spasms: A study employing brainstem evoked potentials and magnetic resonance imaging. *Neuropediatrics* 1993;24:126-30.

[19] Curatolo P, Cardona F, Cusmai R. BAEPs in infantile spasms. *Brain Dev* 1989;11:347-8.

[20] Chugani HT, Shewmon DA, Sankar R, Chen BC, Phelps ME. Infantile spasms: lenticular nuclei and brainstem activation on positron emission tomography. *Ann Neurol* 1992; 31: 212-219.

[21] Haginoya K, Kon K, Tanaka S, et al. The origin of hypsarrythmia and tonic spasms in West syndrome: evidence from a case of porencephaly and hydrocephalus with focal hypsayyhthmia. *Brain Dev* 1999;21:129-131.

[22] Haginoya K, Munakata M, Yokoyama H, et al. Mechanism of tonic spasms in West syndrome viewed from ictal SPECT findings. *Ann Rep Jpn Epi Res Found* 2003;15: 65-70.

[23] Morimatsu Y, Murofushi K, Handa T, Shinohara T, Shiraki H. Pathological studies of severe physically and mentally handicapped - with special reference to four cases of infantile spasms (in Japanese). *Shinkei Kenkyu no Shinpo* 1972;16:465-470.

[24] Satoh J, Mizutani T, Morimatsu Y. Neuropathology of the brainstem in age-dependent epileptic encephalopathy – especially of cases with infantile spasms. *Brain Dev* 1986;8:443-449.

[25] Tominaga I, Yanai K, Kashima H, Kato Y, Sekiyama S, Yokochi A, et al. Observation anatomo-clinique d'une séquelle d'encéhalopathie aiguë. *Rev Neurol (Paris)* 1986; 5: 524-529.

[26] Hayashi M, Itoh M, Araki S, Kumada S, Tanuma N, Kohji T, et al. Immunohistochemical analysis of brainstem lesions in infantile spasms. *Neuropathology* 2000;20:297-303..

[27] Garcia-Rill E. Mechanisms of sleep and wakefulness. In Lee-Chiong Jr TL, Sateia MJ, Carskadon MA (eds) *Sleep medicine*, Hanley & Belfus, Philadelphia, pp31-39, 2002

[28] Lydic R, Baghdoyan HA, Hibbard L, Bonyak EV, DeJoseph MR, Hawkins RA. Regional brain glucose metabolism is altered during rapid eye movement sleep in the cat: a preliminary study. *J Comp Neurol* 1991;304:517-29.

[29] Maquet P Delgueldre C, Delfore G, et al. Functional neuroanatomy of human slow wave sleep. *J Neurosci* 1997;17:2807-12.

[30] Maquet P, Péters J-M, Aerts J, Delfiore G, Degueldre C, Luxen A, et al. Functional neuroanatomy of human rapid-eye-movement sleep and dreaming. *Nature* 1996; 383: 163-166.

[31] Hobson JA, Stickgold R, Pace-Schott EF. The neuropsychology of REM sleep dreaming. *Neuroreport* 1998; 9: R1-R14.

[32] Braun AR, Balkin TJ, Wesensten NJ, Carson RE, Varga M, Baldwin P, et al. Regional cerebral blood flow throughout the sleep-wake cycle. An $H_2{}^{15}O$ PET study. *Brain* 1997; 120: 1173-1197.

[33] Kohyama, J. REM sleep atonia: from basic background to clinical application. *J Med Dent Sci,* 2001, 48, 29-39.

[34] Lai YY, Siegel JM. Muscle tone suppression and stepping produced by stimulation of midbrain and rostral pontine reticular formation. *J Neurosci,* 1990;10:2727-2734.

[35] Lai YY, Siegel JM. Medullary regions mediating atonia. *J Neurosci,* 1998;8:4790-4796.

[36] Takakusaki, K, Shimoda N, Matsuyama K, et al. Discharge properties of medullary reticulospinal neurons during postural changes induced by intra-pontine injections of carbachol, atropine and serotonin, and their functional linkages to hindlimb motoneurons in cats. *Exp Brain Res,* 1994;99:361-374.

[37] Lai YY, Siegel, JM, Wilson WJ. Effect of blood pressure on medial medulla-induced muscle atonia. *Am J Physiol,* 1987;252: H1249-1257.

[38] Lai YY, Siegel J.M Pontomedullary glutamate receptors mediating locomotion and muscle tone suppression. *J Neurosci,* 1991;11: 2931-2937.

[39] Takakusaki, K., Matsuyama K, Kobayashi Y, et al. Pontine microinjection of carbachol and critical zone for inducing postural atonia in reflexively standing decerebrate cats. *Neurosci Lett* 1993; 153:185-188.

[40] Xi MC, Morales FR, Chase MH. The motor inhibitory system operating during active sleep is tonically suppressed by GABAergic mechanisms during other states. *J Neurophysiol* 2001; 86: 1908-1915.

[41] Mori S, Iwakiri H, Honma Y, et al. Neuroanatomical and neurophysiological bases of postural control. *Adv Neurol* 1995;67:289-303.

[42] Tononi G, Pompeiano O. Pharmacology of the cholinergic system. In: Kales, A. (ed), *The pharmacology of sleep*. Springer, Berlin, 195:143-210.

[43] Siegel JM, Wheeler RL, McGinty DJ. Activity of medullary reticular formation neurons in the unrestrained cat during waking and sleep. *Brain Res* 1979; 179: 49-60.

[44] Siegel J.M, Nienhuis R, Fahringer HM, et al. Neuronal activity in narcolepsy: identification of cataplexy-related cells in the medial medulla. *Science* 1991; 252: 1315-1318.

[45] Takakusaki K, KOhyama J, Matsuyama K, et al. Medullary reticulospinal tract mediating the generalized motor inhibition in cats: Parallel inhibitory mechanisms acting on motoneurons and on interneuronal transmission in reflex pathways. *Neuroscience* 2001; 103: 511-527.

[46] Rekling JC, Funk GD, Bayliss DA, et al. Synaptic control of motoneuronal excitability. *Physiol Rev* 2000; 80: 767-852.

[47] Holstege JC, Kuypers, HG.. Brainstem projections to spinal motoneurons: an update *Neuroscience* 1987; 23: 809-821.

[48] Noda H, Adey WR. Changes in neuronal activity in association cortex of the cat in relation to sleep and wakefulness. *Brain Res* 1970; 19: 263-275.

[49] Siegel JM, Tomaszewski KS, Wheeler RL. Behavioral organization of reticular formation in the unrestrained cat. II. Cells related to facial movements. *J Neurophysiol* 1983;50: 717-723.

[50] Trulson ME, Jacobs BL. Activity of serotonin-containing neurons in freely moving cats. In:Jacobs, B.L., et al (eds), *Serotonin, neurotransmission and behavior.* MIT press, Cambridge, 1981:339-365.

[51] Sleep Research Society. *Basic of sleep behavior.* Los Angeles: UCLA,1993.

[52] Okabe S, Kubin L. Role of 5HT1 receptors in the control of hypoglossal motoneurons in vivo. *Sleep* 1996; 19(10 Suppl): S150-S153.

[53] Sakai K, Crochet S. Serotonergic dorsal raphe neurons cease firing by disfacilitation during paradoxical sleep. *Neuroreport* 2000; 11: 3237-3241.

[54] Mileykovskiy BY, Kiyashchenko LI, Kodama T, et al. Activation of pontine and medullary motor inhibitory regions reduces discharge in neurons located in the locus coeruleus and the anatomical equivalent of the midbrain locomotor region. *J Neurosci* 2000; 20: 8551-8558.

[55] Wu MF, Gulyani SA, Yau E, et al. Locus coeruleus neurons: cessation of activity during cataplexy. *Neuroscience* 1999; 91: 1389-1399.

[56] Bourgin P, Huitron-Resendiz S, Spier AD, et al. Hypocretin-1 modulates rapid eye movement sleep through activation of locus coeruleus neurons. *J Neurosci* 2000; 20: 7760-7765.

[57] Chase MH, Morales FR. Control of motoneurons during sleep. In: Kryger, M.H., et al (eds), *Principles and practice of sleep medicine.* WB Saunders, Philadelphia, 2000;155-168.

[58] López-Rodríguez, Chase MH, Morale FR. PGO-Related potentials in lumbar motoneurons during active sleep. *J Neurophysiol* 1992; 68: 109-16.

[59] Kohyama J, Shimohira M, Hasegawa T, Kouji T, Iwakawa Y. Phasic motor activity reduction occurring with horizontal rapid eye movements during active sleep in human. *Exp Brain Res* 1995; 107: 137-144.

[60] Ornitz EM, Ritvo ER, Panman LE, et al. The auditory evoked response in normal and autistic children during sleep. *Electroencephalogr clin Neurophysiol* 1968; 25: 221-30.

[61] Kanamori N, Sakai K, Jouvet M. Neuronal activity specific to paradoxical sleep in the ventromedial medullary reticular formation of unrestrained cats. *Brain Res* 1980; 189: 251-5.

[62] Kohyama J, Lai YY, Siegel JM. Reticulospinal systems mediate atonia with short and long latencies. *J Neurophysiol* 1998; 80: 1839-51.

[63] Connemann BJ, Urban PP, Lüttkopf V, et al. A fully automated system for the evaluation of masseter silent period. *Electroencephalogr clin Neurophysiol* 1997; 105: 53-7.

[64] Ongerboer de Visser BW, Cruccu G, Manfredi M, et al. Effects of brainstem lesions on the masseter inhibitory reflex. *Brain* 1989; 113: 781-92.

[65] Nakamura Y, Mori S, Nagashima H. Origin and central pathways of crossed inhibitory effects of afferents from the masseteric muscle on the masseteric motoneuron of the cat. *Brain Res* 1973; 57: 29-42.

[66] Turman J, Chandler SH. Immunohistochemiicaal evidence for GABA and glycine-containing trigeminal premotoneurons in the guinea pig. *Synapse* 1994; 18: 7-20.

[67] Pedroarena C, Castillo P, Chase MH, et al. The control of jaw-opener motoneurons during active sleep. *Brain Res* 1994; 653: 31-8.

[68] Kohyama J, Shimohira M, Iwakawa Y. Maturation of motility and motor inhibition in REM sleep. *J Pediatr* 1997; 130: 117-122.

[69] Petre-Quadens O. Sleep in mental retardation. In: Clement, C. et al (eds), *Sleep and maturing nervous system*. Academic Press, New York, 1972:383-417.

[70] Seguin JJ, Magherini PC, Pompeiano O. Cholinergic mechanisms related to REM sleep. III. Tonic and phasic inhibition of monosynaptic reflexes induced by an anticholinesterase in the decerebrate cat. *Arch Ital Biol* 1973; 111: 1-23.

[71] Hendricks JC, Kline LR, Davies RO, Pack AI. Effect of dorsolateral pontine lesions on diaphragmatic activity during REMS. *J Appl Physiol* 1990; 68: 1435-1442.

[72] Hendricks JC, Kline LR. Differential activation within costal diaphragma during rapid-eye-movement sleep in cats. *J Appl Physiol* 1991; 70: 1194-1200.

[73] Kyotani K, Taniguchi M, Mikami A, et al. Age-related changes of phasic components during REM sleep: the second report. *Psychiatr Clin Neurosci* 1996; 50 (suppl): S14-15 (abstr).

[74] Fish DR, Sawyers D, Smith SJM, et al. Motor inhibition from the brain stem is normal in torsion dystonia during REM sleep. *J Neurol Neurosurg Psychiatry* 1991; 54: 140-4.

[75] Kohyama J, Tachibana N, Taniguchi M. Development of REM sleep atonia. *Acta Neurol Scand* 1999; 99: 368-373.

[76] Kohyama J. A quantitative assessment of the maturation of phasic motor inhibition during REM sleep. *J Neurol Sci* 1996;143:150-155.

[77] Kimura K, Tachibana N, Kohyama J, et al. onic and phasic inhibition indices are constant among nights: New indices for evaluating the degree of the two types of motor inhibition during REM sleep. *Sleep Med* 2001;2:525-9..

[78] Tachibana N, Sugita Y, Terashima K, et al. Polysomnographic characteristics of healthy elderly subjects with somnambulism-like behaviors. *Biol Psychiatry* 1991; 30: 4-14.

[79] Takakusaki K. *Basal ganglia-brainstem systems that control postural muscle tone and locomotion in cats*. The 30th annual meeting of the Japanese Society of Clinical Neurophysiology (Abstract) 2000: 169.

[80] Inglis WL, Winn P. The pedunculopontine tegmental nucleus: where the striatum meets the reticular formation. *Prog Neurobiol* 1995; 47: 1-29.

[81] Segawa M. Hereditary progressive dystonia with marked diurnal fluctuation. *Brain Dev.* 2000;22 (Suppl 1): S65-80.

[82] Hikosaka O. Changes and disorders in voluntary saccades during development and aging (in Japanese). *No To Hattatsu* 1997; 29: 213-9.

[83] Hikosaka O, Takikawa Y, Kawagoe R. Role of the basal ganglia in the control of purposive saccadic eye movements. *Physiol Rev.* 2000; 80: 953-78.

[84] Kohyama J, Shimohira M, Itoh M, et al. Phasic muscle activity during REM sleep in infancy. - normal maturation and contrastive abnormality in SIDS/ALTE and West syndrome-. *J Sleep Res* 1993; 2: 241-9.

[85] Kohyama J, Kumada S, Shimohira M, et al. Nocturnal enuresis and the pontine reticular formation. *Eur Urol* 2000: 38; 631-4.

[86] Sugimoto J, Itoh M, Hasegawa T, et al. Polysomnographic study in patients with severe myoclonic epilepsy during infancy [abstract]. *Epilepsia* 1998; 39 (suppl 5): 80.

[87] Diomedi M, Curatolo P, Scalise A, et al. Sleep abnormalities in mentally retarded autistic subjects: Down's syndrome with mental retardation and normal subjects. *Brain Dev* 1999;21:548-53.

[88] Araki S, Toyoura T, Kohyama J, et al. Disturbance of active sleep components in neonates with congenital hypothyroidism. *No To Hattatsu (in Japanese)* 1996; 28: 484-9.

[89] Kohyama J, Shimohira M, Kondo S, et al. Motor disturbance during REM sleep in group A xeroderma pigmentosum. *Acta Neurol Scand* 1995; 92: 91-5.

[90] Kohyama J, Hasegawa T, Shimohira M, et al. Rapid eye movement sleep in breath holders. *J Child Neurol* 2000; 15: 449-52.

[91] Takashima S, Becker LE. Developmental abnormalities of medullary 'respiratory centers' in sudden infant death syndrome. *Exp Neurol* 1985; 90: 580-7.

[92] Ornitz EM, Hanna GL, De Traversay J. Prestimulation-induced startle modulation in attention-deficit hyperactivity disorder and nocturnal enuresis. *Psychophysiology* 1992; 29: 437-51.

[93] Schenck CH, Bundlie SR, Mahowald MW. Delayed emergence of a parkinsonian disorder in 38% of 29 older men initially diagnosed with idiopathic rapid eye movement sleep disorder. *Neurology* 1996; 46: 388-93.

[94] Segawa M, Nomura Y. The pathophysiology of the Rett syndrome from the standpoint of polysomnography. *Brain Dev* 1990; 12: 55-60.

[95] Mitchell IJ, Clarke CE, Boyce S, et al. Neural mechanisms underlying parkinsonian symptoms based upon regional uptake of 2-deoxyglucose in monkeys exposed to 1-methyl-4-phenyl-1,2,3,6-tetrahydropyridine. *Neuroscience* 1989; 32: 213-26.

[96] Delwaide PJ, Pepin JL, Maertens de Noordhout A. From basal ganglia to moto-neurons; probable involvement of pathways relaying in the medulla. *Adv Neurol* 1996; 69: 111-6.

[97] Shima F, Ishido K, Sun S-J, Machi T, et al. Surgical control of akinesia in Parkinson's disease. *Eur Neurol* 1996; 36 (suppl 1): 55-61.

[98] Hayashi A, Kagamihara Y, Nakajima Y, et al. Disorder in reciprocal innervation upon initiation of voluntary movement in patients with Parkinson's disease. *Exp Brain Res* 1988; 70: 437-40.

[99] Eisensehr I, Linke R, Noachtar S, et al. Reduced striatal dopamine transporters in idiopathic rapid eye movement sleep behaviour disorder. comparison with Parkinson's disease and controls. *Brain* 2000; 123: 1155-60.

[100] Nakashima K, Wang Y, Shimoda M, et al. Reduced late component of exteroceptive reflex in patients with Parkinson's disease. *Electromyogr clin Neurophysiol* 1997; 37: 503-8.

[101] Parker S, Zuckerman B, Bauchner H. Jitteriness in full-term neonates: prevalence and correlates. *Pediatrics* 1990;85:17-23.

[102] Kramer U, Nevo Y, Harel S. Jittery babies: a short-term follow-up. *Brain Dev* 1994;16:112-4.

[103] Shimohira M, Iwakawa Y, Kohyama J. Rapid-eye-movement sleep in jittery infants. *Early Hum Dev.* 2002;66:25-31.

[104] Kouji T, Kohyama J, Shimohira M, et al. Polysomnographical study in the patients of frontal lobe epilepsy with ictal automatism. *Jpn J Psychiatry Neurol* 1993; 47: 339-41.

[105] Kohyama J, Matsukura F, Kimura K, Tachibana N. Rhythmic movement disorder: polysomnographic study and summary of reported cases. *Brain Dev* 2002;24:33-8.

[106] Werth, E., et al. (2002) Selective REM sleep deprivation during daytime. II. Muscle atonia in non-REM sleep. *Am J Physiol,* 283, R527-R532.

[107] Marcus CL.Sleep-disordered breathing in children. *Am. J. Respir. Crit. Care Med.* 2001; 164:16-30.

[108] Gozal D:Sleep-disordered breathing and school performance in children. *Pediatrics* 1998; 102:616-620.

[109] Kohyama J, Furushima W, Hasegawa T: Behavioral problems in children evaluated for sleep disordered breathing. *Sleep Hypnosis* 5:89-94, 2003.

[110] Rechtschaffen A, Kales A. A Manual of Standardized Terminology, *Techniques and Scoring System for Sleep Stages of Human Subjects.* Washington DC: U. S. Government Printing Office, 1968.

[111] Anders T, Emde R, Parmelee A. *A Manual of Standardized Terminology, Techniques and Criteria for Scoring of States of Sleep and Wakefulness in Newborn Infants.* Los Angeles: UCLA Brain Information Service/BRI Publications Office, 1971.

[112] Guilleminault C, Souquet M. Sleep states and related pathology. In: Korobkin R, Guilleminault C, eds, *Advances in perinatal neurology.* New York: Spectrum Publications, 1979: 225-47.

[113] Whitaker-Azmitia, P.M. Serotonin and brain development: role in human developmental diseases. *Brain Res Bull* 2001; 56: 479-485.

[114] Mann DM, Yates PO, Marcyniuk B, Ravindra CR. Pathological deficits in Down's Syndrome of middle age. *J Ment Defic Res* 1985; 29: 125-135.

[115] Seidl R, Kaehler ST, Prast H, et al. Serotonin (5-HT) in brains of adult patients with Down syndrome. *J Neural Transm Suppl,* 1999; 57:221-232.

[116] Scott BS, Becker LE, Petit TL. Neurobiology of Down's syndrome. *Prog Neurobiol* 1983; 12: 199-237.

[117] Tu JB, Zellweger H. Blood serotonin deficiency in Down's syndrome. *Lancet* 1965; 2: 715-716.

[118] Boullin DJ, O'Brien RA. Abnormalities of 5-hydroxytryptamine uptake and binding by blood platlets from children with Down's syndrome. *J Physiol* 1971; 212: 287-297.

[119] Gedye A. Dietary increases in serotonin reduces self-injurious behavior in a Down's syndrome adult. *J Men Defic Res* 1990; 35: 195-203.

[120] Gedye A. Serotonergic treatment for aggression in a Down's syndrome adult showing signs of Alzheimer's disease. *J Ment Defic Res* 1991; 35: 247-258.

[121] Geldmacher DS, Lerner AJ, Voci JM, et al. Treatment of functional decline in adults with Down syndrome using selective serotonin-reuptake inhibitor drugs. *J Geriatr Psychiatry Neurol* 1997; 10: 99-104.

[122] Wu M-F, Mallick BN, Siegel JM. Lateral geniculate spikes, muscle atonia and startle response elicited by auditory stimuli as a function of stimulus parameters and arousal state. *Brain Res* 1989; 499: 7-17.

[123] Wu M-F, Siegel JM. Facilitation of the acoustic startle reflex by ponto-geniculo-occipital waves: effects of PCPA. *Brain Res* 1990; 532: 237-41.

[124] Rektor IM, Svejdová M, Ménini C. Cholinergic system disturbance in the West syndrome. *Brain Dev* 1990; 12: 790-794.

[125] Maton B, Hirsch E, Vergnes M, Depaulis A, Marescaux C. Dorsal tegmentum kindling in rats. *Neurosci Lett* 1992; 134: 284-287

[126] Baram TZ. Pathophysiology of massive infantile spasms: perspective on the putative role of the brain adrenal axis. *Ann Neurol* 1993; 33: 231-236.

[127] Yoshikura N. *Clinical child neurology* (in Japanese). 6th ed. Tokyo: Nanzando, 1977: 184.

[128] Mori S, Nishimura H, Kurakami C, Yamamura T, Aoki M. Controlled locomotion in the mesencephalic cat: distribution of facilitatory and inhibitory regions within pontine tegmentum. *J Neurophysiol* 1978;41:1580-1591.

[129] Garcia-Rill E. The basal ganglia and the locomotor regions. *Brain Res* 1986;396:47-63.

[130] Rye DB. Contributions of the pedunculopontine region to normal and altered REM sleep. *Sleep* 1997;20:757-788.

[131] Konishi Y, Hayakawa K, Kuriyama M, Saito M, Fujii Y, Sudo M. Effects of ACTH on brain midline structures in infants with infantile spasms. *Pediatr Neurol* 1995;13:134-136.

[132] Zaphiropoulos A, Charnay Y, Vallet P, Constantinidis J, Bouras C. Immunohistochemical distribution of corticotropin-like intermediate lobe peptide (CLIP) immunoreactivity in the human brain. *Brain Res Bull* 1991; 26: 99-111.

[133] Kohyama J, Ohinata J, Hasegawa T. Disturbance of phasic chin muscle activity during REM sleep. *Brain Dev* 2001;23:S104-7.

[134] Snead OC III, Benton JW, Myers GJ. ACTH and prednisone in childhood seizure disorders. *Neurology* 1983; 33: 966-970.

[135] Diomedi M, Curatolo P, Scalise A, Placidi F, Caretto F, Gigli GL. Sleep abnormalities in mentally retarded autistic subjects: Down's syndrome with mental retardation and normal subjects. *Brain Dev* 1999;21:548-553.

[136] Jambaque I, Chiron C, Dulac O, Raynaud C, Syrota P, Benninger CK. Visual inattention in West syndrome: a neuropsychological and neurofunctional imaging study. *Epilepsia* 1993;34:692-700.

[137] Hashimoto T, Tayama M, Murakawa K, Yoshimoto T, Miyazaki M, Harada M, et al. Development of the brainstem and cerebellum in autistic patients. *J Autism Dev Disord* 1995;25:1-18.

[138] Rodier PM, Ingram JL, Tisdale B, Nelson S, Romano J. Embryological origin for autism: developmental abnormalities of the cranial nerve motor nuclei. *J Comp Neurol* 1996;370:247-261.

[139] Rodier PM, Ingram JL, Tisdale B, Croog VJ. Linking etiologies in humans and animal models: studies of autism. *Reprod Toxicol* 1997;11:417-422.

In: Focus on Epilepsy Research
Editor: Shawn M. Benjamin, pp. 105-137

ISBN 1-59454-087-X

Chapter V

MITOCHONDRIAL DYSFUNCTION AND OXIDATIVE STRESS IN EPILEPSY

Hannah R. Cock
Senior Lecturer & Honorary Consultant Neurologist
Clinical Neurosciences, St Georges Hospital Medical School
Cranmer Terrace, London WC1N 3BG
hcock@sghms.ac.uk
Tel: +44 20 8725 4630
Fax: +44 20 8725 3416

ABSTRACT

Mitochondria, in addition to a primary role in energy production, are of increasingly recognized importance in intracellular calcium homeostasis, signalling and ROS (reactive oxygen species or free radicals) production. The role of mitochondria in excitotoxic cell death in many disease states has been extensively studied, and in recent years this has extended to studies of mitochondrial function in seizure related cell death. The process of mitochondrial permeability transition, releasing chemicals into the cytoplasm that initiate cell death pathways, is central in this context. Numerous triggers to permeability transition have now been identified. Many, if not all may act specifically through effects on the redox state of the cell and oxidative stress. There is accumulating evidence that seizures disrupt normal redox homeostasis in the cell. This may be important for seizure related cell death, and have significant functional consequences in surviving neurons. However, which of these changes are compensatory following seizures, and which might be involved both in epileptogenesis and/or neurological damage as a result of seizures requires further study. In addition, many factors including genetic background, seizure type and duration may influence to what extent the biochemical consequences of seizures are detrimental. Reliable markers of pathological, as opposed to physiological, changes are required, which then need to be validated in a clinical setting. This is particularly so given the emerging evidence supporting a role for Reactive oxygen species (ROS or free radicals) in physiological intracellular signalling. At present a range of antioxidant and other neuroprotective strategies appear promising in principle, but detailed studies across a range of in vivo seizure models, in clinically relevant paradigms, are needed before human trials should be considered.

Keywords: Mitochondria; Permeability transition; Apoptosis; Epilepsy; Cell death; oxidative stress

INTRODUCTION

Mitochondria are ubiquitous intracellular organelles, whose primary function is the production of cellular energy in the form of adenosine triphospate (ATP) from food derived fuels. In this capacity alone mitochondria provide crucial support to a diverse range of cellular functions. Mitochondria also play a key role in intracellular calcium homeostasis [1], and are major producers of ROS, which are produced as a by-product of respiration and can be highly toxic. Considering the central position mitochondria thus play in cellular metabolism and physiology, it is no surprise that any disruption to normal mitochondrial function can result in disease states, nor that the nervous system with it's high metabolic demands, and limited capacity for repair, is particularly susceptible when mitochondrial function is compromised. This is illustrated by the prominence of neurological symptomatology within mitochondrial diseases, defined here as diseases in which a disturbance of mitochondrial respiratory chain function, due to either nuclear or mitochondrial DNA (mtDNA) mutations is the primary pathology (reviewed in [2].

Mitochondrial dysfunction has also been shown to be a critical determinant of cell death, with permeabilization of the mitochondrial membrane (mitochondrial permeability transition or MPT) representing a final common pathway through which numerous factors ranging from toxic insults to genetic and developmental signals trigger the process of apoptosis, or programmed cell death [3].

In this context interest in mitochondrial dysfunction, oxidative stress and neurological disease has rapidly expanded over the last 15 years or so, to encompass a broad range of acquired neurodegenerative diseases including Parkinson's disease [4] Huntington's disease [5], Alzheimer's disease [6], ischaemic and traumatic brain injury [7] and Amyotrophic Lateral Sclerosis [8]. Almost any insult to the brain can cause seizures, and epilepsy is a well recognized consequence of traumatic brain injury [9], cerebrovascular disease [10], and of several mitochondrial diseases [11] amonst others. Furthermore that seizures can themselves cause neuronal death is also well established, at least in animal models. Despite this by comparison, interest in mitochondrial dysfunction, oxidative stress and epilepsy is comparatively recent, but rapidly expanding as the focus of epilepsy research is switching from seizure suppression to preventing the consequences of seizures, and the need for antiepileptogenic compounds [12]

This article will discuss the potential role of mitochondrial dysfunction and oxidative stress in epilepsy. Following an introduction to mitochondria and ROS, and a brief overview of some of the methodological issues in this area, I will be primarily discussing this in the context of seizure induced neuronal damage, but also touch on the potentially more interesting, but much less studied, role of mitochondria/oxidative stress in functional changes in epilepsy.

MITOCHONDRIAL STRUCTURE AND FUNCTION

Oxidative Metabolism

Each mitochondrion consists of a double membrane bound structure, with an internal matrix in which many metabolic systems involved in breaking down food fuels reside. These include the fatty acid β-oxidation enzymes, and those of the tricarboxylic acid (TCA/Krebb's) cycle to break down carbohydrates. Electrons from these systems are passed to the mitochondrial respiratory chain (MRC) situated on the inner mitochondrial membrane, which through a series of enzymatic processes (complexes I-IV) passes the electrons to the final acceptor, oxygen, which is reduced to water [13]. At complexes I, III and IV electron transport is coupled to vectoral proton translocation, creating an electrochemical gradient across the inner mitochondrial membrane. This potential energy is then utilized by Complex V to generate adenosine tri-phosphate (ATP). ATP is the basic unit of cellular energy and as such not only a pre-requisite for cell survival, but also essential for a wide range of cellular functions [14], including several ionic homeostasis mechanisms, processing of neurotransmitters, turnover of intracellular messenger systems and repair.

Control of Oxidative Metabolism

Given the additional signalling activities of CNS cells, the brain has particularly high energy demands, and one would expect that energy demand would be inevitably increased during seizures, where there is synchronized hyperactivity of a critical mass of neurons. Under these circumstances, there will be significant changes in both intracellular and extracellular microenvironments, typically with sodium and calcium influx in to neurons, and an increase in extracellular potassium, accompanied by transmembrane chloride fluxes. These fluxes in themselves do not require ATP, but immediately following any discharge, ATP-dependent transport processes are recruited in order to restore ionic gradients, including the Na,K-ATPase, and Ca,Mg-ATPase. It is estimated that about 60% of cerebral ATP consumption is used for operation of the electrogenic Na,-K-pump under physiological conditions, driven primarily by intracellular Na^+ accumulation [15]. At an micro-level, for instance in an unstimulated synaptosome, around 25% of it's respiratory capacity is needed to generate ATP, and compensate for the inherent proton leak across the mitochondrial membrane (see Uncoupling proteins, UCPs, below). Only about 6% of the ATP produced is used by the Na,K-ATPase, under these circumstances, the remainder being available for other functions. However, if sodium channels are fully opened, this goes up to 80% [16]. That this sort of switch can occur demonstrates that needs and capacity must be well matched, and there are various strategies that exist to ensure this. Firstly Increased blood flow will enhance substrate delivery to active regions, probably mediated through local falls in extracellular Ca^{2+}, rises in K^+, adenosine release and nitric oxide generation contributing to local vasodilatation [17].

The role of tissue pO_2 as a factor regulating cellular respiration remains controversial. A recent concept that regulation of cellular respiration is regulated by ADP, O-2 and NO preserves the notion that energy demands drive respiration but places the kinetic control of both respiration and energy supply in the availability of ADP to F-1-ATPase and of O_2 and

NO to cytochrome oxidase [18]. In addition, recent research [18] indicates that NO participates in redox reactions in the mitochondrial matrix that regulate the intramitochondrial steady state concentration of NO itself and other reactive species such as the superoxide radical and peroxynitrite. Thus in addition to known vasodilatory effects, NO may also have an essential role as a mitochondrial regulatory metabolite.

Within the cell, there are several additional coupling strategies that have been characterized, reviewed in detail by Ames [15]. Sites of energy generation are often in close proximity to those with high demands, minimizing the need for trafficking of ATP across the cell. Where there is a local mismatch, creatine kinase and adenylate kinase act to buffer the ATP/ADP ratio at each site, and facilitate the delivery of energy to the required microdomain. There is also evidence that activity induced increases in $[Ca^{2+}]_i$ increase oxidative metabolism, several of the TCA enzymes being regulated by $[Ca^{2+}]_I$ [14]. Energy can also be generated from glucose via lactate (glycolytic metabolism), and glycolysis may also play a particular role in $Ca2^+$ transport, thus also influencing control of glucolysis as well as directly supplying lactate for oxidative metabolism [15]. Neurons in the CNS can also utilize GABA (gamma amino butyric acid) for ATP production through the GABA shunt. GABA is derived from glutamate via GAD (glutamic acid decarboxylase), and broken down by GABA-transaminase, ultimately to succinate, re-entering the TCA cycle as 2-oxoglutarate [19]. It is estimate that between 10-17% of TCA activity is derived from this GABA shunt, and it has been hypothesized that this pathway may contribute to the transition of recurring seizures to status epilepticus, with depletion of the GABA pool [20].

Finally, control of the mitochondrial respiratory chain is arranged such that no single enzyme is rate limiting/has over all control, but instead control is shared between each step (control theory) [16]. This can be assessed by measuring the effect that a small change in the capacity of an individual step in a sequence has upon stead state concentrations of intermediates in the pathway. Thus the control coefficient of an individual step is the fractional change in flux through the whole pathway/the fractional change in activity of the isolated step, induced by slight inhibition of that step. The sum of all control coefficients in the pathway will always be 1. For example the control coefficient of complex I of the MRC assessed in synaptosomes with the complex I inhibitor Rotenone in vitro, is 0.29 (quite high). This means that small changes in complex I activity will have significant effects on electron flux through the whole MRC, and on ATP synthesis, providing a means for subtle demand signals at the level of complex I can result in amplified changes in supply. A common misconception in this context is that increased respiration due to increased ATP demand will increase ROS production. However, the opposite is probably true: ubiquinone is an electron carrier within the mitochondrial chain, providing a link between individual complexes; a major factor in the generation of the oxygen ion is the occupancy of the outer ubiquinone site of Complex II with a semiquinone anion. This occupancy increases when ATP demand is low, and is decreased in state 3 respiration [16]. This would predict that ROS release from a given cell should be maximal sometime after neuronal discharges, and not directly associated in time with the increased activity and immediate cellular response to firing. In practice however we know that even within single neuron membrane potential for example can be different at different locations at any one time, and the same is likely to apply to redox status. Overall, where there are multiple discharging neurons, and massive fluxes in respiratory demand as a result, such as in a seizure, one would expect that free radical production might accumulate through and persist beyond any individual seizure discharge, as will be discussed.

Additional Functions

In addition to their oxidative metabolism function, and mentioned in the in the introduction, mitochondria play a key role in a variety of other cellular processes. Mitochondria are crucial to intracellular calcium homeostasis [21], and possess several calcium transport systems [22]. The concentration of free intracellular calcium is central to normal neuronal functioning, and in turn this has been shown to be critically dependent on functioning mitochondria, as well as secondarily on sodium/calcium exchange [23]. As discussed above intramitochondiral calcium levels also have important regulatory functions, including direct influence on enzymes of the TCA cycle and consequent metabolic rate.

The MRC has also long been recognized as the major source of ROS in the cell [24]. ROS are highly reactive oxygen species, which, unopposed, can damage all cell structures, including lipids, proteins and DNA [25]. Some radicals are toxic via secondary reactions, one of the most important being the production of the highly damaging peroxynitrite from nitric oxide and the superoxide radical. Mitochondria possess a calcium dependent nitric oxide synthase, thus have the potential for peroxynitrite production, in addition to the superoxide and hydroxyl radicals generated by the MRC itself. Under physiological conditions numerous antioxidant systems exist including enzymes such as superoxide dismutase (SOD), catalase, and peroxidases, as well as low molecular weight antioxidant molecules that "mop" up ROS. Of this latter group only glutathione and NADPH are endogenous, others being derived from dietary sources (e.g. vitamin E and Vitamin C, reviewed in [26]). It is thought that under physiological conditions, ROS production is regulated primarily by mitochondrial membrane potential and the NAD(P)H redox state [27]. However, under pathological conditions the normal balance can easily be disturbed, either due to an excess production of ROS, or failure of the normal antioxidant systems, resulting in a state known as oxidative stress. As inhibition of the MRC results in excess ROS production, and ROS themselves are direct inhibitors of the MRC [28] this can result in a vicious cycle, and the potential for secondary oxidative cell damage. This is the context in which ROS have been most studied [29] and the inherent biochemical and physiological characteristics of the brain, including high lipid content and energy requirements make it particularly susceptible to oxidative damage, as will be discussed below. However, as I will also expand upon, there is increasing recognition of the role of mitochondria and ROS in intracellular signalling under physiological conditions [30].

Uncoupling Proteins

Much interest recently has been directed towards mitochondrial uncoupling proteins (UCP). They were first characterised (UCP1) in brown adipose tissue in the context of thermogenesis. Located on the inner mitochondrial membrane, UCPs leak protons from the intramembrane space back into the matrix of the mitochondria. The proton leak effectively deprives ATP synthase of it's proton motive driving force, and dissipates energy, in the form of heat. It was once thought such mitochondrial uncoupling would necessarily be catastrophic, effectively allowing mitochondria to respire without generating ATP. However, UCPs also diminish the production of ROS, and decrease the likelihood of $Ca2^{+}$ entry into the mitochondrial matrix, and additional UCPs have now been identified with specific tissue distributions, and thus must have roles other than simply in thermogenesis. UCP2 is found in muscle, fat, spleen, and the CNS, and there is variance in the distribution of UCP2 in normal brain, suggests there must be a physiological role. UCP2 in brain is found mainly in neuronal populations in subcortical regions involved in autonomic, endocrine and metabolic processes. Where UCP2 expression is abundant you see a higher respiratory control ratio (reflecting more proton leak, and thus less efficient coupling), accompanied by higher local temperatures. Evidence also suggests UCP2 is upregulated in response to excitotoxicity, probably as a protective mechanism to counteract excessive ROS production [31]. This is supported by observations that brain injury induces expression of UCP2mRNA in areas where it is not normally found, and that expression correlates with regional lipid peroxidation. It has also been directly demonstrated that superoxides increase mitochondrial proton conductance, which might be a physiological mechanism for decreasing the concentrations of reactive oxygen species inside mitochondria [32]. Thus there is increasing evidence that the inherent link between uncoupling and respiration may have a role in limiting the change in mitochondrial membrane potential and controlling ROS production despite fluxes in respiratory demand [16], under both physiological and pathological conditions. Whether the accompanying local temperature changes are merely inevitable side effects, or themselves have a role e.g. in neuromodulation at presynaptic terminals is contentious.

Mitochondrial Permeability Transition

Reflecting their central role in cellular metabolism, mitochondria have been proposed to act as the "stress sensor", and in extreme circumstances "executioner" of the cell [33]. Pivotal to this role is a process known as mitochondrial permeability transition (MPT). This is traditionally represented as a pore straddling the two membranes which when opened releases large molecules including cytochrome c in to the cell cytoplasm [34]. This not only directly activates known cell death pathways (e.g. caspases), but also dissipates the mitochondrial membrane potential crucial to oxidative phosphorylation. Caspase activation, and the consequent apoptotic cell death, are in themselves energy requiring, which would seem to be at odds with the concomitant perturbation to mitochondrial respiration. A recent observation that cytochrome c itself, released from the failing mitochondrion, can generate proton motive force and drive ATP synthesis in isolated functioning mitochondria, and thus might contribute to the ATP demands of apoptosis might be part of the explanation for this paradox [35]. To date although it is generally agreed that MPT is protein mediated, no novel inner membrane pore with appropriate characteristics has been identified, and MPT is almost certainly mediated by a group of modified and assembled inner and outer membrane components, including the ADP/ATP translocator, cyclophillin D and possibly porin and hexokinase [36], rather than by a specific pre-formed pore. Numerous factors are known to regulate MPT both from within the mitochondria (e.g. calcium, oxidative stress, membrane potential) and the cytosol (e.g. bcl-2 proteins, nitric oxide) [3], however there is evidence to suggest that oxidative stress links all of these factors and is the critical determinant [36]. Specifically it has been proposed that MPT is not a consequence of the opening of a pre-formed pore, but is the consequence of oxidative damage to pre-existing membrane proteins. As reviewed by [36], MPT can be induced by mitochondrial pyridine nucleotide oxidation (NAD(P)H) is promoted by thiol oxidation or the addition of exogenous ROS, and is inhibited by antioxidants. Furthermore other known triggers (such as Ca2+ accumulation) themselves induce oxidative stress, and thus may act via this process. An extension of this hypothesis is that MPT inside cells is a mechanism for eliminating individual mitochondria ("mitoptosis") which produce excessive ROS, and thus be a last line cellular defence mechanism against mitochondrially generated ROS.

Signal Transduction

With the increased understanding of the diversity of mitochondrial functions has come the realization that mitochondria are active participants in signal transduction pathways, and not simply "power packs" receiving instructions and responding to demands from the rest of the cell. This has been recently reviewed by [30], including discussion of cytochrome c release, hydrogen peroxide formation from the respiratory chain, and the nitric oxide-cytochrome c oxidase signalling pathway.

METHODS FOR ASSESSING MITOCHONDRIAL FUNCTION/OXIDATIVE STRESS

Many of the methods used to study mitochondria and oxidative stress are well established, and have been extensively validated over many years. These include spectrophotometric analysis of MRC and matrix enzyme activities, and substrate linked respiration studies using oxygen electrodes (polarography or respirometry) [37]. These can be applied to tissue homogenates, purified mitochondrial/enzyme preparations, or in the case of polarography to brain slice preparations. Histochemical methods allowing a spatial representation of enzyme activities in a tissue slice are also widely used. HPLC methods can quantify a variety of important metabolites (e.g. glutathione, N-acetyl aspartate [38]), and gene expression and protein synthesis within mitochondria can also be readily studied [37]. Various patterns of enzymatic inactivation in relation to particular insult type/mechanisms are also well recognized. For instance complex I of the respiratory chain is particular susceptible to superoxide damage [28], and the matrix enzyme aconitase is readily inactivated in the presence of peroxynitrite [39]. Methods for measuring ionic transport across mitochondrial membranes (e.g. calcium) and mitochondrial membrane potential are also available, most involving the use of fluorescent dyes (e.g. [40]). Fluorescent dyes can also be used to detect ROS production *in vitro* and *ex-vivo*, but do have limitations with variable auto-oxidation, photoconversion and retention in cells, and possibly direct effects themselves on mitochondrial function [41]. ROS detection, particularly *in vivo*, is difficult due to their short half-life and low concentrations. Direct colorimetric and luminescent probes (e.g. nitro-blue tetrazoleum (NBT), cytochrome *c* reduction [42]) only measure ROS that leave cells, making them of limited value. Most commonly investigators instead look for evidence of ROS damage, and there are established methods for quantifying lipid [43; 44], protein [44] and DNA oxidation [45].

Recent technological advances are also likely to benefit work in this area. Isoprostanes, formed as a product of arachadonic acid oxidation, are checmially stable and of increasing interest as markers of lipid peroxidation as a variety of chromatographic and mass spectrophotmetric detection methods are now in use [46]. It seems likely that in time, particularly given their improved sensitivity and potential application to biological fluids such as CSF from man [47] that these will replace the older colorimetric assays for lipid peroxidation by products. With the streamlining of two-dimensional (2-D) gel technology and the parallel development of facile mass spectrometry for analysis of peptides and proteins, there has been a massive upsurge in protein research [48]. Application of these technologies to the mitochondrial proteome has been limited due to the considerable complement of hydrophobic membrane proteins in mitochondria, which precipitate during first dimension isoelectric focusing of standard 2-D gels, and that functional information regarding protein: protein interactions is lost during 2-D gel separation due to denaturing conditions in both gel dimensions. Some of these technical problems are now being overcome however, and a partial mitochondrial proteome map has been reported [49]. Similarly although study of mtDNA has long been relatively straightforward, due to it's compact and highly conserved nature, nuclear genes important in oxidative stress, epileptogenesis and neuronal damage are now much closer to being understood, with advances in DNA microarray techniques [50].

Consequences of Seizures on the Brain

People with severe epilepsy may experience hundreds to thousands of seizures in their lifetime. Although the time spent actually in a seizure is only a small fraction of their life, their unpredictable and disruptive nature inevitably has a significant morbidity and mortality in itself. For some, the nature of the causative lesion determines their eventual outcome (e.g. malignant brain tumours), and for others the underlying disease is static, and ongoing seizures are their primary problem. However, for at least some patients there appears to be an additional progression of the epileptic process itself, with increasingly frequent seizures, memory disturbance, cognitive decline and decreased quality of life. Though first described under a century ago, an association between epilepsy and brain damage is now well established [51]. As many as 70% of patients with drug refractory temporal lobe epilepsy have accompanying obvious hippocampal sclerosis on neuroimaging, corresponding to neuronal loss particularly in the CA1 and CA3 regions of the hippocampus on histological assessment. This, together with observations that status epilepticus, independent of it's cause, is a risk factor for the subsequent development of epilepsy [52], has formed the context in which much attention has been addressed to the questions surrounding seizure associated brain damage from several perspectives.

Seizure activity continuing beyond 30-120 minutes (status epilepticus) has been clearly shown to result in selective neuronal loss in a wide range of animal models, and specifically demonstrated to be related to the electrical activity and not merely a consequence of often concomitant hyperthermia, hypotension and hypoxia [53]. The extent and pattern of damage varies with the type and duration of insult, the genetic background, and age at the time of the insult. Immature brains appear relatively resistant at least in terms of neuronal death. In man, given the frequent confounding factors/disease processes in patients with epilepsy, difficulty in obtaining control brain tissue for comparison, and the limitations of post-mortem studies, with variable delays to tissue processing, far less definitive histological data is available. However, a small number of case reports where such factors have been considered as best as is possible do show similar patterns of neuronal loss [54; 55]. In addition, clinical observation, neuropsychological assessments, and neuroimaging studies in man infer that damage does occur [56]. The majority of these studies are cross sectional, reflecting the difficulties in conducting longitudinal studies over many years or even decades such as are needed in this field, but the consistency of the findings none the less supports that this is a genuine problem. For example using MR Spectroscopy [57] loss of N-acetyl Asparate (NAA) taken to represent neuronal loss of dysfunction, has been demonstrated to negatively correlate with duration of epilepsy, and occurrence of generalized convulsive seizures. Similar correlations with decreasing cognitive function have been found using psychometric assessments, at least in adult epilepsy populations [58]. Longitudinal studies are also now well underway. Using MRI volumetric methods, a particularly well controlled study including both newly diagnosed and refractory epilepsy patients, has convincingly demonstrated progressive focal neocortical volume loss in a substantial proportion of epileptic individuals over and above that seen in age-matched controls [59]. Of note this included regions distant to the seizure focus, and it may well be that the attention commonly directed just towards hippocampal atrophy represents just the tip of the iceberg.

Thus that cell death as a result of seizures occurs, at least in some circumstances, and that this neuronal death is the likely substrate for some of the morbidity of epilepsy, specifically including cognitive decline, is well accepted. However, to what extent neuronal death contributes to epileptogenesis is much more controversial. It is certainly neither necessary nor sufficient. For example in some epilepsy models in the immature brain, neither the death of neurons nor death-induced abnormalities of surviving neurons appear to underlie the formation of an epileptic circuit, at least within the hippocampus [60]. Similarly amelioration of neuronal death, though to date only partially successful despite a range of attempted neuroprotective strategies, does not prevent the subsequent development of epilepsy in various animal models [61-63]. This is perhaps not surprising. Seizure activity results in a large number of changes and cascades of events at a cellular level, not all of which will lead to neuronal death. Changes in gene expression [64], receptor composition and synaptic physiology [65], activation of inflammatory pathways and growth factors [66] and indeed neurogenesis [67] also occur. Nonetheless, understanding the sequence of events leading to neuronal death in the hope of preventing some of the consequences of seizures is clearly a prerequisite to developing rational neuroprotective strategies. Furthermore neuronal death may be only one end point of processes also resulting in additional functional changes in surviving cells, and which might be involved in epileptogenesis. Any or all of these may play key roles in the epileptogenic process, and a major challenge is sorting out compensatory changes from those directly involved in disease pathogenesis [68].

However, despite the plethora of changes after seizures, given the central role of mitochondria in cellular metabolism, and their ability to influence so many cellular processes directly or indirectly, an understanding of the interaction between mitochondrial function, oxidative stress and epilepsy may be central to the so far elusive goal of developing anti-epileptogenic treatments, as well as preventing some of the other consequences of seizures.

MITOCHONDRIA, OXIDATIVE STRESS, AND EXCITOTOXIC CELL DEATH

Mitochondria and Excitotoxic Cell Death

As has been comprehensively reviewed elsewhere [69], cell death in epilepsy is believed to involve excitotoxicity, whereby excessive glutamate stimulation of the post-synaptic NMDA receptors, and a resultant accumulation of intracellular calcium leads ultimately to cell death. Excitotoxic cell death is also believed to be important in a wide range of other diseases including stroke, trauma and neurodegenerative conditions [70], where it has been extensively studied, both *in vitro* and *in vivo*.

Conventional thinking in recent years has subclassified cell death as either necrotic (acute) or apoptotic (delayed) [71], involving a pre-determined sequence of reactions including enzymatic "chopping" up of DNA giving a "laddered" appearance on DNA gels. Apoptosis is an energy requiring process, thus mitochondrial respiratory function is believed to be a critical determinant of the mode of excitotoxic cell death [72]: essentially where MRC function is significantly impaired, for example due to severe oxidative damage, necrosis occurs; in contrast where there is adequate MRC function to survive the initial insult a delayed cell death by apoptosis occurs. However what is often overlooked/misinterpreted is that the strict definition of apoptosis is primarily a morphological one [73], and other than implying a certain energy reserve within the cell at the time of commitment to death, it presence alone does not tell us what mechanisms initiated the process. Furthermore it is increasingly accepted that neuronal apoptosis in the context of excitotoxicity differs from "classical" apoptosis (originally described in a developmental context). The primary event in the latter has been considered to be independent of mitochondrial function, being genetically based and protein activated, and focused on the caspase-8 activation pathway [74]. In contrast in excitotoxicity, as will be discussed, the primary event probably centres on mitochondrial dysfunction, involving calcium influx and oxidative stress, with secondary MPT and caspase-9 activation. Confusingly secondary changes in mitochondrial function including MPT can and undoubtedly do occur in classical apoptosis as well, and in the context of excitotoxicity and neurodegenerative diseases features of both necrosis and apoptosis may identifiable in individual cells. Furthermore in neural tissue "apoptosis" can be variably triggered by a variety of "necrotic" insults [75] further confounding the issue. A final contributor to this puzzle lies with the relative non-specificity of some of the methods used (e.g. TUNEL histochemistry) to identify "apoptotic" changes [76]. Thus some authors have argued that the distinction between apoptosis and necrosis in excitotoxic cell death is somewhat artificial, each representing one end of a continuum depending on the nature/severity of the causative insult and properties of the cell in question [77]. From a pragmatic perspective, in the context of seizure related cell death, many of the involved mechanisms are probably common to both "excitotoxic apoptosis" and "necrosis" and drawing mechanistic conclusions from morphological data is not appropriate.

Studies *in vitro* and in other disease status have highlighted a number of mechanisms contributing to excitotoxic cell death. These include calcium influx into the cell [78-80], nitric oxide (NO) production via $Ca2^+$ stimulation of cGMP [81], oxidative damage via the production of ROS [82;83], including specifically mitochondrial nitric oxide/peroxynitrite production [84], and activation of mitogen activated protein kinases (MAPK) [85]. As discussed previously peroxynitrite, formed from superoxide and NO, is one of the most toxic ROS and may play a key role both in excitotoxicity, and in NO toxicity. Tyrosine residues on proteins exposed to peroxynitrite are readily nitrated, resulting in a permanent modification that can be both immunologically and electro-chemically detected, and with functional consequences. In neuronal culture systems, peroxynitrite inhibits complex II/II activity and cytochrome oxidase (complex IV) [86]. Astrocytes are relatively protected probably via higher glutathione levels (see below). The TCA enzyme aconitase is also particularly susceptible [39], and subject to increased proteosomal digestion [87]. Various synaptic vesicle proteins such as synaptophysin are also affected, with likely functional consequences on exocytosis via modified protein-protein interactions [88]. Peroxynitrite may also however be involved in compensatory mechanisms, via feedback inhibition of NADH oxidase, indirectly reducing superoxide generation [89], and there is circumstantial evidence that peroxynitrite activates glucose-6-phosphate dehydrogenase, an enzyme in the pentose-phosphate pathway, and at low levels may even be neuroprotective [90]. Furthermore it has been proposed that mitochondrial ubiquinone, the aforementioned electron carrier within the MRC, is involved in protection against peroxynitrite mediate damage [91], illustrating that the relationship between the MRC and peroxynitrite is far from simple. Thus it is not really known what effect blocking peroxynitrite production might have on mitochondrial respiration in vivo, or in the long term.

Of note from a mitochondrial perspective it appears that ATP depletion, although it may lower the threshold for cell death, is not the crucial step. Eloquent studies have demonstrated that impairment of mitochondrial calcium sequestration is the key determinant [92]. This in turn requires ATP, but is also in part potential driven, involving the MPT process mentioned previously [93]. Thus even in the presence of adequate ATP, if the mitochondrion is unable to sequester calcium cell death ensues. As discussed previously, ROS may be mediators through which this occurs [36].

Glutathione

That mitochondria are the primary source of ROS in the cell has already been discussed, and in this context metabolism of a major intracellular antioxidant, glutathione also appears to be centrally involved in both neuronal and astrocytic excitotoxic cell death. Reduced glutathione (GSH) is synthesized from glycine, cystein and glutamate by a series of enzymatic reactions. It can also be regenerated from the oxidised form (glutathione disulfide, GSSG) by glutathione reductase. In addition to being an efficient ROS scavenger, it is irreversibly consumed in detoxification of electrophilic metabolites and xenobiotics, and present in cells throughout the body [94]. Glutathione also reacts directly with NO forming GSNO, serving as a "sink" for NO within cells. Thus GSH is quickly consumed in the presence of high NO levels, and GNSO can itself also contribute to nitrosylation of protein sulphydryl groups, and damage. Brain glutathione is mainly found in astroglial cells at concentrations of around 2-5mmol/l. It is also found in nanomolar concentrations in CSF. Importantly it is also possible to supplement glutathione levels in deficiency states, most studied in malnutrition/chronic infection. In this scenario providing substrate in the form of n-acetyl cysteine repletes stores more efficiently than administering intravenous GSH itself

[94]. GSH itself also has poor brain penetration, which may be overcome by the use of n-acetyl cysteine, although this has not been rigorously demonstrated. Glutathione deficiency results in neuronal death and mitochondrial damage, probably in part via accumulation of hydrogen peroxide. As the turnover of glutathione is rapid, in the order of 30 minutes in adults, in states of oxidative stress, stores may be quickly depleted confounding the situation [95]. Impaired calcium handling [96] and reduced complex 1 activity, probably via thiol modification of the protein [97], have been demonstrated in GSH depleted cells in vitro, and GSH levels predict the vulnerability of cells to a range of stimuli. Otherwise "safe" levels of glutamate NMDA activation [98] and nitric oxide [99-101] are rendered toxic in the setting of concomitant glutathione depletion, at least in vitro, and astrocytic protection of neurons from NO appears to involve a glutathione dependent mechanism [99]. GSH depletion may occur in excitotoxicity both due to ROS consumption, and because extracellular glutamate levels are rate limiting for the glutamate/cysteine antiporter, thus indirectly contributing to impaired glutathione synthesis [102], commonly referred to as oxidative glutamate toxicity [103]. This process is proposed to be the mechanisms of glutamate induced astrocytic death [104].

Escalation Cycles

It will be clear by now that none of these processes function in isolation, and there are several overlap points, which could contribute to escalation of damage once the excitotixic process/oxidative stress has initiated, and probably to continuing damage even after the initial insult/trigger has ceased. For example: NMDA activation increases NO production via Calcium, cGMP and nNOS (neuronal nitric oxide synthase) activation; NO (and peroxynitrite) inhibit Complexes II/II and IV of the respiratory chain; an inhibited MRC produces more ROS; superoxide inhibits Complex I, thus constituting a vicious cycle once the initial oxidative balance is disturbed; the failing mitochondria will handle Calcium less well, and another feedback loop is established. Where there is neuronal death there is usually accompanying microglial activation, yet more NO release (Calcium independent, via iNOS), and this may result in an astrocytic calcium wave, and release of astrocytic glutamate, possible further contributing to the excitotoxicity, though this is controversial [105]. Zinc is known to accumulate in excitotoxicity, and although at low leves this increases oxygen consumption and decreases ROS production, at higher levels the opposite occurs. This certainly appears to be a factor in *in vitro* excitotoxicity [106], though the role *in vivo* is uncertain. As discussed above, GSH depletion exacerbates glutamate, NO and ROS toxicity, representing a further potential mechanisms for escalation and perpetuation of damage following an initial insult. Calcium is recognised as a key messenger in a range of cell functions [21], including probable feedback inhibition of the NMDA receptor [107], and regulation metabolic activity, so impaired homeostasis with mitochondrial dysfunction may have other widespread effects in the cell. Finally dysfunction the endoplasmic reticulum, important in calcium handling and in the folding and processing of proteins, may also be involved, and is influence by calcium levels and NO [108]. Untangling what the key determinants is inevitably not a straightforward process, and many questions in this respect remain unanswered.

MITOCHONDRIA AND OXIDATIVE STRESS IN EPILEPSY

On this background, I will now go on to discuss the evidence implicating mitochondrial dysfunction an oxidative stress in epilepsy.

The first observation to make is that compared to the wealth of *in vitro* data on excitotoxicity, and the large number of studies in other disease states, both using animal models and human samples, there has been relative paucity of data about mitochondrial function and oxidative stress in epilepsy. For example of the nearly 21,000 matches since 1981 relating to "mitochondria*, excitotoxic*, oxidative stress, free radical*" and "brain or neuron" on the Web of Knowledge Database (wok.mimas.ac.uk), only 0.03% relate to epilepsy or seizures, and nearly 50% of these are from the last 5 years alone, despite that epilepsy is the commonest serious neurological disease. In part this probably reflects that human epilepsy, is not a condition easily modelled, and the study of human tissue is largely confined to surgical specimens or post-mortem material, which inevitably represents the end stage of whatever processes are occurring. What data there is largely relates to prolonged seizures (status epilepticus) *in vivo*. Following discussion from *in vitro* studies, I will review this first, before going on to the sparse data on brief seizures, and drawing some conclusions.

PROLONGED SEIZURES ARE ASSOCIATED WITH OXIDATIVE STRESS AND MITOCHONDRIAL DYSFUNCTION

In Vitro Evidence of Oxidative Stress/Mitochondrial Dysfunction

Strictly speaking epilepsy cannot be modelled in vitro, as alluded to above, given that the hall mark feature, a seizure, defined as the clinical manifestation of an abnormal synchronized discharge of cortical neurons, requires a behavioural as well as an electrographic component. Neuronal cultures with or without glial co-culture have been commonly used for studies of excitotoxicity, and although lacking even the most basic of networks, epileptiform discharges from single cells can be identified and may provide insights at the cellular level. In addition hippocampal slices are widely used to study synaptic physiology and ionic changes in seizures, and have in recent years been used in the context of excitotoxicity and oxidative stress, with persuasive results. The electrographic discharges can reasonably be considered the *in vitro* equivalent of seizures, and this preparation does allow some eloquent real-time studies.

Studies in an electrical stimulation hippocampal slice model using rhodamine dyes and digital microfluorimetry have demonstrated that both mitochondrial depolarization and intracellular Ca2+ accumulation correlate with the intensity of electrical activity [109]. Furthermore these changes were send to migrate in a wave along the circuit, and were sensitive to glutamate blockers as would be expected if related to synaptic avtivity. These dyes have limitations, as discussed previously, but with appropriate methodological controls, useful results are achievable, and they do permit real time studies. Frantseva et al [110] have reported some eloquent studies using fluorescent dyes to detect ROS production in hippocampal slice preparations. Rhythmic synchronous activity was induced with topical bicuculline, and increased ROS production was apparent within 10-15 minutes, particularly in the CA3 region where neurons subsequently degenerated. Both the ROS production and cell death correlated with a persistent and progressive increase in intracellular calcium, beyond the duration of activity. It was also shown that ROS scavengers (Vitamin E and glutathione) significantly reduced the seizure-induced neurodegeneration, suggesting causative involvement of ROS in the neuronal death.

Methods have also been developed for monitoring energy metabolism using NAD(P)H autofluorescence signals in hippocampal slices or cultures [111], which can be combined with fluorescent dyes sensitive to $Ca2^+$, ROS and mitochondrial membrane potential respectively in the same experiment. Such studies have demonstrated early intramitochondrial calcium accumulation and mitochondrial depolarization in response to seizure-like event provoked by Mg2+ withdrawal, accompanied by increased NADH production and some ROS generation [20]. The authors suggest that Ca2+ has a role in adapting NADH synthesis and thus ATP supply to the neuron. However, during recurrent or prolonged seizures NADH production was observed to fail, and there was simultaneously increased ROS production, coinciding with increased cell death in the vulnerable hippocampal subfields. As with the earlier studies, many of these changes following prolonged seizures were prevented with Vitamin E. Thus work from both these groups suggests that ROS overproduction is directly related to seizure-induced cell death, and not only develops during but continues after prolonged insults. That oxygen presence is an obligate step in glutamate excitotoxicity [112] in slice systems also implicates ROS.

In Vivo Studies of Oxidative Stress/Mitochondrial Function after Prolonged Seizures

There are numerous well established models of seizures, which all have there limitations and have been comprehensively reviewed elsewhere [113;114]. The majority are actually acute seizure provocation models, rather than true epilepsy (with spontaneous unprovoked seizures), but when studying the consequences of seizures this is less problematic than is the case for e.g. studies of anti-epileptic drug efficacy, and in some cases is advantageous, where the duration and intensity of the seizure stimulus can be reasonably controlled, such as with electrical stimulation models.

There have been a number of studies looking for evidence of oxidative damage following seizures, though in many cases it is not possible to definitively separate the effect of the agent used (e.g. iron, bicuculline, kainate) from the seizures per se. This is particularly true for iron, which is well recognized as a potent stimulant of ROS production in its own right [115]. Intra-cortical iron, used as a model of post traumatic epilepsy, certainly produces both seizures and ROS as assessed by chemiluminescence [116] and markers of lipid peroxidation in brain [117], but this association does not establish cause and effect. Using electron-spin trapping methods, it has also been possible to detect evidence of ROS in hippocampal microdialysate [118] in an iron model, and with more sensitive methods it is hoped detection in CSF might also be possible and thus applicable to man. Pre-treatment with the ROS scavenger adenosine [119] or melatonin [120] has been shown to reduce iron induced hydroxyl radical production *in vitro*, and melatonin to variably delay/prevent the occurrence of spike discharges [116;120] *in vivo* in this model. Thus it might be that ROS are causing seizures, rather than the reverse, though both adenosine and melatonin have actions in additional to their antioxidant capacities, and the conclusion that ROS scavenging suppresses the epileptogenesis following iron injection is perhaps premature.

A number of groups have looked at oxidative stress in kainate-induced seizures. Kainate administered systemically, via the ventricles, or directly to the hippocampus results in prolonged seizures in rat and mouse models. Although kainate may be neurotoxic in itself and thus confound interpretation of results from this model, that following unilateral hippocampal application, bilateral seizure activity and bilateral hippocampal cell death in a characteristic pattern ensue, supports that it is the seizure activity *per se* causing at least some of the observed changes. Bruce et al [121] demonstrated that in the early stages (8-16 hours) after prolonged (5-6 hour) seizure activity, there was increased lipid peroxidation and protein oxidation in regional brain homogenates, correlating with and preceding histological cell damage that was most apparent at 5 days post-status (predominantly affecting CA1 and CA3 in mature, but not young animals). There was also a later (5 days post status) increase in antioxidant enzyme activities (glutathione peroxidase), postulated to reflect compensatory microglial activation and proliferation. Others have reported similar findings with evidence of lipid peroxidation [122-124], mtDNA damage [123;125;126], aconitase activity [126] and decreased GSH [122] levels at time points including up to 3 days after kainate-induced status. One group reported no such change in brain glutathione [124] but it is not clear whether the reported results represent total glutathione (GSH and GSSG, which may be unchanged), or just GSH, and an unconventional method was used. Nitric oxide production is also increased following kainate induced seizures [127;128], as a very early change, occurring within minutes or the insult [128], and preceding both seizures and significant later falls in ATP and phospho-creatine [127], in keeping with known activation pathways following excitotoxicity. As discussed previously the combination of nitric oxide and ROS production provides ideal circumstances for peroxynitrite to form.

A handful of studies in other chemoconvulsant models have also been reported: Bauknight et al [42] demonstrated increased ROS (assessed by spectrophotometric analysis of the SOD inhibitable reduction of nitroblue tetrazoleum (NBT) in the CSF overlying a bicuculline induced seizure focus in cats; Rauca et al [129] studied ROS production after acutely provoked and kindled seizures following pentylenetetrazole administration to rats. The method used is reported to detect free hydroxyl radicals, trapped by systemically applied salicylate, resulting in a stable and quantifiable product. Increased ROS production was seen in the early minutes (1-15 mins) after acute or kindled seizures, but had normalized by 60 minutes; In the same model, markers of lipid peroxidation and nitric oxide production have also been reported following seizures [130]. However despite the small number and limitations of some of these studies, the overall message is consistent – supporting ROS production as a consequence of seizures.

A small number of groups have looked specifically at mitochondrial function following seizures. Kunz et al [131] initially reported polarography and fluorescent spectroscopy on hippocampal slices prepared from kainate treated rats. The animals were sacrificed at least a month after initial kainate treatment, having exhibited both initial status and subsequent spontaneous seizures. The main finding was an increase in oxidative metabolic rates in the seizure animals compared to controls, suggested to represent increased mitochondrial energy turnover, in turn possibly reflecting futile calcium cycling, which would fit with existing hypotheses. In keeping with this, others have reported increased expression of mitochondrial respiratory enzymes in the brains of genetically epilepsy prone (EL) mice [132], postulated to reflect an intrinsic upregulation of neuronal activity even prior to seizures. Markers of oxidative stress, or individual enzyme activities were not however reported so no conclusions can be drawn in this respect.

Our own work has been in the perforant path stimulation model of status epilepticus, which avoids the potentially confounding effects of extrinsic chemoconvulsants [133], and allows careful control of stimulus duration and intensity. We have observed significant decreases in the activities of aconitase and α-ketoglutarate dehydrogenase, two mitochondrial enzymes known to be critically sensitive to oxidative stress, particularly involving nitric oxide (peroxynitrite), as well as reduced levels of glutathione, in the brain homogenates of status animals compared to sham operated controls. These changes were detectable up to 44 hours after the 5 hours of seizure activity, and preceded maximal histological neuronal damage (assessed at up to8 days post status in this study), again supporting a role for ROS production in the pathogenesis of cell death after prolonged seizures. Although changes in aconitase [126] and glutathione [122] have also been reported following kainate seizures, that we can demonstrate this in an electrical stimulation model further supports that these changes are specifically related to the seizure activity. Subsequent studies have included earlier time points, and microdissected hippocampi in order to compare changes in CA3, CA1 and Dentate gyrus and hilar regions. These studies confirm the previous findings, and further suggest that glutathione depletion is an early and critical determinant of cell death [134] and paper in preparation). This data might at first consideration seem at odds with the reports of increased mitochondrial activity in association with epilepsy [131;132]. However, firstly the studies each use a different model, different seizure duration and different time points, making direct comparisons difficult. Secondly a general up regulation of mitochondrial activity is not inconsistent with specific defects such as we have described, and might in fact reflect early attempts to compensate for these. Overall the data consistently support mitochondrial dysfunction and oxidative stress as a result of seizure activity.

In Vivo Studies of Oxidative Stress/Mitochondrial Dysfunction after Brief Seizures

There has been less work looking for oxidative stress after brief seizures or in chronic epilepsy models. In cortical iron induced epileptogenesis, in the interitcal state, persistent markers of lipid peroxidation and impaired antioxidant capacity has been demonstrated [118], but as discussed previously as iron is pro-oxidant in itself this is difficult to interpret.

More convincingly following electroconvulsive shock in rats, avoiding any confounding chemoconvulsants, an acute decrease in regional brain antioxidant levels has been reported [135]. This was said to persist for at least 48 hours after a single seizure, although exact seizure duration is not specified in the paper. The decrease was even more marked where there had been repeated brief seizures. This could be either as a result of, or contributing to oxidative stress in this model, and direct evidence of ROS production was not sought. Arnaiz et al [136] used a chemilluminesent assay to look for lipid peroxidation after 3-mercaptopropionic acid induced seizures in rats. Even in animals sacrificed during the seizures (3-6mins after onset), a 20-40% increase in lipid peroxidation was found in some vulnerable brain regions, although not in all. This had largely normalized 20 minutes later, which is somewhat surprising given the rate of lipid turnover, and that total antioxidant capacity did not change at all throughout, and this is not adequately explained by the authors. An immediate increase in ROS production following individual seizures has also been demonstrated in PTZ-kindled animals [129]. Thus, although there is sparse data it is consistent, and suggests that even brief seizures can increase ROS production, though perhaps only very transiently and the pathophysiological consequences of this have not been sufficiently elucidated to draw further conclusions.

A few groups have evaluated mitochondrial function in chronic epilepsy: Following on from their earlier work in the kainate model (discussed above, [131]) the same group [137] used a pilocarpine model in which following 40 minutes of status epilepticus, seizures were terminated with diazepam, and the rats then monitored for seizures over prior to sacrifice for biochemical studies at 30 days. At this time point substantial neuronal death in CA1 and CA3 has already occurred, and the reported observations must predominantly reflect activity in surviving neurons and glia, rather than being necessarily related to ongoing cell death. Significant decreases in the activities of complex I and complex IV (cytochrome oxidase) are reported in the CA3 and CA1 subfields, accompanied by reduced mitochondrial membrane potential were reported, with relative preservation of all in the dentate and parahippocampal gyri. Succinate dehydrogenase was unaffected, and all MRC activities were reported as a ratio to citrate synthase (CS: a marker of mitochondrial content), indicating that these are specific changes, and not simply a reflection of reduced cell/mitochondrial numbers in the damaged subfields, assuming that CS and succinate dehydrogenase are not independently upregulated. The observed enzyme defects were sufficient to result in reduced respiration, and shown to be of sufficient magnitude to themselves lower mitochondrial membrane potential. The authors also found mtDNA copy number to be reduced in CA3, and suggest that this is the underlying mechanism, given that mtDNA contributes significantly to complex I and IV, but not to succinate dehydrogenase or CS. However complex III activity (also with mtDNA components) was not directly assessed, and there was no significant decrease in mtDNA copy number in CA1 despite biochemical changes of similar magnitude, which is not really accounted for. Ongoing oxidative stress could equally account for the findings, especially given that reduced respiration would be expected to increase ROS production. Endogenous antioxidant capacity was not assessed, and although *in vitro* high doses of Hydrogen peroxide did not mimic the findings, other ROS or antioxidant strategies were not assessed, so their conclusion that oxidative enzymatic modifications were not contributors cannot be considered certain.

Human Studies of Oxidative Stress/Mitochondrial Function in Epilepsy

Studies of mitochondrial dysfunction or oxidative stress in human brain are obviously limited by tissue availability, and whether peripheral markers such as erythrocyte lipid peroxidation are of any relevance at all is uncertain. CSF markers of oxidative status might be of value, but are not readily obtained expect in patients where the causes of the seizures (e.g. encephalitis, meningitis) would confound interpretation of the results. Most patients with epilepsy are also on antiepileptic drugs which themselves may influence parameters of interest, independent of effects on seizures. On this background, few studies in human epilepsy have been undertaken.

Studies of mitochondrial function using spectrophotometric enzyme analysis on regional brain homogenates, and polarography on hippocampal slices have been reported from 40 surgical resection specimens from patients with hippocampal sclerosis [138]. Control tissue is of course difficult to obtain for such studies, and the 3 "controls" had pathologically normal hippocampi, but did also have epilepsy associated with other lesions. Complex I activity was found to be decreased in the CA3 region in the sclerosed specimens, and the authors speculate that this might be of significance in the pathogenesis of temporal lobe epilepsy. However whilst clearly of interest, it is difficult to draw mechanistic conclusions from such work as the tissue clearly represents the end stage of a very long process, both in terms of neuronal damage and epileptogenesis.

The antioxidant status in blood was ascertained in 29 patients with active epilepsy (also on a range of antiepileptic drugs), and compared to that of 10 patients well controlled on phenobarbitone, and 50 healthy controls [139]. Higher erythrocyte lipid peroxidation *ex vivo* in response to exogenous hydrogen peroxide, accompanied by lower levels of glutathione reductase, Vitamin A and C were reported in the active epilepsy group, with reversal of all features (except the lipid peroxidation response) in those who were well controlled. However, though the authors conclude that this provides support for oxidative stress in the pathogenesis of seizures, it is a small study, and quite apart from the confounding effect of antiepileptic drug regimes, neither the distinction between cause vs effect, nor the validity of these peripheral markers in CNS oxidative damage are established.

Newer functional imaging techniques, though with poor spatial resolution, may provide further insights, but have as yet been sparsely applied in this area, despite that magnetic resonance spectroscopy (MRS) may provide insights into energy metabolism [140]. Reduced GSH levels have been reported using MRS in 19 epilepsy patients compared to 8 healthy controls, although of note all the patients were also on antiepileptic drugs, and nearly half of the epilepsy patients were in remission following surgery at the time of imaging, making it difficult to ascertain the basis for this. In addition the changes were widespread, seen both adjacent to and in the opposite hemisphere from the epileptic focus. Nonetheless this is an interesting observation, and should be extended, perhaps to include other measures (e.g. in CSF) as validation. It has also been proposed that the interitcal hippocampal hypometabolism detected by FDG(fluoro-deoxy-glucose)-PET in patients with temporal lobe epilepsy is correlated to the glucose-oxygen capacity of the CA3 hippocampal subfield as a result of impaired oxidative metabolism [141]. Whilst another interesting observation, and a carefully conducted study including imaging in patients later undergoing hippocampal resection, and respirometry of *ex-vivo* hippocampal slice sub fields, given that this is a study at the end-point of the disease process, it is again difficult to draw firm mechanistic conclusions from the observed associations. A better understanding of events at the cellular and tissue level is probably needed before we can usefully interpret such imaging approaches, other than as markers of abnormal (epileptic) foci.

What Determines Susceptibility to Seizure Related Neuronal Damage?

That there is differential vulnerability to excitotoxicity and seizure related injury amongst neuronal populations is well recognised, the striking difference between CA1, CA3 and the relatively resistant dentate granule cell layer in the hippocampus being the most cited example. It is also well recognized that age is important, the immature brain being relatively resistant to seizure induced neuronal death [142], although functional changes do occur. Clearly an understanding of the molecular basis of vulnerability (or resistance) to toxic stimuli may be helpful in designing appropriate neuroprotective treatments, and this remains an important question in the field. In the kainate model, markers of mitochondrial oxidative stress (aconitase inhibiton and mtDNA damage) have been reported to be absent in immature brains (postnatal days 12 and 21 in rat), in contrast to the significant changes reported in adult (postnatal day 30 and beyond) animals [126]. These markers also correlated with the presence/absence of cell death, both in terms of age and sub-region, and the authors conclude that mitochondrial oxidative stress is a critical factor, though do not discuss a molecular basis for this.

Age related differences in the production of ceramide after status epilepticus has also been proposed as a potential mechanism. Ceramide is a naturally occurring membrane sphingolipid known to affect a number of diverse signal transduction pathways, is also a potent apoptotic agent, believed to act via activation of a mitochondrial membrane phosphatase [143]. Studies following kainate induced status have reported increases in ceramide and DNA fragmentation correlating with neuronal death in adult rats, prevented by pre-treatment with the NMDA antagonist MK801 [144]. No such changes were observed in day 7 rat pups, but as with other studies whether these is merely an association, or whether ceramide response is responsible for the age related differences in neuronal vulnerability as the authors propose, remains unclear.

More interesting is a recent study of UCP2 in immature brains, and kainate induced seizures [145]. Kainate was administered systemically in doses to achieve similar seizure severity in both adults and neonatal rats, with studies of mitochondrial respiration (polarography of homogenates), mitochondrial membrane potential (immunofluorescence), ROS production (fluorescent probe), and immunohistochemical assessments of neuronal damage undertaken 6 and 24h after seizures. The immature brain was resistant not only to neuronal death but also showed no evidence of mitochondrial dysfunction or ROS production, in contrast to the adults. UCP2 was found to be basally increased in neonatal brain compared to adults, and they authors postulate that increased mitochondrial uncoupling (with consequent reduction in ROS) is the mechanism affording protection. This is consistent with previous results from this model also [126]. In parallel however, upregulation of UCP2 was also seen following seizures in adults, and postulated to represent a compensatory protective mechanism. This was further supported by experiments in which UCP2 expression in neonates was reduced by a low fat diet, and shown to restore mitochondrial coupling and permit ROS production and seizure induced neuronal injury. That UCP2 expression might define neuronal vulnerability is an attractive hypothesis, which might also be relevant to the reported benefits of high fat, low glucose (ketogenic) diets in epilepsy [146], though clearly confirmatory studies in other models are required. What the long term consequences of UCP2 upregulation as a therapeutic manoeuvre might be also remains uncertain.

Neuroprotection in Epilepsy

Various putative neuroprotective agents have been studied using kainate provoked seizures. It is accepted that pre-treatment with NMDA antagonists such as MK801 is at least partially effective, with reduction in neuronal damage [147] and markers of oxidative stress [116] in various animal models. However not surprisingly given it's site of action, this strategy largely fails when employed after seizures have occurred [148], and thus though of mechanistic interest is unlikely to be of clinical relevance. Caspase inhibitors are also of obvious interest, as caspase activation is well documented following seizures both in animals and in man (reviewed in [149]), but have at best provided only partial protection, and often none at all administered after status epilepticus [61;150]. Furthermore at least one study [63] found no antiepileptogenic effect following despite in this instance reasonably successful neuroprotection with a caspase inhibitor. Again this is perhaps not unexpected, as earlier intracellular events including mitochondrial dysfunction and ROS production would not be expected to be affected by this strategy. Previous milder seizures do seems to be neuroprotective in a variety of models [151;152], and it is interesting to speculate that this might reflect physiological upregulation of antioxidant strategies and/or mitochondrial function, affording partial protection against a later insult, though of insufficient magnitude to be damaging in itself. However there is no direct evidence in support of this at present.

Pre-treatment with melatonin, a potent scavenger of hydroxyl radicals, has been shown to partially ameliorate the development of acute seizures [123;153], neuronal damage [153;154], mtDNA damage [125] and lipid peroxidation [123] following kainate, in keeping with the hypothesis that oxidative stress plays an early role in the cascade to cell death in kainate-induced excitotoxicity. Melatonin has been similarly effective in iron induced seizures [120]. However the anticonvulsant vs. antioxidant effects of melatonin cannot be distinguished in these studies as in all, even administered after the onset of status, melatonin ameliorates seizures as well as damage. The same is true for trans-resveratrol, shown to have potent ROS scavenging activity in vitro, which administered prior to kainate reduces both lipid peroxidation and seizure latency and severity [124]. However that a range of alternative antioxidants, with no/little effect on the seizures themselves, also at least partially ameliorate both indices of oxidative stress and of neuronal damage, suggest that antioxidants are independently neuroprotective. For example the synthetic antioxidant (EUK-134) had no effect on kainate induced seizures, but did significantly reduce early evidence of oxidative stress (specific gene induction, and nitrotyrosine immunohistochemistry at 8 - 16hours post status) and histological damage evident at 5 days [155]. Similarly pre-treatment with Vitamin E or N-tert-butyl-alpha-phenylnitrone (PBN, an ROS spin-trapping agent) significantly attenuated observed losses in ATP and phospho-creatine after kainate seizures [127]. The efficacy of antioxidants in vitro as neuroprotectants has already been discussed [20;110]

CONSEQUENCES OF MITOCHONDRIAL DYSFUNCTION & OXIDATIVE STRESS BEYOND CELL DEATH

As discussed previously, cell death itself may not be the key event in epileptogenesis, and just be one marker of pathogenic mechanisms with more widespread consequences in surviving cells. ROS, probably through membrane (lipid) oxidation may influence channel/receptor function (reviewed by [156]). Oxidative protein modifications [157] have wide potential ramifications, Thus understanding of cell death mechanisms could have a wider application in preventing perhaps more widespread non-fatal functional damage, although to date this possibility has been little explored.

In the previously discussed hippocampal slice studies of mitochondrial depolarization and Ca2+ changes [109], it was also noted that the observed changes following electrical stimulation outlasted the actual stimulus, and might thus serve as a "memory" of recent activity and be involved in synaptic activity. Synaptic plasticity is known to involve calcium dependent processes, and to be affected by dysfunction of mitochondrial calcium buffering. For example mice deficient in mitochondrial voltage-dependent anion channels, thought to contribute to the outer membrane component of the MPT "pore", have impairments in learning and hippocampal synaptic plasticity, and blocking MPT with cyclosporin A has similar effects [158]. Although cyclosporin A is also known to have additional mechanisms of action, including on calcium binding proteins, *in vitro* studies on isolated mitochondria reported in the same paper suggested that mitochondrial calcium buffering was the important factor. Various other potential contributors such as effects of calcium or cyclosporin A on GABA receptors were not excluded. Nonetheless, if this proposal proves valid, oxidative stress and mitochondrial dysfunction as a result of seizures could result in memory and learning difficulties not only due to neuronal loss, but also as a result of similar functional changes in the surviving cells. Similarly, modulation of synaptic function in the context of mitochondrial dysfunction could have implications for epileptogenesis. ROS have also been shown to modulate neuronal activity, including synaptic transmission. For example, hydrogen peroxide applied to hippocampal slices can depress the population spike, alter neurotransmitter release, cause hyperpolarization of CA1 neurons and modulate synaptic plasticity [159]. These *in vitro* studies suggest that this is via activation of normally silent NMDA receptors, possibly via inhibition of a redox-sensitive glutamate uptake pathway. This is supported by observations that the changes were prevented by NMDA antagonists or by ascorbate, which mops up hydroxyl radicals, but not by isoascorbate (which does not enter cells) and thus probably due to intracellular actions of hydroxyl radicals. Thus it appears that mechanisms whereby mitochondrial dysfunction and/or oxidative stress might contribute to significant functional changes in epilepsy are beginning to be understood, with obvious implications in terms of preventing the consequences of seizures.

CONCLUSIONS AND AREAS FOR FUTURE ATTENTION

Overall, the fairly consistent data from a range of animal models, suggests that mitochondrial dysfunction and significant ROS production occur following prolonged seizures, and furthermore that there is local oxidative cell damage preceding neuronal death in vulnerable brain regions. Many of the models studied have only complex partial seizures, without additional cardio-respiratory compromise, and the changes observed can be reasonably ascribed directly to the seizure activity, particularly where extrinsic chemoconvulsants have been avoided. Following status epilepticus there appears to be a potential therapeutic window following status of at least a few hours, although all the antioxidant neuroprotective studies to date in this area have included pre-treatment, so this is at present speculative. However it is by no means clear which ROS are of particular importance in epilepsy, where they come from, or which cell components are especially vulnerable (e.g. lipid membranes, MRC or other enzymes, channels or receptors etc.). Different antioxidant neuroprotective strategies may apply depending on the particular mechanisms operating (e.g. Glutathione mainly protects against complex I damage, Vitamin E against complex IV), and "random" neuroprotective attempts without a good understanding are probably inappropriate [160]. Perhaps more important to establish is to what extent the various pathways activated act in parallel or in series. If the former applies then multiple neuroprotective strategies would be needed to prevent cell death/damage, either via a single agent with multiple actions, or using multiple agents. Such an approach is clearly likely to have more widespread, perhaps damaging, implications on other cell functions and may account for why antioxidant/neuroprotective strategies in the clinical arena have been so disappointing to date [160]. It is further possible that different mechanisms will prove important in different models and in different epilepsy syndromes, which will need to be considered in experimental design. Factors related to the seizure eitology, the seizure itself, and to the individual in which they apply (encompassing both genetic and environmental influences) may all be relevant. However despite these hurdles, there are a number of well-established techniques in this area, which have been sparsely applied to epilepsy models, so further laboratory based work addressing these questions is clearly not only necessary but possible, and a prerequisite to rationale and appropriately designed clinical trials.

The question of whether repeated brief seizures might be trigger the same mechanism(s) also needs addressing from the mitochondrial/oxidative stress perspective. The results of Rauca et al [129] suggest that any oxidative stress with brief seizures may be short lived. If this finding is replicated in other models, it would suggest a very short window of opportunity for antioxidant therapy in the acute situation, but there may be a cumulative effect with frequent seizures such that prophylaxis in patients with chronic epilepsy may be justified. A randomized double blind trial of Vitamin E in children with epilepsy [161] showed that 10 of the 12 in the treatment group had at least a 60% improvement in seizure frequency over 3 month period compared to none in the placebo group. Although this is a single small study, and it has perhaps surprisingly not been replicated on a larger scale, this surely should fuel the need for more work in this area, both in animal models, and ultimately in man.

In terms of neuroprotection and antiepileptogenesis, oxidative stress and ROS production are attractive targets, and there is accumulating evidence of their importance in seizure related neuronal damage, and potentially in epileptogenesis. Reliable and markers of damage and dysfunction need to be established from animal models, and translated into clinical tools. Although in other diseases such as stroke promising results from the laboratory have failed to translate into effective clinical strategies, with the exception of hypothermia, much of this can be ascribed to methodological flaws at both ends [160;162]. The challenge for epilepsy is to learn from these mistakes, and conduct carefully controlled in vivo studies in clinically relevant paradigms, and to ensure statistical significance is not confused with clinical significance.

ACKNOWLEDGEMENTS

I would like to thank the Medical Research Council (UK), Welcome Trust, Brain Research Trust, Epilepsy Research Foundation, Johnson & Johnson, UCB pharma, St. Georges Hospital Charitable Foundation and Pfizer (UK) for research support, Hannah Sleven (St Georges Hospital Medical School), Andrew Fisher, Simon Heales, Matthew Walker and Simon Shorvon (Institute of Neurology, London) for intellectual support and scientific discourse.

REFERENCES

[1] Ganitkevich VY. The role of mitochondria in cytoplasmic Ca2+ cycling. *Experimental Physiology 88[1]*, 91-97. 2003.

[2] McFarland R, Taylor RW, Turnbull DM. The neurology of mitochondrial DNA disease. *Lancet Neurology 1[6]*, 343-351. 2002.

[3] Kroemer G, Reed JC. Mitochondrial control of cell death. *Nature Medicine 6[5]*, 513-519. 2000.

[4] Schapira AHV. Evidence for mitochondrial dysfunction in Parkinson's disease - a critical apraisal. *Movement Disorders 9*, 125-138. 1994.

[5] Gu M, Gash MT, Mann VM, Javoy-Agid F, Cooper JM, Schapira AHV. Mitochondrial defect in Huntington's disease caudate nucleus. *Annals of Neurology 39[3]*, 385-389. 1996.

[6] Corral-Debrinski M, Horton T, Lott MT, Shoffner JM, McKee AC, Beal MF et al. Marked changes in mitochondrial DNA deletion levels in Alzheimer's brains. *Genomics 23*, 471-476. 1994.

[7] Leker RR, Shohami E. Cerebral ischemia and trauma - different etiologies yet similar mechanisms: neuroprotective opportunities. *Brain Research (Reviews) 39[1]*, 55-73. 2002.

[8] Orrell RW, Schapira AHV. Mitochondria and amyotrophic lateral sclerosis. *Mitochondrial Function and Dysfunction 53*, 411-426. 2002.

[9] Frey LC. Epidemiology of posttraumatic epilepsy: A critical review. *Epilepsia 44*, 11-17. 2003.

[10] Silverman IE, Restrepo L, Mathews GC. Poststroke seizures. *Archives of Neurology 59[2]*, 195-201. 2002.

[11] Cock HR. Mitochondrial diseases and epilepsy. *Epilepsy Monitor 7[3]*. 2003.

[12] Cole AJ, Dichter M. Neuroprotection and antiepileptogenesis - Overview, definitions, and context. *Neurology 59[9]*, S1-S2. 2002.

[13] Darley-Usmar VM, Ragan CI, Smith PR, Wilson MT. The proteins of the mitochondrial inner membrane and their role in oxidative phosphorylation. Darley-Usmar VM, Schapira AHV, editors. *Mitochondria:DNA, proteins and disease. [1]*, 1-27. 1994. London, Portland Press. Portland Press Research Monographs.

[14] McCormack JG, Denton RM. Mammalian mitochondrial metabolism and its regulation. Darley-Usmar VM, Schapira AHV, editors. *Mitochondria:DNA, proteins and disease. 1[4]*, 81-112. 1994. London, Porton Press.

[15] Ames A. CNS energy metabolism as related to function. *Brain Research (Reviews) 34[1-2]*, 42-68. 2000.

[16] Nicholls DG. Mitochondrial function and dysfunction in the cell: its relevance to aging and aging-related disease. *International Journal of Biochemistry & Cell Biology 34[11]*, 1372-1381. 2002.

[17] Dirnagl U. Metabolic aspects of neurovascular coupling. *Optical Imaging of Brain Function and Metabolism 2 413*, 155-159. 1997.

[18] Boveris A, Costa LE, Poderoso JJ, Carreras MC, Cadenas E. Regulation of mitochondrial respiration by oxygen and nitric oxide. *Annals Of The New York Academy Of Sciences 899*, 121-135. 2000.

[19] Waagepetersen HS, Sonnewald U, Schousboe A. The GABA paradox: Multiple roles as metabolite, neurotransmitter, and neurodifferentiative agent. *Journal of Neurochemistry 73[4]*, 1335-1342. 1999.

[20] Heinemann U, Buchheim K, Gabriel S, Kann O, Kovacs R, Schuchmann S. Cell death and metabolic activity during epileptiform discharges and status epilepticus in the hippocampus. *Do Seizures Damage the Brain 135*, 197-210. 2002.

[21] Duchen MR. Mitochondria and calcium: from cell signalling to cell death. *Journal of Physiology 529[1]*, 57-68. 2000.

[22] Nicholls DG. A role for the mitochondrion in the protection of cells against calcium overload? *Progress in Brain Research 63*, 97-106. 1985.

[23] White RJ, Reynolds IJ. Mitochondria and Na+/Ca2+ exchange buffer glutamate-induced calcium loads in cultured cortical neurons. *Journal of Neuroscience 15[2]*, 1318-1328. 1995.

[24] Cadenas E, Boveris A, Ragan CI, Stoppani AOM. Production of superoxide radicals and hydrogen peroxide by NADH-ubiquinone reductase and ubiquinol-cytochrome c reductase from beef heart mitochondria. *Archives of Biochemistry and Biophysics 180*, 248-257. 1977.

[25] Halliwell B, Gutteridge JMC. *Free radicals in biology and medicine*. 1985. Oxford, Clarendon Press.

[26] Gilgun-Sherki Y, Melamed E, Offen D. Oxidative stress induced-neurodegenerative diseases: the need for antioxidants that penetrate the blood brain barrier. *Neuropharmacology 40[8]*, 959-975. 2001.

[27] Starkov AA, Fiskum G. Regulation of brain mitochondrial H2O2 production by membrane potential and NAD(P)H redox state. *Journal of Neurochemistry 86[5]*, 1101-1107. 2003.

[28] Zhang Y, Marcillat O, Giulivi C, Ernster L, Davies JA. The oxidative inactivation of mitochondrial electron transport chain components and ATPase. *Journal of Biological Chemistry 265*, 16330-16336. 1990.

[29] Cock HR. The role of mitochondria and oxidative stress in neuronal damage after brief and prolonged seizures. *Do Seizures Damage the Brain 135*, 187-196. 2002.

[30] Brookes PS, Levonen AL, Shiva S, Sarti P, Darley-Usmar VM. Mitochondria: Regulators of signal transduction by reactive oxygen and nitrogen species. *Free Radical Biology And Medicine 33[6]*, 755-764. 2002.

[31] Horvath TL, Diano S, Barnstable C. Mitochondrial uncoupling protein 2 in the central nervous system: neuromodulator and neuroprotector. *Biochemical Pharmacology 65[12]*, 1917-1921. 2003.

[32] Echtay KS, Roussel D, St Pierre J, Jekabsons MB, Cadenas S, Stuart JA et al. Superoxide activates mitochondrial uncoupling proteins. *Nature 415[6867]*, 96-99. 2002.

[33] Green DR, Reed JC. Mitochondria and apoptosis. *Science 281*, 1309-1310. 1998.

[34] Martinou JC. Apoptosis: Key to the mitochondrial gate. *Nature 399*, 411-412. 1999.

[35] Atlante A, de Bari L, Bobba A, Marra E, Calissano P, Passarella S. Cytochrome c, released from cerebellar granule cells undergoing apoptosis or excitotoxic death, can generate protonmotive force and drive ATP synthesis in isolated mitochondria. *Journal of Neurochemistry 86[3]*, 591-604. 2003.

[36] Kowaltowski AJ, Castilho RF, Vercesi AE. Mitochondrial permeability transition and oxidative stress. *FEBS Letters 495[1-2]*, 12-15. 2001.

[37] Mitochondria:a practical approach. Darley-Usmar VM, Rickwood D, Wilson MT, editors. 1. 1987. Oxford, IRL Press. *Practical approach series*. Rickwood, D. and Hames, B. D.

[38] Heales SJ, Davies SEC, Bates T, Clark JB. Depletion of brain glutathione is accompanied by impaired mitochondrial function and decreased N-acetyl aspartate concentration. *Neurochemistry Research 20[1]*, 31-38. 1995.

[39] Gardner PR, Nguyen DD, White CW. Aconitase is a sensitive and critical target of oxygen poisoning in cultured mammalian cells and in rat lungs. *Proceedings of the National Academy of Sciences of the United States of America 91[25]*, 12248-12252. 6-12-1994.

[40] Schuchmann S, Luckermann M, Kulik A, Heinemann U, Ballanyi K. Ca(2+)- and metabolism-related changes of mitochondrial potential in voltage-clamped CA1 pyramidal neurons in situ. *J.Neurophysiol. 83[3]*, 1710-1721. 2000.

[41] Buckman JF, Hernandez H, Kress GJ, Votyakova TV, Pal S, Reynolds IJ. MitoTracker labeling in primary neuronal and astrocytic cultures: influence of mitochondrial membrane potential and oxidants. *Journal Of Neuroscience Methods 104[2]*, 165-176. 2001.

[42] Bauknight GC, Wei EP, Kontos HA. Superoxide production in experimental seizures in cats. *Stroke 23[10]*, 1512-1514. 1992.

[43] Gerard-Monnier D, Erdelmeier I, Regnard K, Moze-Henry N, Yadan JC, Chaudiere J. Reactions of 1-methyl-2-phenylindole with malondialdehyde and 4-hydroxyalkenals. Analytical applications to a colorimetric assay of lipid peroxidation. *Chemical Research In Toxicology 11[10]*, 1176-1183. 1998.

[44] Cini M, Moretti A. Studies on lipid peroxidation and protein oxidation in the ageing brain. *Neurobiology of Ageing 16*, 53-57. 1995.

[45] Williams MD, Van Remmen H, Conrad CC, Huang TT, Epstein CJ, Richardson A. Increased oxidative damage is correlated to altered mitochondrial function in heterozygous manganese superoxide dismutase knockout mice. *Journal of Biological Chemistry 273[43]*, 28510-28515. 23-10-1998.

[46] Lawson JA, Rokach J, FitzGerald GA. Isoprostanes: Formation, analysis and use as indices of lipid peroxidation in vivo. *Journal of Biological Chemistry 274[35]*, 24441-24444. 1999.

[47] Greco A, Minghetti L, Levi G. Isoprostanes, novel markers of oxidative injury, help understanding the pathogenesis of neurodegenerative diseases. *Neurochemical Research 25[9-10]*, 1357-1364. 2000.

[48] MacBeath G. Protein microarrays and proteomics. *Nature Genetics 32*, 526-532. 2002.

[49] Brookes PS, Pinner A, Ramachandran A, Coward L, Barnes S, Kim H et al. High throughput two-dimensional blue-native electrophoresis: A tool for functional proteomics of mitochondria and signaling complexes. *Proteomics 2[8]*, 969-977. 2002.

[50] Del Rio JA, Barlow C. Genomics and neurological phenotypes: applications for seizure-induced damage. *Progress in Brain Research 135*, 149-160. 2002.

[51] Meldrum BS. Concept of activity-induced cell death in epilepsy: historical and contemporary perspectives. *Progress in Brain Research 135*, 3-11. 2002.

[52] Hesdorffer DC, Logroscino G, Cascino G, Annegers JF, Hauser WA. Risk of unprovoked seizure after acute symptomatic seizure: Effect of status epilepticus. *Annals of Neurology 44[6]*, 908-912. 1998.

[53] Holmes GL. Seizure-induced neuronal injury - Animal data. *Neurology 59[9]*, S3-S6. 2002.

[54] DeGiorgio CM, Tomiyasu U, Gott PS, Treiman DM. Hippocampal pyramidal cell loss in human status epilepticus. *Epilepsia 33[1]*, 23-27. 1992.

[55] Fujikawa TG, Itabashi HH, Wu AG, Shinmei SS. Status epilepticus-induced neuronal loss in humans without systemic complications of epilepsy. *Epilepsia 41[8]*, 981-991. 2000.

[56] Duncan JS. Seizure-induced neuronal injury - Human data. *Neurology 59[9]*, S15-S20. 2002.

[57] Bernasconi A, Tasch E, Cendes F, Li LM, Arnold DL. Proton magnetic resonance spectroscopic imaging suggests progressive neuronal damage in human temporal lobe epilepsy. *Progress in Brain Research 135*, 297-304. 2002.

[58] Dodrill CB. Progressive cognitive decline in adolescents and adults with epilepsy. *Progress in Brain Research 135*, 399-407. 2002.

[59] Liu RSN, Lemieux L, Bell GS, Hammers A, Sisodiya SM, Bartlett PA et al. Progressive neocortical damage in epilepsy. *Annals of Neurology 53[3]*, 312-324. 2003.

[60] Baram TZ, Eghbal-Ahmadi M, Bender RA. Is neuronal death required for seizure-induced epileptogenesis in the immature brain? *Progress in Brain Research 135*, 365-375. 2002.

[61] Ebert U, Brandt C, Loscher W. Delayed sclerosis, neuroprotection, and limbic epileptogenesis after status epilepticus in the rat. *Epilepsia 43[Supplement 5]*, 86-95. 2002.

[62] Andre V, Ferrandon A, Marescaux C, Nehlig A. Vigabatrin protects against hippocampal damage but is not antiepileptogenic in the lithium-pilocarpine model of temporal lobe epilepsy. *Epilepsy Research 47[1-2]*, 99-117. 2001.

[63] Narkilahti S, Nissinen J, Pitkanen A. Administration of caspase 3 inhibitor during and after status epilepticus in rat: effect on neuronal damage and epileptogenesis. *Neuropharmacology 44[8]*, 1068-1088. 2003.

[64] Becker AJ, Wiestler OD, Blumcke I. Functional genomics in experimental and human temporal lobe epilepsy: powerful new tools to identify molecular disease mechanisms of hippocampal damage. *Progress in Brain Research 135*, 161-173. 2002.

[65] Cohen AS, Lin DD, Quirk GL, Coulter DA. Dentate granule cell GABA(A) receptors in epileptic hippocampus: enhanced synaptic efficacy and altered pharmacology. *European Journal of Neuroscience 17[8]*, 1607-1616. 2003.

[66] Jankowsky JL, Patterson PH. The role of cytokines and growth factors in seizures and their sequelae. *Progress in Neurobiology 63[2]*, 125-149. 2001.

[67] Parent JM, Lowenstein DH. Seizure-induced neurogenesis: are more new neurons good for an adult brain? *Progress in Brain Research 135*, 121-131. 2002.

[68] Walker MC, White HS, Sander JWAS. Disease modification in partial epilepsy. *Brain 125*, 1937-1950. 2002.

[69] Meldrum BS. Excitotoxicity and selective neuronal loss in epilepsy. *Brain Pathology 3[4]*, 405-412. 1993.

[70] Sattler R, Tymianski M. Molecular mechanisms of calcium-dependent excitotoxicity. *Journal Of Molecular Medicine 78[1]*, 3-13. 2000.

[71] Bonfoco E, Krainc D, Ankarcrona M, Nicotera P, Lipton SA. Apoptosis and necrosis: two distinct events induced, respectively, by mild and intense insults with N-methyl-D-aspartate or nitric oxide/superoxide in cortical cell cultures. *Proceedings of the National Academy of Sciences of the United States of America 92[16]*, 7162-7166. 1-8-1995.

[72] Ankarcrona M, Dypbukt JM, Bonfoco E, Zhivotovsky B, Orrenius S, Lipton SA et al. Glutamate-induced neuronal death: a succession of necrosis or apoptosis depending on mitochondrial function. *Neuron 15[4]*, 961-973. 1995.

[73] Kerr JFR. Shrinkage necrosis:a distinct mode of cellular death. *Journal of Pathology 105*, 13-20. 1971.

[74] Ashkenazi A, Dixit VM. Death receptors: signalling and modulation. *Science 281*, 1305-1308. 1998.

[75] Roy M, Sapolsky R. Neuronal apoptosis in acute necrotic insults: why is this subject such a mess? *Trends in Neurosciences 22[10]*, 419-422. 1999.

[76] Charriaut-Marlangue C, Ben-Ari Y. A cautionary note on the use of the TUNEL stain to determine apoptosis. *Neuroreport 7[1]*, 61-64. 29-12-1995.

[77] Martin LJ, Al Abdulla NA, Brambrink AM, Kirsch JR, Sieber FE, Portera-Cailliau C. Neurodegeneration in excitotoxicity, global cerebral ischemia, and target deprivation: A perspective on the contributions of apoptosis and necrosis. *Brain Research Bulletin 46[4]*, 281-309. 1998.

[78] Hartley DM, Kurth MC, Bjerkness L, Weiss JH, Choi DW. Glutamate receptor induced $^{45}Ca^{2+}$ accumulation in cortical cell culture correlates with subsequent neuronal degeneration. *Journal of Neuroscience 13[5]*, 1993-2000. 1993.

[79] Arundine M, Tymianski M. Molecular mechanisms of calcium-dependent neurodegeneration in excitotoxicity. *Cell Calcium 34[4-5]*, 325-337. 2003.

[80] Limbrick DD, Sombati S, DeLorenzo RJ. Calcium influx constitutes the ionic basis for the maintenance of glutamate-induced extended neuronal depolarization associated with hippocampal neuronal death. *Cell Calcium 33[2]*, 69-81. 2003.

[81] Bolanos JP, Almeida A, Stewart V, Peuchen S, Land JM, Clark JB et al. Nitric oxide-mediated mitochondrial damage in the brain: mechanisms and implications for neurodegenerative diseases. [Review] [173 refs]. *Journal of Neurochemistry 68[6]*, 2227-2240. 1997.

[82] Lafoncazal M, Pietri S, Culcasi M, Bockaert J. NMDA-dependent superoxide production and neurotoxicity. *Nature 364[6437]*, 535-537. 1993.

[83] Beal MF. Mitochondria, free radicals, and neurodegeneration. *Current Opinion in Neurobiology 6[5]*, 661-666. 1996.

[84] Almeida A, Heales SR, Bolanos JP, Medina JM. Glutamate neurotoxicity is associated with nitric oxide-mediated mitochondrial dysfunction and glutathione depletion. *Brain Research 790[1-2]*, 209-216. 20-4-1998.

[85] Hughes JP, Staton PC, Wilkinson MG, Strijbos PJ, Skaper SD, Arthur JS et al. Mitogen and stress response kinase-1 (MSK1) mediates excitotoxic induced death of hippocampal neurones. *Journal of Neurochemistry 86[1]*, 25-32. 2003.

[86] Bolanos JP, Heales SJR, Land JM, Clark JB. Effect of peroxynitrite on the mitochondrial respiratory chain differential susceptibility of neurons and astrocytes in primary culture. *Journal of Neurochemistry 64[5]*, 1965-1972. 1995.

[87] Grune T, Blasig IE, Sitte N, Roloff B, Haseloff R, Davies KJ. Peroxynitrite increases the degradation of aconitase and other cellular proteins by proteasome. *Journal of Biological Chemistry 273[18]*, 10857-10862. 1-5-1998.

[88] Di Stasi AMM, Mallozzi C, Macchia G, Maura G, Petrucci TC, Minetti M. Peroxynitrite affects exocytosis and SNARE complex formation and induces tyrosine nitration of synaptic proteins. *Journal of Neurochemistry 82[2]*, 420-429. 2002.

[89] Martin-Romero FJ, Gutierrez-Martin Y, Henao F, Gutierrez-Merino C. The NADH oxidase activity of the plasma membrane of synaptosomes is a major source of superoxide anion and is inhibited by peroxynitrite. *Journal of Neurochemistry 82[3]*, 604-614. 2002.

[90] Garcia-Nogales P, Almeida A, Bolanos JP. Peroxynitrite protects neurons against nitric oxide-mediated apoptosis - A key role for glucose-6-phosphate dehydrogenase activity in neuroprotection. *Journal of Biological Chemistry 278[2]*, 864-874. 2003.

[91] Schopfer F, Riobo N, Carreras MC, Alvarez B, Radi R, Boveris A et al. Oxidation of ubiquinol by peroxynitrite: implications for protection of mitochondria against nitrosative damage. *Biochemical Journal 349*, 35-42. 2000.

[92] Stout AK, Raphael HM, Kanterewicz BI, Klann E, Reynolds IJ. Glutamate-induced neuron death requires mitochondrial calcium uptake. *Nature Neuroscience 1[5]*, 366-373. 1999.

[93] Schinder AF, Olson EC, Spitzer NC, Montal M. Mitochondrial dysfunction is a primary event in glutamate neurotoxicity. *Journal of Neuroscience 16[19]*, 6125-6133. 1-10-1996.

[94] Reid M, Jahoor F. Glutathione in disease. *Current Opinion in Clinical Nutrition and Metabolic Care 4[1]*, 65-71. 2001.

[95] Jain A, Mårtensson J, Stole E, Auld PAM, Meister A. Glutathione deficiency leads to mitochondrial damage in brain. *Proceedings of the National Academy of Sciences of the United States of America 88*, 1913-1917. 1991.

[96] Jurma OP, Hom DG, Andersen JK. Decreased glutathione results in calcium-mediated cell death in PC12. *Free Radical Biology And Medicine 23[7]*, 1055-1066. 1997.

[97] Balijepalli S, Annepu J, Boyd MR, Ravindranath V. Effect of thiol modification on brain mitochondrial complex I activity. *Neuroscience Letters 272[3]*, 203-206. 1999.

[98] Shaw CA, Bains JS. Synergistic versus antagonistic actions of glutamate and glutathione: The role of excitotoxicity and oxidative stress in neuronal disease. *Cellular and Molecular Biology 48[2]*, 127-136. 2002.

[99] Chen YM, Vartiainen NE, Ying WH, Chan PH, Koistinaho J, Swanson RA. Astrocytes protect neurons from nitric oxide toxicity by a glutathione-dependent mechanism. *Journal of Neurochemistry 77[6]*, 1601-1610. 2001.

[100] Bolanos JP, Heales SJR, Peuchen S, Barker JE, Land JM, Clark JB. Nitric oxide-mediated mitochondrial damage: A potential neuroprotective role for glutathione. *Free Radical Biology And Medicine 21[7]*, 995-1001. 1996.

[101] Canals S, Casarejos MJ, de Bernardo S, Rodriguez-Martin E, Mena MA. Glutathione depletion switches nitric oxide neurotrophic effects to cell death in midbrain cultures: implications for Parkinson's disease. *Journal of Neurochemistry 79[6]*, 1183-1195. 2001.

[102] Bannai S. Exchange of cystine and glutamate accross plasma-membrane of human fibroblasts. *S. Journal of Biological Chemistry 261[5]*, 2256-2263. 1986.

[103] Had-Aissouni L, Re DB, Nieoullon A, Goff LKL. Importance of astrocytic inactivation of synaptically released glutamate for cell survival in the central nervous system-are astrocytes vulnerable to low intracellular glutamate concentrations? *Journal of Physiology-Paris 96[3-4]*, 317-322. 2002.

[104] Re DB, Boucraut J, Samuel D, Birman S, Kerkerian-Le Goff L, Had-Aissouni L. Glutamate transport alteration triggers differentiation-state selective oxidative death of cultured astrocytes: a mechanism different from excitotoxicity depending on intracellular GSH contents. *Journal of Neurochemistry 85[5]*, 1159-1170. 2003.

[105] Bal-Price A, Moneer Z, Brown GC. Nitric oxide induces rapid, calcium-dependent release of vesicular glutamate and ATP from cultured rat astrocytes. *Glia 40[3]*, 312-323. 2002.

[106] Sensi SL, Ton-That D, Sullivan PG, Jonas EA, Gee KR, Kaczmarek LK et al. Modulation of mitochondrial function by endogenous Zn2+ pools. *Proceedings of the National Academy of Sciences of the United States of America 100[10]*, 6157-6162. 2003.

[107] Rosenmund C, Feltz A, Westbrook GL. Calcium-dependent inactivation of synaptic NMDA receptors in hippocampal neurons. *J.Neurophysiol. 73[1]*, 427-430. 1995.

[108] Paschen W, Frandsen A. Endoplasmic reticulum dysfunction - a common denominator for cell injury in acute and degenerative diseases of the brain? *Journal of Neurochemistry 79[4]*, 719-725. 2001.

[109] Bindokas VP, Lee CC, Colmers WF, Miller RJ. Changes in mitochondrial function resulting from synaptic activity in the rat hippocampal slice. *Journal of Neuroscience 18[12]*, 4570-4587. 1998.

[110] Frantseva MV, Velazquez JLP, Hwang PA, Carlen PL. Free radical production correlates with cell death in an in vitro model of epilepsy. *European Journal of Neuroscience 12[4]*, 1431-1439. 2000.

[111] Schuchmann S, Kovacs R, Kann O, Heinemann U, Buchheim K. Monitoring NAD(P)H auto fluorescence to assess mitochondrial metabolic functions in rat hippocampal-entorhinal cortex slices. *Brain Research Protocols 7[3]*, 267-276. 2001.

[112] Dubinsky JM, Kristal BS, Elizondofournier M. An obligate role for oxygen in the early stages of glutamate-induced, delayed neuronal death. *Journal of Neuroscience 15[11]*, 7071-7078. 1995.

[113] Loscher W. Animal models of epilepsy and epileptic seizures. Eadie MI, Vajda RJE, editors. *Antiepileptic drugs:phramacology and therapeutics.* 19-62. 1999. Handbook of experimental pharmacology.

[114] Stables JP, Bertram EH, White HS, Coulter DA, Dichter MA, Jacobs MP et al. Models for epilepsy and epileptogenesis: report fromt he NIH workshop, Bethesda, Maryland. *Epilepsia 43[11]*, 1410-1420. 2002.

[115] Gutteridge JMC. Iron and oxygen radicals in brain. *Annals of Neurology 32*, S16-S21. 1992.

[116] Kucukkaya B, Aker R, Yuksel M, Onat F, Yalcin AS. Low dose MK-801 protects against iron-induced oxidative changes in a rat model of focal epilepsy. *Brain Research 788[1-2]*, 133-136. 1998.

[117] Srivastava AK, Gupta SK, Jain S, Gupta Y. Effect of melatonin and phenytoin on an intracortical ferric chloride model of posttraumatic seizures in rats. *Methods and Findings in Experimental and Clinical Pharmacology 24[3]*, 145-149. 2002.

[118] Ueda Y, Nakajima A, Tokumaru J. Antioxidant ability and lipid peroxidation in the hippocampus with epileptogenesis induced by Fe3+ injection into the amygdaloid body of rats. *Neurochemical Research 28[12]*, 1895-1900. 2003.

[119] Yokoi I, Toma J, Liu JK, Kabuto H, Mori A. Adenosines scavenged hydroxyl radicals and prevented post-traumatic epilepsy. *Free Radical Biology And Medicine 19[4]*, 473-479. 1995.

[120] Kabuto H, Yokoi I, Ogawa N. Melatonin inhibits iron-induced epileptic discharges in rats by suppressing peroxidation. *Epilepsia 39[3]*, 237-243. 1998.

[121] Bruce AJ, Baudry M. Oxygen-free radicals in rat limbic structures after kainate-induced seizures. *Free Radical Biology And Medicine 18[6]*, 993-1002. 1995.

[122] Gulyaeva NV, Stepanichev MY, Onufriev MV, Chernyavskaya LI, Moiseeva YV, Lazareva NA et al. Seizure severity in kainic acid-treated rats correlates with transcriptional activity, oxidative stress, and apoptosis in the hippocampus. *Journal of Neurochemistry 73*, S9.

[123] Mohanan PV, Yamamoto H. Preventive effect of melatonin against brain mitochondria DNA damage, lipid peroxidation and seizures induced by kainic acid. *Toxicology Letters 129[1-2]*, 99-105. 2002.

[124] Gupta YK, Briyal S, Chaudhary G. Protective effect of trans-resveratrol against kainic acid- induced seizures and oxidative stress in rats. *Pharmacology Biochemistry And Behavior 71[1-2]*, 245-249. 2002.

[125] Yamamoto H, Mohanan PV. Ganglioside GT1B and melatonin inhibit brain mitochondrial DNA damage and seizures induced by kainic acid in mice. *Brain Research 964[1]*, 100-106. 2003.

[126] Patel M, Li QY. Age dependence of seizure-induced oxidative stress. *Neuroscience 118[2]*, 431-437. 2003.

[127] Milatovic D, Gupta RC, Dettbarn WD. Involvement of nitric oxide in kainic acid-induced excitotoxicity in rat brain. *Brain Research 957[2]*, 330-337. 2002.

[128] Canafoglia L, Franceschetti S, Antozzi C, Carrara F, Farina L, Granata T et al. Epileptic phenotypes associated with mitochondrial disorders. *Neurology 56[10]*, 1340-1346. 2001.

[129] Rauca C, Zerbe R, Jantze H. Formation of free hydroxyl radicals after pentylenet-etrazol- induced seizure and kindling. *Brain Research 847[2]*, 347-351. 1999.

[130] Bashkatova V, Vitskova G, Narkevich V, Vanin A, Mikoyan V, Rayevsky K. Nitric oxide content measured by ESR-spectroscopy in the rat brain is increased during pentylenetetrazole-induced seizures. *Journal of Molecular Neuroscience 14[3]*, 183-190. 2000.

[131] Kunz WS, Goussakov IV, Beck H, Elger CE. Altered mitochondrial oxidative phosphorylation in hippocampal slices of kainate-treated rats. *Brain Research 826[2]*, 236-242. 1999.

[132] Nakagawa Y, Mishima T, Murashima YL, Nakano K. Increased expression of mitochondrial respiratory enzymes in the brain of epilepsy-prone, naive EL mice. *Brain Research (Molecular) 101[1-2]*, 59-61. 2002.

[133] Cock HR, Tong X, Hargreaves IP, Heales SJ, Clark JB, Patsalos PN et al. Mitochondrial dysfunction associated with neuronal death following status epilepticus in rat. *Epilepsy Research 48*, 157-168. 2002.

[134] Sleven HJ, Cock HR. Evidence of free radical production continuing up to 44 hours after termination of status epilepticus in an animal model. *Epilepsia 44[Suppl.9]*, 197.

[135] Erakovic V, Zupan G, Varljen J, Radosevic S, Simonic A. Electroconvulsive shock in rats: changes in superoxide dismutase and glutathione peroxidase activity. *Brain Research (Molecular) 76[2]*, 266-274. 2000.

[136] Arnaiz SL, Travacio M, Llesuy S, Arnaiz GRD. Regional vulnerability to oxidative stress in a model of experimental epilepsy. *Neurochemical Research 23[12]*, 1477-1483. 1998.

[137] Kudin AP, Kudina TA, Seyfried J, Vielhaber S, Beck H, Elger CE et al. Seizure-dependent modulation of mitochondrial oxidative phosphorylation in rat hippocampus. *European Journal of Neuroscience 15[7]*, 1105-1114. 2002.

[138] Kudin A, Vielhaber S, Beck H, Elger EC, Kunz WS. Mitochondrial respiratory chain complex I deficiency in human epileptic hippocampus. *Journal of Neurochemistry 73*, S217. 1999.

[139] Sudha K, Rao AV, Rao A. Oxidative stress and antioxidants in epilepsy. *Clinica Chimica Acta 303[1-2]*, 19-24. 2001.

[140] Duncan J. The current status of neuroimaging for epilepsy. *Current Opinion in Neurology 16[2]*, 163-164. 2003.

[141] Vielhaber S, von Oertzen JH, Kudin AF, Schoenfeld A, Menzel C, Biersack HJ et al. Correlation of hippocampal glucose oxidation capacity and interictal FDG-PET in temporal tobe epilepsy. *Epilepsia 44[2]*, 193-199. 2003.

[142] Lado FA, Laureta EC, Moshe SL. Seizure-induced hippocampal damage in the mature and immature brain. *Epileptic Disorders 4[2]*, 83-97. 2002.

[143] Ruvolo PP, Deng X, Ito T, Carr BK, May WS. Ceramide induces Bcl2 dephosphorylation via a mechanism involving mitochondrial PP2A. *J Biol.Chem. 274[29]*, 20296-20300. 16-7-1999.

[144] Mikati MA, Abi-Habib RJ, El Sabban ME, Dbaibo GS, Kurdi RM, Kobeissi M et al. Hippocampal programmed cell death after status epilepticus: Evidence for NMDA-receptor and ceramide-mediated mechanisms. *Epilepsia 44[3]*, 282-291. 2003.

[145] Sullivan PG, Dube C, Dorenbos K, Steward O, Baram TZ. Mitochondrial uncoupling protein-2 protects the immature brain from excitotoxic neuronal death. *Annals of Neurology 53[6]*, 711-717. 2003.

[146] Amanda E.Greene, Mariana TT, Thomas NS. Perspectives on the metabolic management of epilepsy through dietary reduction of glucose and elevation of ketone bodies. *Journal of Neurochemistry 86[3]*, 529-537. 1-8-2003.

[147] Clifford DB, Zorumski CF, Olney JW. Ketamine and MK-801 prevent degeneration of thalamic neurons induced by focal cortical seizures. *Experimental Neurology 105[3]*, 272-279. 1989.

[148] Prasad A, Williamson JM, Bertram EH. Phenobarbital and MK-801, but not phenytoin, improve the long- term outcome of status epilepticus. *Annals of Neurology 51[2]*, 175-181. 2002.

[149] Liou AKF, Clark RS, Henshall DC, Yin XM, Chen J. To die or not to die for neurons in ischemia, traumatic brain injury and epilepsy: a review on the stress-activated signaling pathways and apoptotic pathways. *Progress in Neurobiology 69[2]*, 103-142. 2003.

[150] Fujikawa DG, Shinmei SS, Nguyen PQ. Caspase inhibition does not protect against seizure-induced neuronal necrosis with internucleosomal DNA cleavage. *Epilepsia 40*, 19-20.

[151] Kelly ME, McIntyre DC. Hippocampal kindling protects several structures from the neuronal damage resulting from kainic acid-induced status epilepticus. *Brain Research 634[2]*, 245-256. 1994.

[152] Kondratyev A, Sahibzada N, Gale K. Electroconvulsive shock exposure prevents neuronal apoptosis after kainic acid-evoked status epilepticus. *Brain Research (Molecular) 91[1-2]*, 1-13. 2001.

[153] Giusti P, Lipartiti M, Franceschini D, Schiavo N, Floreani M, Manev H. Neuroprotection by melatonin from kainate-induced excitotoxicity in rats. *FASEB J 10[8]*, 891-896. 1996.

[154] Uz T, Giusti P, Franceschini D, Kharlamov A, Manev H. Protective effect of melatonin against hippocampal DNA damage induced by intraperitoneal administration of kainate to rats. *Neuroscience 73[3]*, 631-636. 1996.

[155] Rong YQ, Doctrow SR, Tocco G, Baudry M. EUK-134, a synthetic superoxide dismutase and catalase mimetic, prevents oxidative stress and attenuates kainate-induced neuropathology. *Proceedings of the National Academy of Sciences of the United States of America 96[17]*, 9897-9902. 1999.

[156] Cock HR, Schapira AHV. Mitochondrial DNA mutations and mitochondrial dysfunction in epilepsy. *Epilepsia 40*, 33-40. 1999.

[157] Orrenius S, Burkitt MJ, Kass GEN, Dypbukt JM, Nicotera P. Calcium ions and oxidative cell injury. *Annals of Neurology 32*, S33-S42. 1992.

[158] Levy M, Faas GC, Saggau P, Craigen WJ, Sweatt JD. Mitochondrial regulation of synaptic plasticity in the hippocampus. *Journal of Biological Chemistry 278[20]*, 17727-17734. 2003.

[159] Avshalumov MV, Rice ME. NMDA receptor activation mediates hydrogen peroxide-induced pathophysiology in rat hippocampal slices. *Journal Of Neurophysiology 87[6]*, 2896-2903. 2002.

[160] Delanty N, Dichter MA. Antioxidant therapy in neurologic disease. *Archives of Neurology 57[9]*, 1265-1270. 2000.

[161] Ogunmekan AO, Hwang PA. A randomised double-blind, placebo-controlled, clinical trial of D-alpha-tocophorol acetate (vitamin E), as add on therapy for epilepsy in children. *Epilepsia 30[1]*, 84-89. 1989.

[162] Chauhan N, Zhao ZH, Barber PA, Buchan AM. Lessons in experimental ischemia for clinical stroke medicine. *Current Opinion in Neurology 16[1]*, 65-71. 2003.

In: Focus on Epilepsy Research
Editor: Shawn M. Benjamin, pp. 139-198

ISBN 1-59454-087-X

Chapter VI

ICTOGENESIS AND EPILEPTOGENESIS IN EPILEPTIC MUTANT EL MICE

Yoshiya L. Murashima**, *Jiro Suzuki and Mitsunobu Yoshii
Department of Neural Plasticity, Tokyo Institute of Psychiatry, Tokyo, Japan

ABSTRACT

Purposes

In EL mice, ictogenesis has been established at around 10 weeks of age, whereas epileptogenesis will be established through experience of repetitive seizures during development. It is suggested that an "abnormal neural plasticity" may play a crucial role in the establishment of ictogenesis and epileptogenesis, and therefore, can be a potential target for the development of a new pharmacotherapy to the epilepsy.

It is reported that some isoforms of nitric oxide synthetases (nNOS and eNOS) are both necessary for the establishment of long-term potentiation (LTP) phenomena. LTP and Abnormal neural plasticity will play the key roles in the establishment of physiological brain function and pathogenesis of epileptic disorder.

To investigate the role of abnormal neural plasticity in the ictogenesis and epileptogenesis in EL mice brain, epileptic mutant were analyzed by biochemical and molecular biological methods.

Recently, antiapoptotic, proapoptotic factors and neurotrophic factors are suggested to play a key role not only in the cell survival but also in the epileptogenesis. In the brain of EL, DNA fragmentation without cell loss was observed in the parietal cortex and hippocampus which play the key role in the seizure initiation and generalization respectively.

To investigate the the role of antiapoptotic, proapoptotic factors and neurotrophic factors in the ictogenesis and epileptogenesis in EL mice brain, developmental changes of these factors are determined.

* Address correspondence to: Dr. Y. L. Murashima, Department of Neural Plasticity, Tokyo Institute of Psychiatry, 2-1-8 Kamikitazawa, Setagaya-ku, Tokyo 156-8585, Japan, TEL: +81-3-3304-5701, FAX: +81-3-3329-8035, E-mail: murasima@prit.go.jp

Methods

Immediate Early Gene (IEG) (c-fos and zif) expression in EL mice were developmentally analyzed by in situ hybridization by using ^{35}S.

Distribution of GABA concentrations and GAD activities in the parietal cortex of EL mice were quantitatively determined by using ultra micro enzymatic amplification method.

Three isoforms of NOS were assayed by immunoblotting analysis for hippocampal tissues of developing EL and control DDY mice.

DNA fragmentation were detected by in situ terminal transferase-mediated dUTP Nick end labeling (Tunnel method).

The activities of two isozymes of SOD were determined enzymatically.

Proapoptotic Bax, antiapoptotic Bcl-2 and Bcl-XL, Neurotrophic factors; Brain derived neuro trophic factor (BDNF), Neurotrophin-3 (NT-3) and Fibroblast growth factor-2 (FGF-2) were semiquantitatively analyzed by using Western Blot and NIH image with macros and compared with those of control DDY.

Results

In EL mouse brains, IEG expression is related to the seizure history, seizure threshold and age. Even in the interictal period, the animals produce IEG expression continuously when their seizure thresholds are very low. Among IEG expression sites in the brain, it is most remarkable in the hippocampal CA1 and the parietal cortex.

These IEG expression sites are almost identical, with respect to the spatio-temporal specificity, to the brain regions of EL mice where GABA concentrations and GAD activities are altered.

Unexpectedly, eNOS content of EL was very small despite the fact that eNOS appears to be responsible for NO that mediates an increase in local cerebral blood flow during focal seizures. nNOS, iNOS and relatively lower concentration eNOS are essential to establish either ictogenesis or epileptogenesis.

DNA fragmentation has been observed in the hippocampal CA1 of EL mice in the interictal period. Once epileptogenesis was established, EL mice had abnormally low levels of Cu,Zn-superoxide dismutase (SOD) activities in the hippocampal area. After allopurinol (ALP) was given orally to EL, Cu,Zn-SOD activiities increased dramatically in the hippocampus and seizure was deceased.

In the control DDY mice, very low steady-state levels of Bcl-2 and Bax remained constant throughout development. In EL mice, these Bcl-2 and Bax levels increased predominantly after experiencing frequent seizures. However, once epileptogenesis was established, Bax and Bcl-2 levels decreased to the control level. The level of BDNF in EL mice showed a significant increase corresponding to those of Bcl-2 and Bax during the periods of epileptogenesis.

Conclusions

Continuous IEG expression and abnormal GABAergic function may be involved in epileptogenesis in EL mice. It is likely that transiently expressed IEG is involved in the ictogenesis. iNOS is more conspicuous than eNOS, it is conceivable that excess iNOS (and subsequent increase in antimicrobial NO) and relatively lower concentration eNOS (and subsequent decrease in NO identified as endothelium derived relaxing factor (EDRF) may work together to contribute to a focus complex and ictogenesis.

The DNA fragmentation may be associated with the formation of epileptogenesis. And drugs which can suppress free radicals generation and protect brain - such as allopurinol (ALP) - may be promising in new antiepileptic agents.

DNA fragmentation without cell loss in EL mice, the susceptibility of hippocampal neurons to DNA fragmentation increases after experiencing repetitive seizures during development probably due to a change in the balance between protective mechanism and proapoptotic pathway's inactivation. Neurotrophic factors may also play a role in ictogenesis and epileptogenesis through the developmental stages by promoting abnormal synaptic plasticity.

Key Words: Epileptic mutant, EL mouse, Focus complex, Abnormal plasticity, Ictogenesis, Epileptogenesis, Immediate Early Genes (IEG), GABA, GAD (Glutamate decarboxylase), Nitric Oxide (NO), Nitric Oxide Synthetase (NOS), Superoxide dismutase (SOD), free radical, DNA fragmentation, Pro and Antiapoptotic factors (Bax, Bcl-2, Bcl-XL), Neurotrophic factors (BDNF, Nt-3, FGF-2)

1. Ictogenesis and Epileptogenesis in EL Mice Brain Related to Immediate Early Gene Expression

Introduction

Rapid genomic responses to neural stimulation may play a critical role in long-term synaptic plasticity. Recent works have strengthened this idea by demonstrating that neurotransmitter-induced long-term synaptic plasticity requires RNA and protein synthesis during a critical time window immediately following stimulation. These studies prompted the suggestion that genes, such as *c-fos*, which are rapidly induced by cell-surface-receptor stimulation by growth factors or neurotransmitters might be involved in the early genomic response underlying long-term synaptic plasticity [5]. Activation of immediate early genes (IEGs) occurs by increased transcription and is thought to represent the primary genomic response to stimulations, because it does not require protein synthesis. Several IEGs code for transcription factors. These include members of the *fos* families, which dimerize to form the transcription regulatory complex AP1 as well as *zif* which is a member of a family of proteins characterized in the DNA-binding domains.

Developmentally, the site of IEG expression shifted from one site to another and the three dimensional expression area was gradually expanded, suggesting a change in the regional active site during epileptogenesis [6].

These lines of evidence suggest that during development as well as repetitive seizures, frequent expressions of IEGs and syntheses of Fos and Zif proteins might facilitate synaptic conductivity involved in epileptogenesis [6].

We found that IEG expression after seizures is not related to the seizure pattern, but is related to the seizure history, seizure threshold and development of EL [6, 7]. Even in the interictal period, EL mice with long seizure histories and very low seizure thresholds demonstrate IEG expression continuously [6]. This is probably strengthened by repeated seizures. The IEG expression site is however located in the hippocampal CA1, which is the final terminal of various inputs from other areas of the limbic system. It is proposed that the continuous expression of IEGs might play a different role from that of transiently expressed IEGs.

During development of the animals as well as through repetitive seizures, the *zif* expression site shifted gradually from the primary input system of the hippocampus (i.e., the pyriform cortex, the entorhinal cortex and the dentate gyrus), to the hippocampal CA1 [8]. In the parietal cortex, the *zif* expression site was initially localized and ictogenesis was obtained. And then the *zif* expression site became universal and epileptogenesis was established. In general, the initially localized expression site finally became universal and weak all over the cortex [8].

To examine the hypothesized role of the immediate early gene (IEG) response in synaptic plasticity and in epileptogenesis, we studied the spatial specificity of the expression of IEG in EL mice, a well known mutant model of epilepsy.

We observed previously that *zif* was expressed in both cerebrum and cerebellum maximally 30 min after seizure. There were no regional differences [9].

In parallel with the seizure phenomena, the maximum *zif* expression site in the limbic system shifted from the pyriform and the entorhinal cortex to the dentate gyrus subsequently and further to the hippocampal CA3 and CA1 [10].

To understand the role of IEG responses in epileptogenesis in terms of the "abnormal" synaptic plasticity [12] and epileptogenesis [11], we studied the three dimensional spatial specificity of the expression of IEG in the EL mice [11].

Materials and Methods

EL Mice

EL mice had experienced tossing-up stimulations once every week since 5 weeks of age and had a very low seizure threshold. These stimulated EL mice (EL[s]) had experienced the last seizure 30 min before being sacrificed. On the other hand, non-stimulated EL mice (EL[ns]) experienced only one seizure by tossing up stimulation 30 min before being sacrificed. The seizure threshold of EL[ns] was very high compared with EL[s] **(Table 1., 2 Fig. 1, 2, 3, 4)**

Preparation of c-fos and zif Probes

[^{35}S]-labeled probes were prepared by using uridine 5'-[-[^{35}S]thio]triphosphate and T7 or T3 RNA polymerase (Takara) to synthesize RNA transcripts. RNA antisense probes for the 3' non-translated plasmid with a restriction enzyme that cuts 3' to coding sequences [13].

In Situ Hybridization

Whole brains including the cerebellum were obtained from seizure-induced EL[s]/[ns] and control DDY mice. Frozen 10-12 μm-thick sections of the brain were mounted on slide glass and prepared for hybridization with RNA probes as described by Largent et al [14]. *In situ* hybridization was performed as described by Segal and Shilo [11], with modifications as follows: ^{35}S-labeled RNA probes were not denatured with alkali; prehybridization was omitted; hybridization was performed in a moist chamber under unsealed, silicone-treated coverslips at 46°C, using 5 x 105 to 1 x 106 c.p.m. probe for each section; slides were washed twice in 2 x SSC (1 x SSC is 150 mmol/L NaCl/15 mmol/L sodium citrate, pH7), incubated for 30 min at 37°C in 2 x SSC containing RNAase A (Sigma, St. Louis, MO, USA) at 10(g/mL and washed once in 2 x SSC and rinsed once in double distilled water to remove surface salts of sections; and after washing, sections were dehydrated by absolute ethanol, air dried, and exposed to Ultrofilm (LKB) at room temperature for 4 days [14].

Table 1. Epileptic mutant EL mouse

EL mouse: mutant epileptic model

EL[s]: experienced frequent seizures and very low seizure threshold
EL[ns]:experienced no induced seizures and high seizure threshold

The EL mouse is a mutant epileptic model. It shows secondarily generalized seizures.

(1) The susceptibility to seizures has gradually increased during development and repetitive seizures. - **Abnormal Plasticity** -
(2) The initiation site is the parietal cortex and the hippocampus shows a high electrical excitability during generalization of seizures. - **Focus Complex** -

EL[s] have been stimulated once a week since three weeks of age and EL[ns] have been bred without adding tossing up stimulation and have no history of exhibiting seizures. As the control of EL, DDY/ TIP (mother strain of EL) were used.

Table 2. Developmental programs in the ictogenesis and epileptogenesis in EL

Developmental Programs of Epileptogenesis and Abnormal Plasticity

During the establishment of epileptogenesis, two major factors are very important, so that one is genetically determined abnormalities and the other is postnatal acquired abnormalities caused by the repeated frequent seizure history. EL[s] has both factors and EL[ns] has only genetic factors and control DDY has no factors of theestablishment of epileptogenesis.

In the relation of the epileptogenesis and the abnormal plastic phenomena, we have examined the ***developmental changes of***...

1. GABAergic activities,
2. Cu,Zn-superoxide dismutase activities,
3. *c-fos* expression,
4. DNA fragmentation without cell loss,
5. Nitric oxide (NO) metabolites and NO synthetase (NOS) in the hippocampus,
6. Expression of Bcl family (anti- and pro-apoptotic factors) and neurotrophic factors

Seizure Susceptibility of EL Mice Depends on the Development and Seizure History

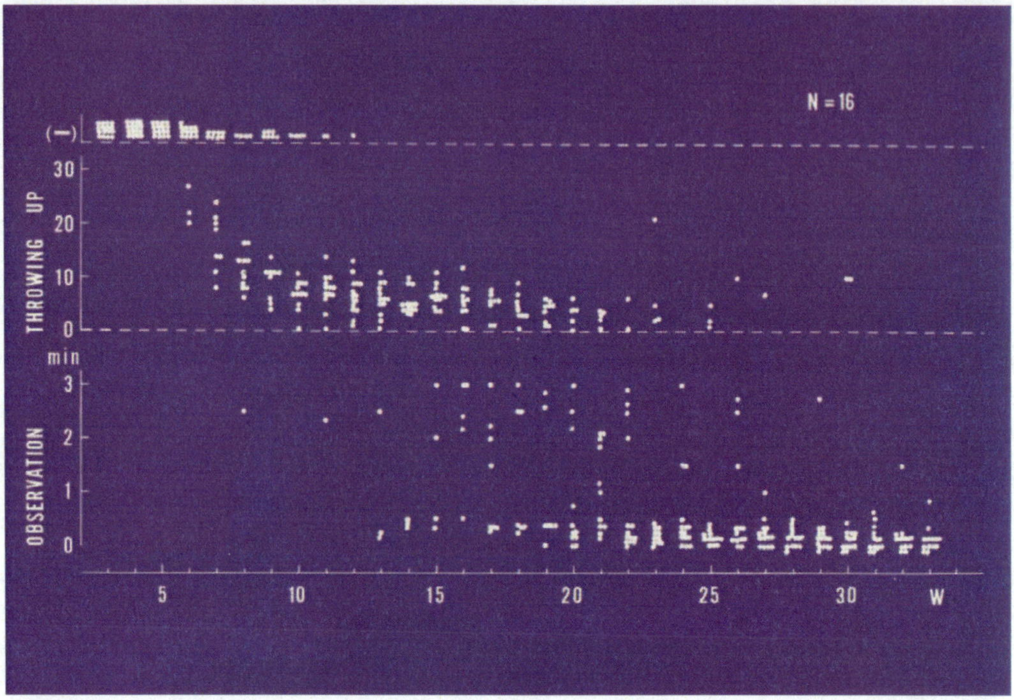

Fig. 1. Seizure susceptibility increase during development in EL

Field Potential Recording of EL Mouse Seizure

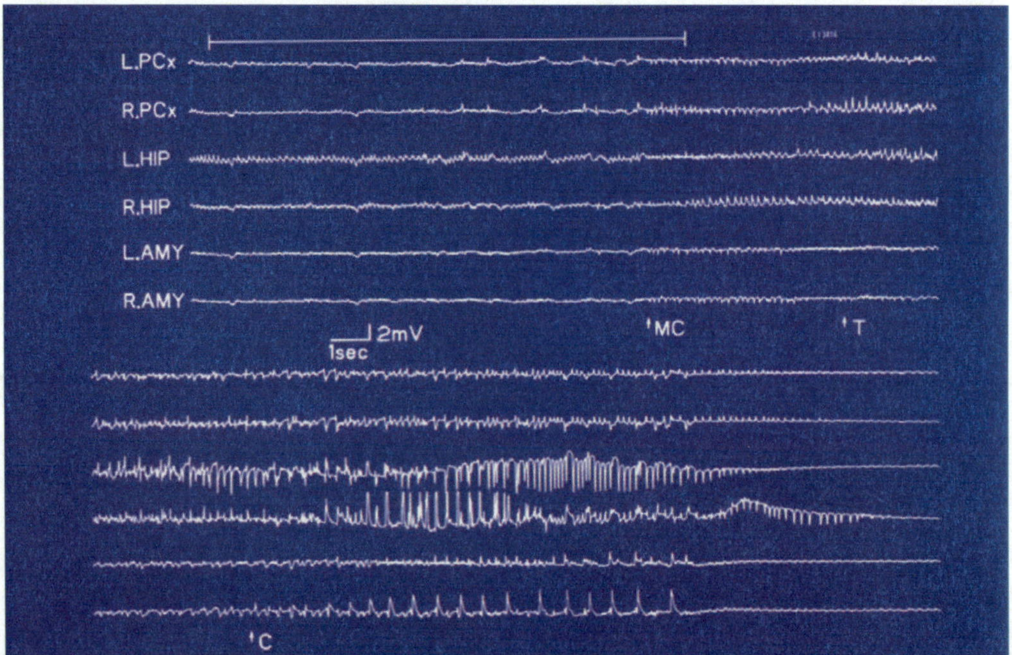

Fig. 2. EEG recording of EL

Seizure Initiation Site is the Parietal Cortex

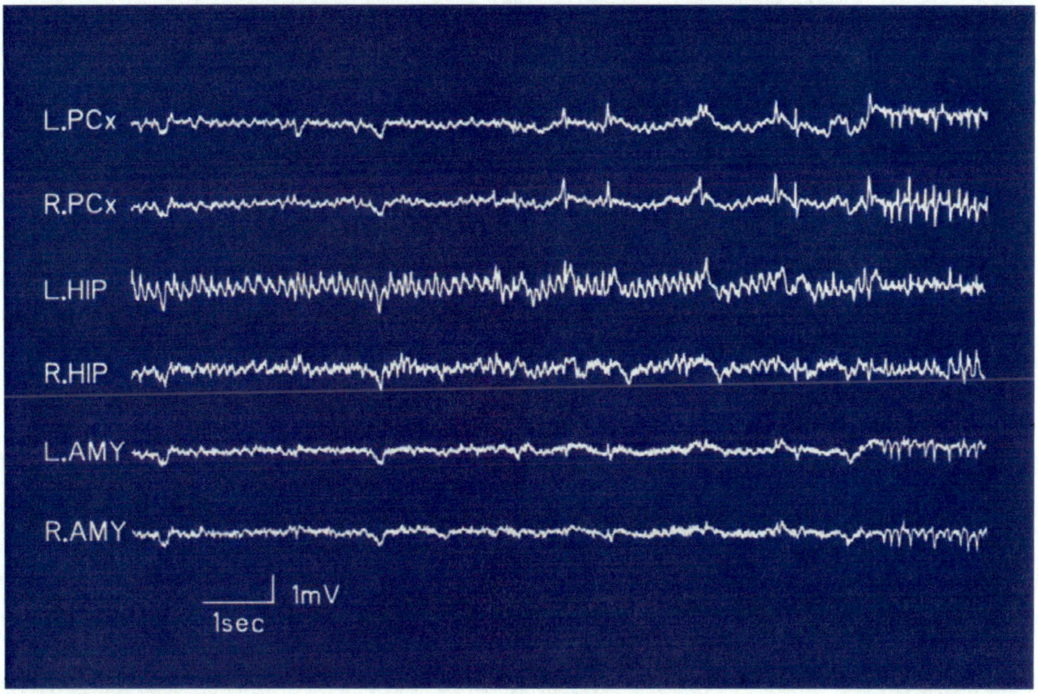

Fig. 3. Seizure initiation site is the parietal cortex in EL

Initiation and Propagation Site of EL Mice Seizure

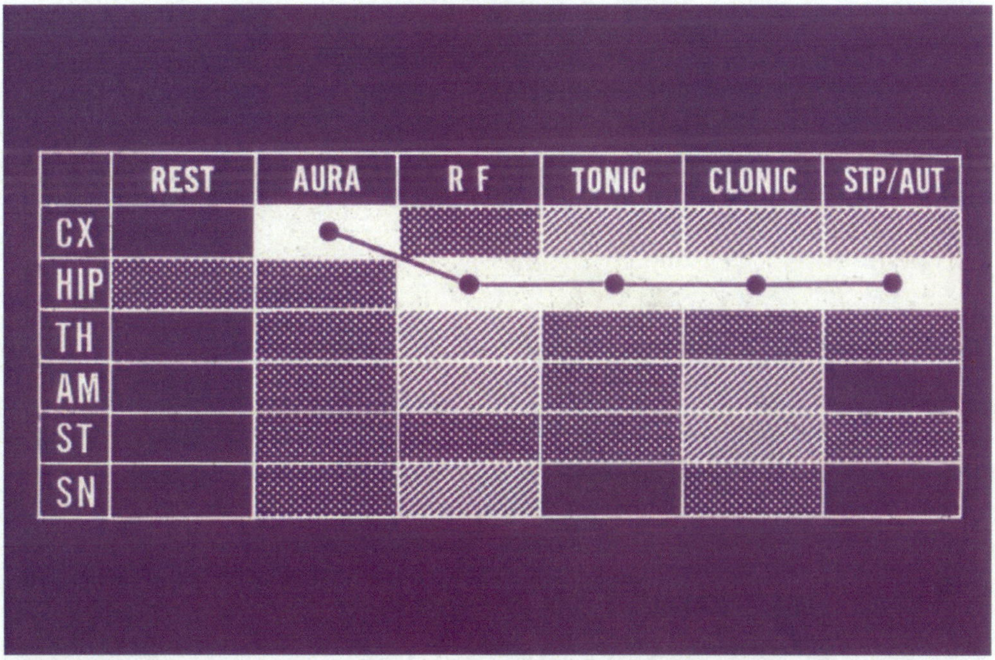

Fig. 4. Schematic representation of the high electrical activity sites during the epileptic seizure

X-ray Emulsion Autoradiography

For autoradiography, Kodak NTB-2 emulsion was used in a 1:1 mixture with distilled water at 42°C. The exposure was done at 4°C for 8 weeks in complete darkness in Pb-sealed chamber. Slides were also developed in complete darkness, and then stained weekly with 0.5% cresyl fast violet for 5 min [16].

GABA and Glutamate Decarboxylase (GAD) Assay

The GAD reaction was allowed to proceed in the standard reaction mixture containing glutamate to yield GABA [16]. GABA was converted to the corresponding amount of NADPH. Then NADPH was amplified by using NADP cycling and assayed fluorometrically [18].

Freeze-Dried Microbrain Region Samples

Fifteen µm thick serial freeze-dried samples of the whole mouse brain were obtained according to the number of Sidman atlas [19]. Micro brain region samples (10-300 ng) were cut out from the parietal cortex and hippocampal pyramidal layer. The samples were weighed on the fish pole quartz fiber balance and applied to the reaction mixture in the oil well [18]. In the parietal cortex [20] samples of 500 µm width were obtained from the rostral to caudal side through 3400 µm. In the hippocampal pyramidal layer samples were obtained from the coronal sections of EL mice which are parallel to the Sidman atlas No. 321 [20]. And the data were obtained from the average of serial two, four or eight samples of each animal in the parietal cortex and single serial 5 samples for the hippocampal CA1, CA2 and CA3 each. Data of one animal were connected by solid line [20]. The number of animals was three for each age, both the DDY and EL.

Results

Effects of Tossing-up Stimulation in DDY

In order to exclude the possibility that *c-fos* and *zif* might be expressed in the handling procedure of tossing up, 20 times tossed up, 30 week old DDY and control DDY mice were examined. The levels of *c-fos* and *zif* expressions of both stimulated and non stimulated DDY were almost silent.

IEG Expression after Abortive and Tonic Clonic Seizures and During Interictal Period in the Cerebrum and Cerebellum of 30-W EL[S]

We have examined whether the expression of IEG might be affected by the pattern of the last seizure experienced. In the case of EL[s], the seizure threshold of which was very low, *zif* expression showed a similar pattern either after abortive or full seizures. There was almost no difference between EL[s] mice after very mild myoclonic seizures for 5 sec (abortive seizure) and those after severe tonic clonic seizures (GTC) for over 30 sec (full seizure). In the pyriform cortex, the parietal cortex and the hippocampus, especially in the dentate gyrus, *zif* expression was remarkably strong. Control EL[s] mice were in an interictal state. The mice experienced the last tonic clonic seizure 4 days earlier. They showed a weak *zif* expression in the parietal cortex, hippocampal CA1 and cerebellum [20].

Time Course of zif Expression after Induced Seizure in 30w EL[s]

We examined when the transient strong IEG expression following an induced-seizure would recover to a weak, continuous level during the interictal period. One hour after seizure, *zif* expression was stronger in the EL[s] with tonic clonic seizure than in EL[s] after abortive seizure. In both cases the regions showing *zif* expression were the same (the parietal cortex and the hippocampal CA1). In the dentate gyrus *zif* expression was no longer detected. In the interictal control there was a weak *zif* expression in the parietal cortex and the hippocampal CA1, the findings of which were very similar to *zif* expression after 30 min. Two hours and 8 hours after seizure, there were no significant differences of *zif* expression between the seizure-induced and control interictal EL[s] mice [20].

Developmental Change of IEG Expression in EL[s]

The expression of *zif* was examined developmentally using EL[s]. When EL[s] mice were 10 weeks old, the expression was localized to the parietal cortex and was almost silent in the limbic system. When 20 weeks old, the expression was increased in the dentate gyrus but was weak in the pyriform cortex and the entorhinal cortex. In the parietal cortex, the expression was almost universal. When 30 weeks old, *zif* expression was prominent in the dentate gyrus and hippocampal CA1 but not in the pyriform cortex and entorhinal cortex. In the parietal cortex, the expression was universal and not localized, although its layers were clearly identified **(Fig. 5)**.

Interictal IEG Expression

We have excluded the possibility that the weak *zif* expression during the interictal period of EL[s] might be an artifact. X-ray emulsion and cresyl fast violet double-stained samples showed a *zif* expression in pyramidal cells in the parietal cortex and in pyramidal cells in hippocampal CA1, but no expression in the hippocampal CA2, CA3 pyramidal cells and dentate gyrus granule cells. Similarly, *c-fos* expression was also examined **(Fig. 6)**. Samples showed a *c-fos* expression in pyramidal cells of the parietal cortex and the hippocampal CA1, and no expression in the hippocampal CA2, CA3 and the dentate gyrus. In the interictal period, the expression of *c-fos* and *zif* showed a very similar pattern.

Effects of Seizure History on IEG Expression

How seizure history would affect the IEG expression was examined using EL[s] and EL[ns]. In EL[ns], the expression of *zif* was prominent in the pyriform cortex, entorhinal cortex and dentate gyrus, a primary input system to the hippocampus. The expression in the parietal cortex was focal and the layers with strong expression were clearly identified. On the other hand, the expression in EL[s] was prominent in the dentate gyrus and hippocampal CA1. The expression in the pyriform cortex and the entorhinal cortex was universally prominent and not localized in the parietal cortex [20].

In our preceding studies [10], it was observed that *zif* was expressed maximally 30 min after seizure in both cerebrum and cerebellum under the same condition of the seizure threshold. There were no regional differences.

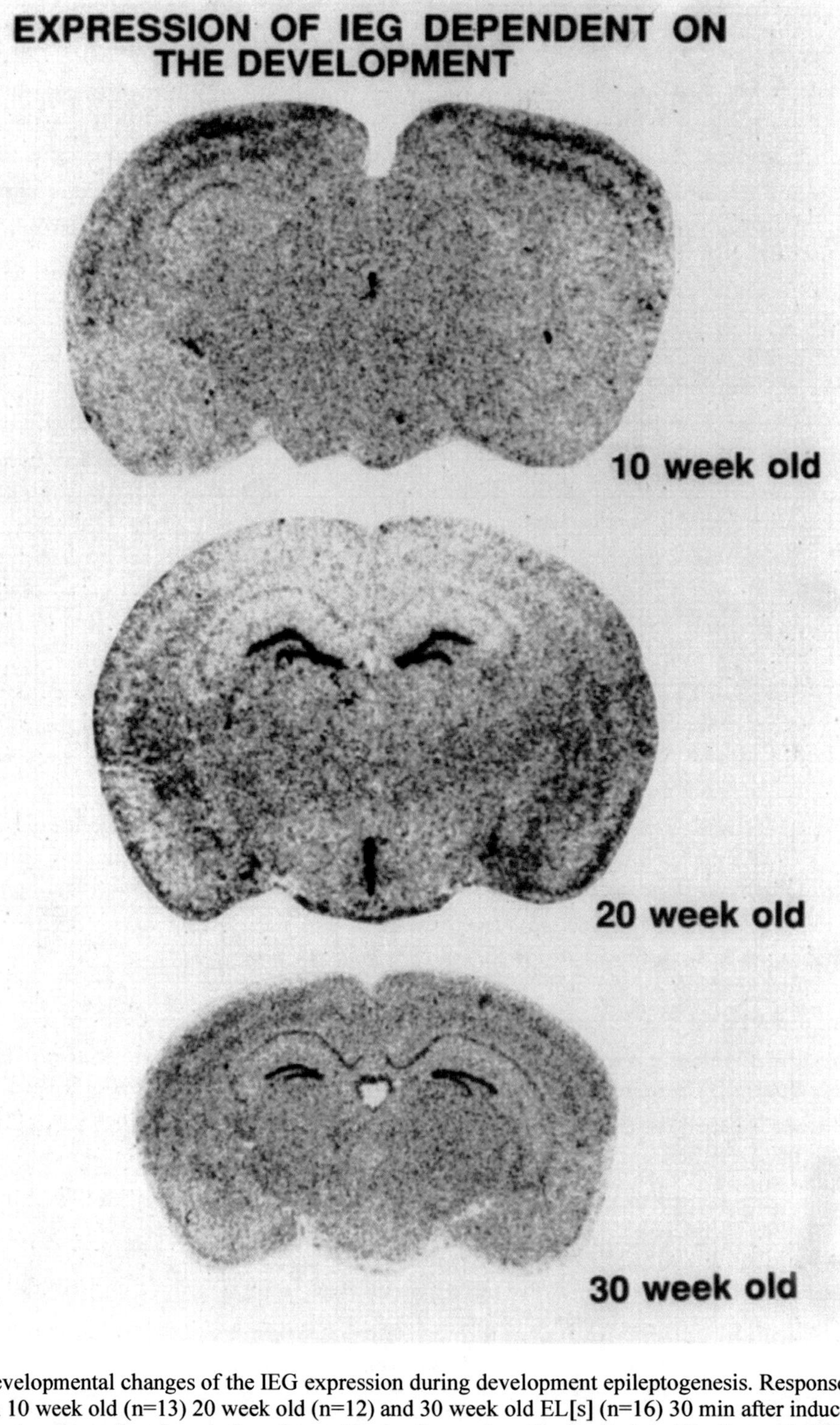

Fig. 5. Developmental changes of the IEG expression during development epileptogenesis. Response of *zif* mRNA in 10 week old (n=13) 20 week old (n=12) and 30 week old EL[s] (n=16) 30 min after induced seizure. Autoradiographs of coronal sections of brains from mice after in situ hybridization with 35S-labeled probes. Exposure time, 3 days.

c-fos Expression in the Parietal Cortex and Hippocampal CA1 in EL[s] Brain by using X-ray Emulsion

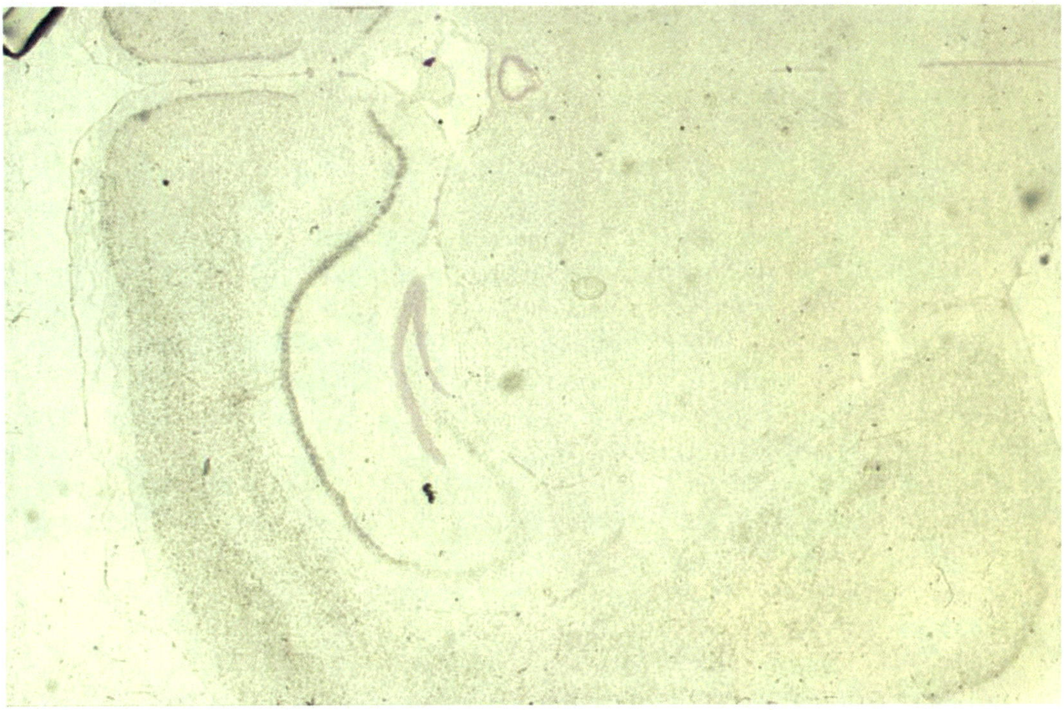

Fig. 6. Interictal continuous expression of IEG in EL[s] (low threshold group) in the parietal cortex and hippocampus. Response of IEG mRNA in 30 W EL[s] IEG expressions were developed by using X-ray emulsion and cresyl fast violet double staining. Autoradiographic grains were seen in black (parietal cortex pyramidal cells and hippocampal CA1). The counter staining by cresyl fast violet gave a very pale purple without black grains in the dentate gyrus. For the detection of *c-fos* mRNA expression, 30 W EL[s] (n=16) were used. Autoradiographs of coronal sections of brain tissues of the mice after in situ hybridization with ^{35}S-labeled probes. Exposure time, 8 weeks in complete darkness.

Results as examined with seizure history indicate that in the limbic system, the maximum expression site shifts from the pyriform cortex and entorhinal cortex to the dentate gyrus and further to the hippocampal CA3 and CA1 by frequent seizures during development.

On the other hand, results during development indicate that through the development as well as repetitive seizures, the *zif* expression site shifts gradually from the primary input system of the hippocampus; i.e., the pyriform cortex, entorhinal cortex and dentate gyrus, to the hippocampal CA1. In the parietal cortex, *zif* expression site is initially localized and then becomes universal. It is further demonstrated that the *zif* expression site finally becomes universal and weak in all over the cortex.

However, these phenomena were observed in a limited A-P area which corresponds to the Sidman atlas coronal section No.301-321 (315 μm length of rostro-caudal axis). To determine the precise localization of IEGs, three dimensional region specific localization should be studied. We have drawn schematic representations of IEG positive cell groups on the Sidman atlas coronal section No. 261,281,301,321 and 335 level. Data were obtained from the *zif* response by using X-ray emulsion autoradiographies [20].

Schematic Representation of Developmental Changes of *zif* Expression after 30 Min of Tonic Clonic Seizures [20]

Developmental changes of *zif* expression after 30 min of tonic clonic seizures were investigated. In 10week old EL[s] (number of animals; n=13) *zif* expression was diffusely localized to the area from No. 281 to 321. No signal was found in the hippocampus. In 20week old EL[s] (n=12) very strong expression was found in the dentate gyrus granule cells from the wide area No.281 to 335. In contrast, no expression was found in the parietal cortex and hippocampal pyramidal cells. In the 30week old EL[s] (n=16), strong and wide expression were found in the cortex from the area No.281 to 335. These areas cover both the parietal cortex and temporal cortex. The expression pattern showed a dense layered form. In the hippocampus, strong, universal expression was found in the granule cells of the dentate gyrus and the pyramidal cells of the hippocampal CA1, from the area No. 281 to 335 very widely. In the CA2 and CA3 pyramidal cells no signal was found [20].

Schematic representation of developmental changes of *zif* expression after 30 min of induced abortive seizures: Developmental changes of *zif* expression after 30 min of induced abortive seizure were investigated. In 10 week old EL[ns] (n=10) *zif* expression was very localized to the area No. 301. The expression area was very narrow compared with the area in case of tonic clonic full seizures. In the hippocampus weak and diffuse expression were found in CA1, CA2 and CA3 pyramidal cells. There were no spatial specificity as was found in the full seizure. In 20 week old EL [ns] (n=9) *zif* expression was a little bit strengthened, however the tendency that the expression site area was very narrow was the same [20]

DISCUSSION

In the present study, it was found that IEG expression after induced seizures was not related to the seizure pattern, but related to the seizure history, seizure threshold and development of EL[s]. Even in the interictal period, EL mice with long seizure histories and very low seizure thresholds expressed IEG continuously, which were probably strengthened by repeated seizures. However, the expression site was localized in the hippocampal CA1 (which is the final terminal of various inputs from other areas of the limbic system) and in the parietal cortex. Contrary, after seizures were induced, the expression was most remarkable in the dentate gyrus. It was supposed that the continuous expression of IEG might play a different role from that of the transiently expressed IEG **(Table 3, 4)**.

Table 3. IEG (Immediate Early Gene) expression in EL mice

c-fos expression after 30 minutes of seizure dependent on the seizure history
The expression sites have moved from the parietal cortex to the hippocampus during development.
c-fos expression in the interictal period dependent on the seizure history
Once epileptogenecity was obtained, *c-fos* was expressed in the hippocampal CA1 in the interictal period in the EL [s].

Table 4. Meanings of IEG expression in the brain of EL mice

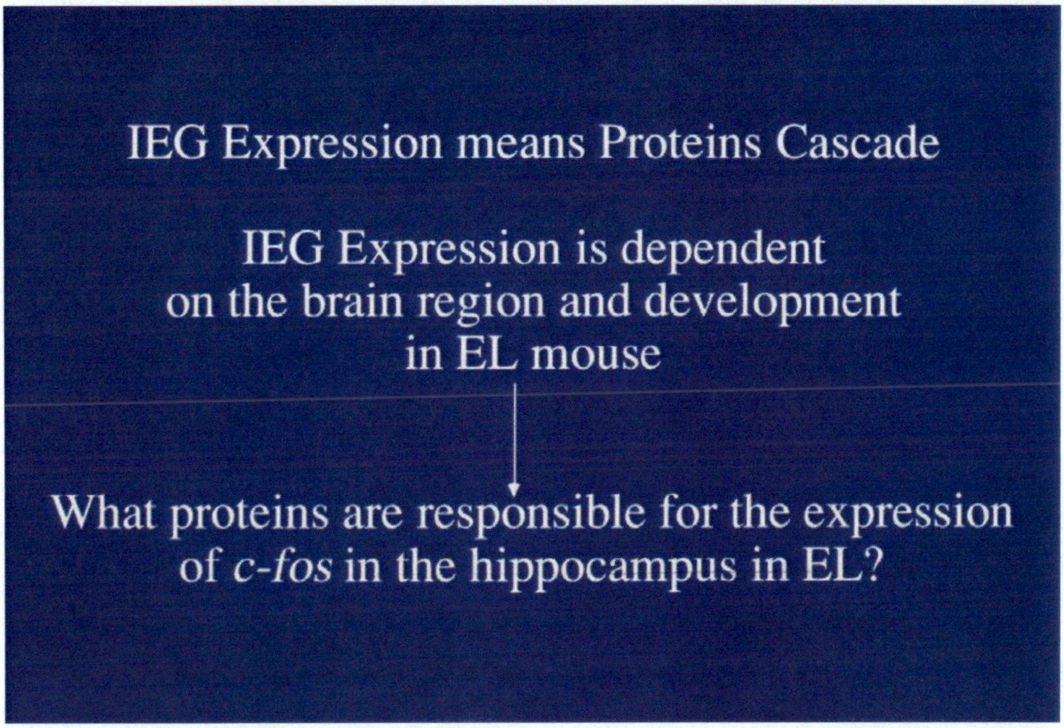

We have demonstrated previously the time courses of *zif* expression after induced seizures using 30week old EL[s] [15]. In the hippocampus and the parietal cortex, the expression of *zif* was weak 15 min after seizures but it reached a maximum level 30 min after and then became very weak 45 min after. One hour after, there was a significant difference in *zif* expression between abortive and full seizures, although the expressed regions were the same. Two hours after, however, there was no difference in *zif* expression between seizure-induced and control interictal EL[s] mice. The transient *zif* expression, especially remarkable in the dentate gyrus, might cease in 2 hours and then might decrease to the continuous expression level [15].

2. Ictogenesis and Epileptogenesis in EL Mice Brain Related to GABAergic Abnormalities

To examine the "GABA hypothesis" in epilepsy, GABA concentrations and GAD activities were determined in micro brain regions (10-300ng) of EL mice related to the focus complex; the parietal cortex and the hippocampus [20].

The sites which shows abnormal GABA concentrations and GAD activities were almost the same in the parietal cortex (around Sidman atlas coronal section No. 300) and in the hippocampal CA1 pyramidal cells, as compared with the sites of the spatio-temporal specific IEG expression. These findings strongly suggest that IEG expression and abnormal GABAergic function are involved in epileptogenesis in EL mice.

Which neurotransmitters mediate the expression of IEGs in the process of epileptogenesis is not known. Recently the "GABA hypothesis" of epilepsy was revived [24] in the context of the postsynaptic inhibition of GABA, Benzodiazepine receptor complex and epileptogenesis. The "GABA hypothesis" of epilepsy implies that a reduction of GABAergic inhibition results in epilepsy and raises the question of where this reduction of GABAergic inhibition occurs.

It has been proposed that a failure of GABA mediated inhibition is one of the bases of induction and generalization of seizures in the kindling model. To examine the "GABA hypothesis", abnormalities of GABAergic activity have been thoroughly investigated in micro brain regions [21, 22, 23].

It was shown that low GABAergic activity area in the parietal cortex was specifically localized just around Sidman atlas No.300 [20] where IEG expression was also localized. Then the epileptogenesis of EL was established. In the hippocampal pyramidal layer, high GABAergic activity area was localized in the CA1 where IEG expression was also localized, contrary in the CA3, GABAergic activities were low compared with control DDY [21]. In EL the parietal cortex has an important role for the initiation of seizure [26], the failure of GABAergic inhibition at the seizure initiation site may result in the abnormal augmentation of excitability in this region and the transcription factor IEG will be repeatedly expressed and then specific protein synthesis cascades may occur to support the epileptogenesis. These phenomena might be the beginning of epileptogenesis, so that, the established ictogenesis. The hippocampus has an important role in the seizure propagation and generalization in EL [23].

The dentate gyrus receives a primary input from entorhinal cortex, pyriform cortex and so on and transmits via mossy fibers to pyramidal CA3 and via Schaffer collaterals to pyramidal CA1. After the seizure initiation, in the CA3 GABAergic inhibition will be decreased and IEG expressed strongly at the age of 20 weeks when ictogenesis of EL was established. In this stage only in the CA3, some specific protein cascades which may relate to the long term potentiation will occur. Then the abnormal excitability reached the CA1 pyramidal cell, IEG expression has the final pattern. It may be contradictory that in the CA1 of EL[s] (most remarkable expression site of IEG in the interictal period), GABAergic activities remarkably increased compared with that of control DDY and CA2, CA3 of EL[s]. The so called "GABAergic disinhibition hypothesis" may explain this contradiction. The hypothesis implies that the increase of inhibitory GABAergic interneuron which synapse to the other inhibitory neuron will lead to the increase of local excitability and ictogenesis may be established. And then strong expression of IEG occur and CA1 specific protein cascade will be activated, because in this stage other region except CA1 so that CA2 and CA3 were silent. These phenomena will be the last step to the formation of the abnormal plasticity and further epileptogenesis [25].

3. Ictogenesis and Epileptogenesis in EL Mice Brain Related to Nitric Oxide Synthetase (NOS) Abnormalities

Introduction

Nitric oxide (NO) has been identified as a source of free-radical oxidants with special relevance to pathological conditions in the brain, and reactive nitrogen intermediates could damage DNA as an important target **(Table 5)**. In addition, NO, identified as an endothelium-derived relaxing factor (EDRF), is a potent vasodilatator regulating cerebral blood flow in basal conditions and during certain types of neuronal activation including seizures.

Table 5. Role of Nitric oxide in the ictogenesis and epileptogenesis

Nitric Oxide (NO) Free radical or Messenger ?
Recently, it is suggested that long term potentiation (LTP) might be involved in the neural plasticity and further epileptogenesis. LTP is a postsynaptic phenomena through a retrograde messenger from post- to pre-synaptic transmission, which potentiates the release of presynaptic neurotransmitters. Nitric oxide (NO) is one of candidates of retrograde messengers. We have investigated the role of NO by measuring the NO metabolites, nitrite (NO2-) and Nitrate (NO3-) in the parietal cortex (PCx) and hippocampus (Hipp) of EL mice which have acquired before and after the epileptogenesis.

NO is also associated with a variety of brain functions including synaptic plasticity and involved in glutamate neurotoxicity [30]. In the central nervous system, NO is synthesized from L-arginine by a Ca^{2+}-calmodulin-dependent NO synthetase (NOS) that is activated mainly by the stimulation of NMDA receptors [30].

In association with such distinct functions of NO, three isoforms of NOS have been identified: the constitutive neuronal (nNOS) and endothelial (eNOS) forms and the inducible (iNOS) form [31]. It remains to be seen, however, how seizure activities are regulated by NO in the developing EL mice.

To understand the role of NO in the regulation of seizures, three isoforms of NOS were assayed by immunoblotting analysis for hippocampal tissues of developing EL[s] [32] and control DDY mice [41]. The results indicate that nNOS and iNOS are major and minor components, respectively in EL[s].

Unexpectedly, eNOS content was very small despite the fact that eNOS appears to be responsible for NO that mediates an increase in local cerebral blood flow during focal seizures [33]. One would wonder whether or not relatively lower concentration of eNOS in EL mouse brain may result in anoxia in neurons, particularly in those active neurons associated with focus complex, and subsequent neural damage.

NO has been proposed as a retrograde messenger for sustaining long-term potentiation (LTP) In the hippocampus [31]. LTP is a phenomenon thought to be involved in learning and memory function. Recently, Kandel's group carried out an elegant study in which mice that lack either nNOS or eNOS have essentially normal LTP, whereas mutant mice deficient in both nNOS and eNOS have substantially decreased LTP [34]. This implies that both nNOS and eNOS are essential for neural plasticity.

The process of development of EL mouse seizure has been referred to as "abnormal plasticity" based on electroencephalogram studies [35,36], biochemical analysis of neurotransmitters, mitochondrial function and gene expressions [27, 31]. By analogy with the neural plasticity in normal brains, both nNOS and eNOS may participate in this abnormal plasticity and further epileptogenesis in EL mice. Given the fact that iNOS is more conspicuous than eNOS, it is conceivable that excess iNOS (and subsequent increase in harmful antimicrobial NO) and relatively lower concentration eNOS (and subsequent decrease in NO identified as EDRF) may work together to contribute to a focus complex and ictogenesis.

Materials and Methods

Preparation of Tissues

For Determination of Nitric Oxide (NO) Metabolites

EL[s] mice (low seizure threshold group) and EL[ns] mice (high threshold group) of 20 weeks and 30 weeks of age (before and after establishment of epileptogenesis, number of the animals used was six for each group. Six DDY/TIP mice (mother strain of EL) were used as control. After decapitation, brains were removed and then the parietal cortex (PCx), the temporal cortex (TCx) and the hippocampus (Hipp) were dissected out. Homogenates were prepared with 20 mM Tris-HCl buffer (pH 8.0). The homogenates were centrifuged for 40 min at 2000 x g before use.

For Immunoblotting Analysis

EL[s] of 10, 20 and 30 weeks of age were used (6 animals for each group). As described above, the hippocampus was dissected out and 10% homogenates were prepared. Just before use, homogenates with dye were boiled for 3 min and the were centrifuged for 5 min at 2000 x g.

Determination of Nitric Oxide (NO) Metabolites

Nitric oxide (NO) is very rapidly decreased by oxidation to nitrite (NO^-) and nitrate. Nitric oxide was determined photometrically via its oxidation products, nitrite and nitrate. The nitrate present in the sample was reduced to nitrite by reduced NADPH in the presence of the enzyme nitrate reductase. The nitrite formed reacted with sulfanilsmide and N-(1-naphthl)-ethyl-enediamine dihydrochloride to give a red-violet diazodye. The diazodye was measured on the basis of its absorbance in the visible range at 550 nm. Concentrations of nitrite and nitrate in the samples were measured as follows: the concentration of nitrite was measured by skipping the reduction step. The concentration of nitrate was obtained by subtracting the nitrite concentration from the total concentration of nitrite and nitrate. The standard curve was obtained from the authentic nitrate using Nitric Oxide Colormetric Assay (Boelinger Mannheim, Germany).

Primary Antibodies and Their Specificities

Three kinds of the primary antibodies; namely, anti-nNOS antibody, anti-iNOS antibody and anti-eNOS antibody, were purchased from SIGMA (Saint Louis, Missouri, USA). According to SIGMA, the anti-nNOS antibody does not cross react in immunoblotting with activated mouse macrophage (iNOS). The anti-iNOS antibody reacts specifically with iNOS from the activated murine macrophage cell line RAW 264.7 (130 kDa) and does not cross react with NOS derived from rat brain (n-NOS). The anti-eNOS does not cross react with NOS derived from rat brain (nNOS) or activated mouse macrophage (iNOS).

Immunoblotting Procedures

Western blot studies were carried out according to the partially modified procedures by Arima and Ueda [37, 38] For the immunoblotting analysis, 10% mouse brain homogenates (total protein of applied samples: 8.33 - 8.43 μg) were separated through 7.5 - 10% SDS-PAGE and transfered to a PVDF membrane (Millipore, Bedford, MA, USA), blocked and then incubated with either of nNOS (251 - 270, 1409 - 1429) (1:5,000), or iNOS (1:3000 - 1:5000), or eNOS (596 - 609, 1185 - 1205). After washing, the membrane was incubated with goat anti-rabbit IgG conjugated with horseradish peroxidase (1:20,000; SIGMA), followed by the Western blot-chemiluminescence reagent (DuPont NEN, Boston, MA, USA).

The immunoreactivities on the membrane were detected using Hyperfilm-ECL (Amersham, Little Chalfont, UK) **(Table 6)**.

Results

Nitric Oxide (NO) Metabolites in EL Mice Brain

In EL mice, the parietal cortex plays an important role in the initiation of seizures, and the hippocampus is responsible for their generalization The epileptogenesis is completely established at the 30 weeks of age [29].

The major component of NO metabolites in the mouse brain was nitrite [41]. In the parietal cortex [41], EL[ns] group showed a statistically high content of nitrate (stable form) compared with DDY and EL[s] groups ($p<0.01$ by t-test), whereas in the total level of NO metabolites which approximates nitrite content, there was no significant change among DDY, EL[ns] and El[s].

In the hippocampus [41], the content of nitrite in EL[s] at the age of 30 weeks old was higher than that of EL[s] at the age of 20 weeks, or higher than those of EL[ns] and DDY groups at the age of 20 and 30 weeks ($p<0.001$ by t-test).

In the temporal cortex [41], which is not involved in the epileptogenesis of EL mouse, no significant changes were detected among DDY, EL[ns] and EL[s] mice.

Immunoblotting of Nitric Oxide Synthetase (NOS) in the EL Hippocampus during Development

Relative contents of three NOS isoenzymes were determined by SDS-PAGE for samples obtained from the hippocampus that contained identical amount of proteins. Immunoblotting bands were identified by N-terminal NOS antibody, C-terminal NOS antibody, and an authentic ladder marker of the molecular weights. In the case of iNOS in which only N-terminal antibody was available, the specific single band was identified by further dilution of the primary antibody.

Table 6. Procedure of Immunoblotting of iNOS

Western Blotting of i-NOS

Western blotting
DDY iNOS

Gel: SDS-PAGE 10%
Blotting membrane: Millipore membrane (PVDF) pore size 0.45 μm
primary antibody dilution: 1:3,000 - 5,000
secondary antibody dilution: 1:20,000
total protein of applied samples: 9,18,36 μg
hyperfilm ECL (Amersham)

i-NOS has not detected in the hippocampus of DDY mice during

Western blotting
EL iNOS

Gel: SDS-PAGE 10%
Blotting membrane: Millipore membrane (PVDF) pore size 0.45 μm
primary antibody dilution: 1:3,000 - 5,000
secondary antibody dilution: 1:20,000
total protein of applied samples: 8.33 -8.43 μg
hyperfilm ECL (Amersham)

i-NOS has gradually increased in the hippocampus of EL[s] mice during development.

In the hippocampus of EL[s] mice, nNOS was the major component of the NOS family from 10 weeks to 30 weeks of age.

iNOS was a minor component compared with the nNOS and often difficult to be identified at earlier stages **(Fig. 7)**. However, the presence of iNOS was detectable at the age of 10 weeks, at which the animals (EL[s]) experienced the first seizures with seizure thresholds that had not been lowered yet. Like nNOS, iNOS showed a gradual increase, reaching a maximum level at the age of 30 weeks.

In the case of eNOS [41], the isoform could not be identified under the present experimental conditions in which applied sample volume was 8.33 - 8.43 μg,

These results, together with previous observations, indicate that in the hippocampus of EL[s] mice, nNOS and iNOS increase in parallel with development of epileptogenesis. It remains to be seen, however, how eNOS participates in the process of developing epileptogenesis.

Increased i-NOS Expression in the Hippocampus of EL

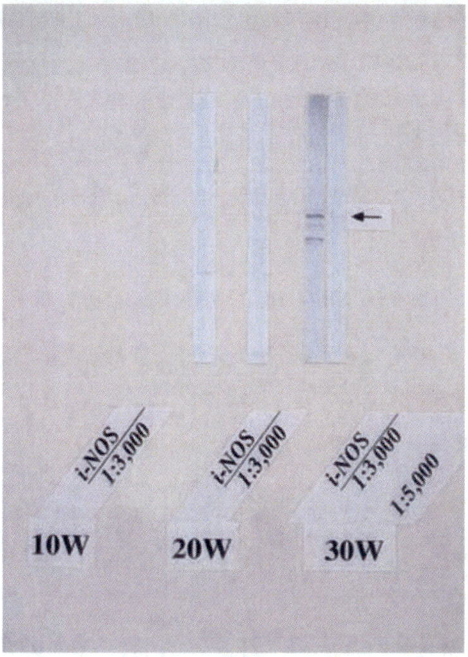

i-NOS Bands Densities of EL Mice Brain

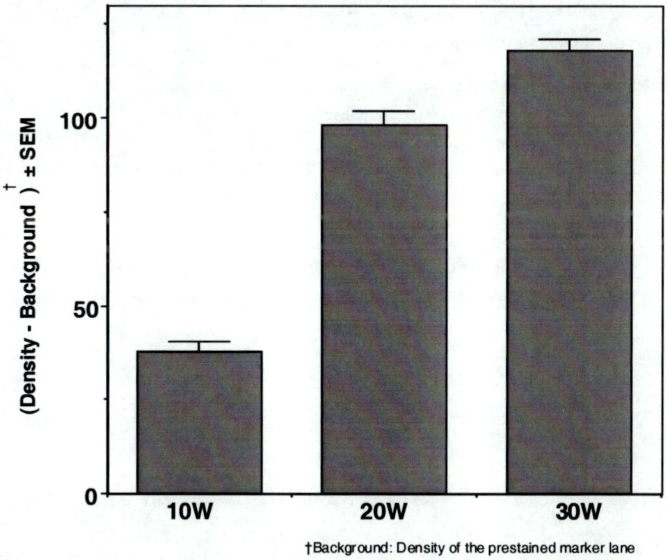

Fig. 7. Western blotting of iNOS in the hippocampus of EL mice. Anti-iNOS antibody (rabbit polyclonal antibody raised against a synthetic peptide corresponding to amino acids 1126 - 1141 of nitric oxide synthetase (NOS) of mouse macrophage origin (iNOS) (1:3,000 - 5,000) was used. Total protein of applied samples: 8.33 - 8.43 µg, Gel: 10% SDS-PAGE, Blotting membrane: Millipore membrane (PVDF), Pore size 0.45 µm, Secondary antibody dilution: 1:20,000, The immunoreactivities on the membrane were detected using Hyperfilm ECL. The arrows indicate the specific separated band of iNOS

Discussion

In the present study, we measured the extracellular levels of the NO metabolites as indices of NO generation in the brains of epileptic mutant EL mice and their control animal, DDY mice. It was found that EL mice that experienced repetitive seizures (EL[s]) showed a remarkable increase in nitrite (NO^-) in the hippocampus at 30 weeks of age when compared with EL mice that had no experience of seizures (EL[ns]). The results suggest that NO is involved in the formation of epileptogenesis in EL mice as may be expected from our previous studies [29] **(Table 7)**

Table 7. Role of NOS and NO in the abnormal plasticity

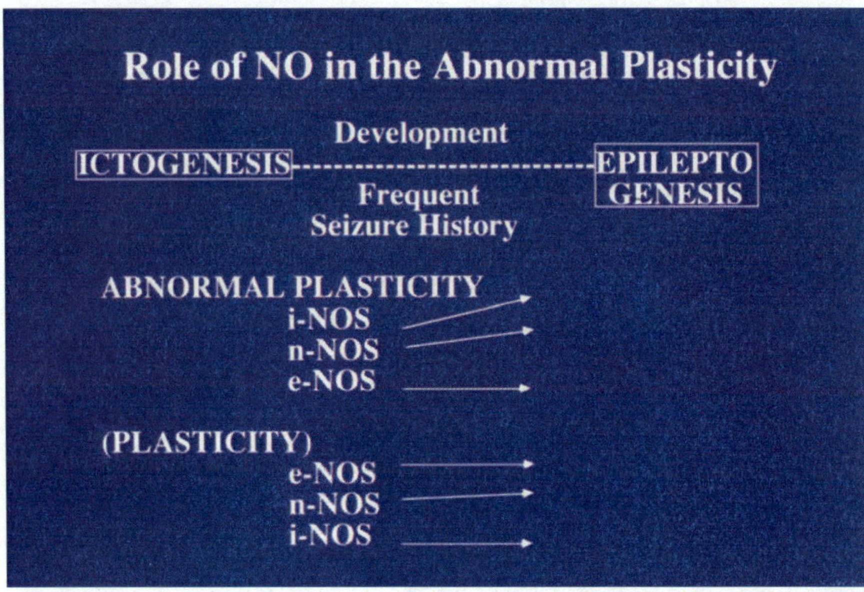

To further understand the role of NO in the regulation of seizures, three isoforms of NOS were assayed by immunoblotting analysis for hippocampal tissues of developing EL[s] mice. The results indicate that nNOS and iNOS are major and minor components, respectively **(Table 8)**.

Table 8. Role of Nitric Oxide

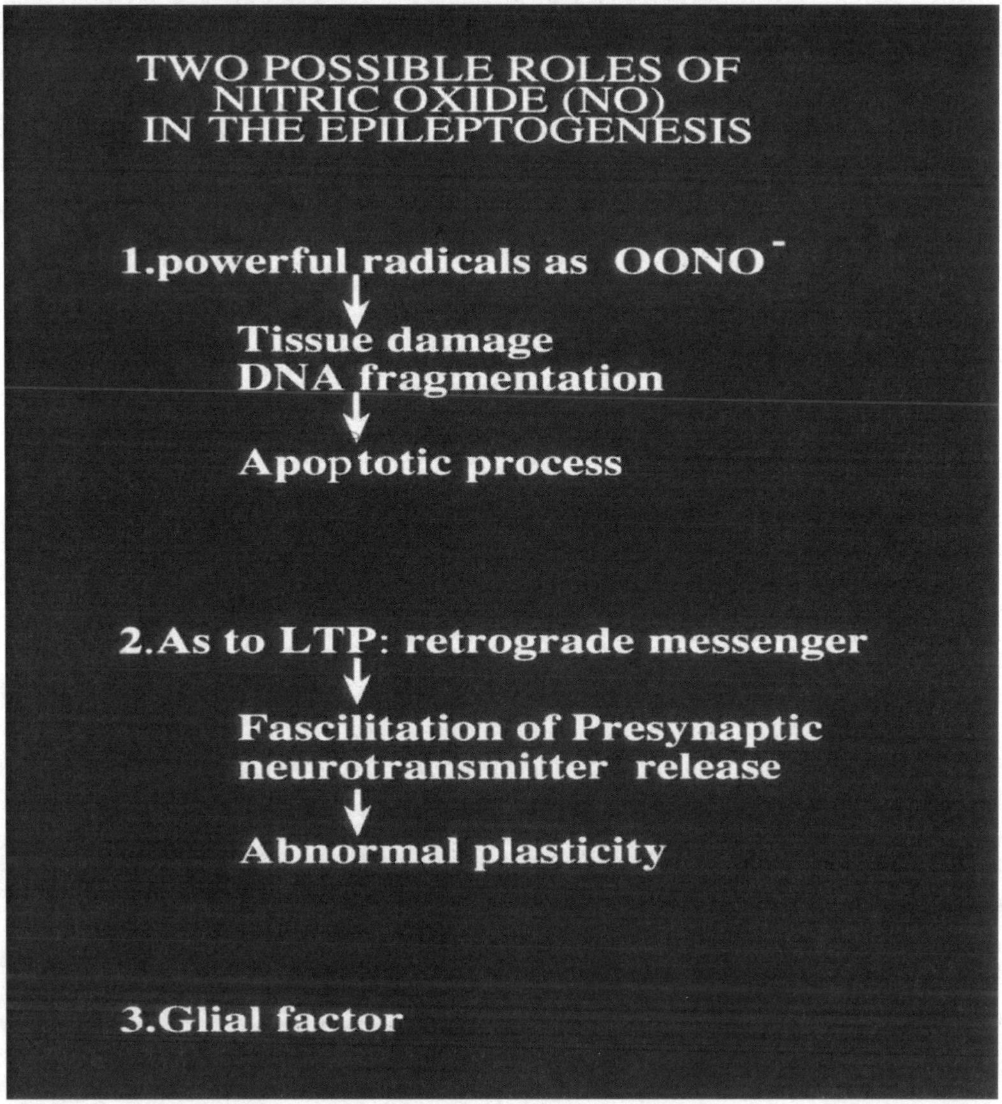

Neuromodulator in the Central Nervous System

NO is produced by neurons in many parts of the brain. It can both link local blood flow to neuronal activity and modulate neurotransmitter release. In postsynaptic terminal, binding of glutamate to N-methyl-D-aspartate-(NMDA)-type receptors leads to Ca^{2+} influx, which would activate nNOS. nNOS binds via its N-terminal PDZ domain to certain postsynaptic density proteins (PSD-95, PSD-93) in the brain. Peptides binding with high affinity to the PDZ domain of nNOS were found to potentially and selectively uncouple NOS activity from NMDA receptor stimulation, suggesting that the interaction with postsynaptic proteins target nNOS to the NMDA receptors, creating the link between postsynaptic glutamate binding and NO synthesis.

The function of NO in normal physiology of the brain is controversial. It has been proposed to play a role in long-term potentiation (LTP) of excitatory neurotransmission in the hippocampus, a phenomenon thought to be involved in learning and memory formation. LTP involves glutaminergic neurotransmission, and NOS inhibitors both inhibited presynaptic glutamate release and reduced LTP

Induction of LTP by NO appears to depend on cGMP formation. cGMP can trigger Ca^{2+}-influx through cyclic nucleotide gated ion channels, causing release of glutamate from presynaptic terminals. NO is supposed to act as a retrograde messenger completing the feedback loop responsible for sustaining LTP.

Mice lacking the nNOS gene were found to be less susceptible to experimental stroke than control animals, whereas infarct size was significantly increased in animals without eNOS.

Both endotherial NOS (eNOS) and nNOS activities are found in hippocampus. Mice that lack either eNOS and nNOS have essentially normal LTP, whereas mutant mice deficient in both eNOS and nNOS have substantially decreased LTP.

Through regulation of synaptic plasticity, NO mediates complex influences on brain development, memory formation, and behavior. For Example in adult animals, NOS inhibitors hinder motor learning and the formation of olfactory memories.

However, nNOS knock out mice display normal sensitization to peripheral tissue damage in this model, and NOS inhibitors do not block sensitization in the nNOS knockout mice. Again the deficiency of nNOS is compensated by an NO independent pathway.

Cell Toxicity in the Central Nervous System

Thus, the positive effect of endotherial-derived NO on blood flow appears to protect the brain from exitotoxicicity. While neuronal NO contributes the neurodegeneration. This last effct might be explained by the ability of nNOS to synthesize superoxide and/or peroxidase. Therefore, NO signaling must allow for rapid and localized NO production and immediate termination of biosynthesis, This tight control of NO signaling is largely regulated at the level of NO biosynthesis. Indeed, the NOS proteins are among the most highly regulated of all neuronal enzymes.

Simultaneous production of reactive nitrogen and oxygen intermediates may lead to the formation of a variety of antimicrobial molecular species, each with distinct stability, compartmentalization, and reactivity. In addition to NO radical (NO*) itself, potentially important NO congeners include peroxynitrite ($OONO^-$), nitrogendioxide (NO^-), dinitrogentrioxide (N_2O_3), dinitrogen tetroide (N_2O_4), formed from the rapid interaction of NO* and superoxide ($O_2{}^{*-}$), from the combination of hydrogen peroxide (H_2O_2) and nitrous acid (HNO_2), which would exist in equilibrium with nitrite ($NO_2{}^-$) within an acidified phagolysosomal vacuole, or from the interaction nitroxyl (NO^-) and oxygen, and all these variety of radicals might damage brain tissue. especially the DNA.

Several lines of evidence indicate that DNA is an important target of reactive nitrogen intermediates. First, NO can deaminate DNA in vitro, evidently acting via an intermediate (perhaps N_2O_3) since deamination requires the presence of air NO_2 and peroxynitrite can also oxidatively damage DNA, resulting in strand breaks, and a variety of other DNA alterations. We have found DNA fragmentation in the hippocapus of 30-week old EL[s] mice. Repeated seizures and overproduced radicals from NO will damage DNA and cause DNA fragmentation. Cell defenses against reactive nitrogen intermediates. Cell systems which repair oxidative injury appear to be similarly involved in repairing nitrosative injury. Cu,Zn-superoxide dismutase (SOD) may protect against both oxidative and nitrosative stress by removing periplasmic superoxide and limiting peroxynitrite formation, however, in the EL[s] mice, the activities of Cu,Zn-SOD level is decreased compared with that of control DDY. EL[s] mice are very susceptible to radicals and cell damage and further DNA fragmentation.

4. Ictogenesis and Epileptogenesis in EL Mice Brain Related to Cu,Zn-SOD Abnormalities

Introduction

Recently, the xanthine oxidase inhibitor, allopurinol (ALP), has been clinically demonstrated to exert antiepileptic effects [63, 68], particularly, on secondarily generalized seizures [47, 75]. The EL mouse is an epileptic mutant model of secondarily generalized seizures [55, 73]. Several lines of evidence indicate that in EL mice, the parietal cortex plays an important role for the initiation of seizures and the hippocampus is responsible for the generalization of them [55]. Furthermore, the developmental formation of the "Focus Complex [74]", which is mainly constituted from the parietal cortex and the hippocampus, should be deeply involved in the epileptogenesis [74].

In our recent study [65], the antiepileptic effects of ALP were examined in EL[s]. Six hours after administration of ALP (75mg/kg, p.o.), no seizure was provoked, and the effect lasted for 24 hours and was abolished after 48 hours. The ED_{50} determined was 7.5mg/kg, p.o.

Several isoforms of superoxide dismutase (SOD) are essential enzymes involved in the cellular defense against oxidative processes occurring with the generation of superoxide anion [69]. Manganese SOD (Mn-SOD) [42, 45, 57] is located in mitochondria and preferentially induced in terminally differentiating cells, and copper/zinc SOD (Cu,Zn-SOD) is located in cytoplasm and more closely associated with postnatal exposure to environmental sources of oxygen free radicals [51, 57]. Cu,Zn-SOD is a metalloenzyme that catalyzes the dismutation of the superoxide radical into hydrogen peroxide and molecular oxygen, being a defense system against free radical formation. Free radical reactions are implicated in a variety of physiological processes as aging, apoptosis and neurodegenerative diseases, and abnormalities associated with SOD have been recently documented in several neurodegenerative processes [47, 49]. Further it has been suggested that free radicals might be involved in the enhancement of long term potentiation (LTP) [66].

We have investigated the potential antiepileptic action of superoxide dismutase (SOD) activities in the brain of the epileptic mutant EL mouse [44]. EL mice which had experienced frequent seizures (EL[s]) which had abnormally low levels of SOD isoenzyme activity in the hippocampal area. Once epileptogenesis was established, SOD activities, especially cyanide sensitive Cu,Zn-SOD was maintained at significantly lower levels than in control mice in the hippocampal area. However, cyanide-insensitive Mn-SOD activity was not different from non-epileptic controls [44]. Six hours after allopurinol (ALP) was given orally (75 mg/kg, p. o.), Cu,Zn-SOD activities increased drastically in the hippocampus. Even after 48 hr, when antiepileptic action of ALP was lost, the SOD activity was maintained at the high levels associated with initial ALP administration [44].

In EL mice which had not experienced seizure provoking stimulations and shown relatively high seizure threshold (EL[ns]), there was moderately lower levels of SOD isoenzyme activities compared to control even at the age of 30 weeks. However, EL[ns] has already acquired ictogenesis [44].

In spite of the low level of Cu,Zn-SOD activity in EL[s] mice, Cu,Zn-SOD protein content was high in the hippocampus of these animals, suggesting that inactive Cu,Zn-SOD might be induced during development and then epileptogenesis of EL may be established.

It may therefore be useful to investigate the isoenzyme patterns of SOD in parallel with the mode of antiepileptic effects of ALP, using EL mice.

To address these issues, we examined the developmental changes of SOD isoenzyme activities and protein contents in the parietal cortex (PCx) and the hippocampus (Hipp) in both EL mice and their control animal, DDY mice.

Materials and Methods

Breeding of EL and DDY Mice and the Preparation of Brain Region Homogenate

EL mice were carefully reared in our experimental animal center. More than 100 of them were F136-145 of an inbred strain and susceptible to seizures. They were bred with free access to pelleted food and water, at a constant temperature (24°C) and a humidity (50%). Lights were turned on from 6:00h to 18:30h. In the present study, our standard method for inducing seizures [71] was applied to EL[s] subjects once a week at a rule. This method consists of two steps: a mouse is carefully removed from the home cage, placed on the metal mesh of the cage, and observed for 3 minutes; then it is thrown or tossed 30 times in the air about 10 cm above the mesh. Although specificity of various types of stimulation provoking seizures in EL mice was reported [72], seizures could be elicited uniformly through these two step. DDY/TIP (DDY) mice were used as the control animals of EL, which were also inbred in our institute (TIP) from the DDY which was the mother's strain of EL.

Mice were sacrificed by decapitation and the brains were removed and placed on ice. The parietal cortex and the hippocampus were cut out from the brains and weighed (8-20mg). Adding 20mM Tris-HCl (pH 8.0), 8-12% brain region homogenates were obtained.

Measurement of SOD Isoenzyme Activities

SOD activities were determined by the modified procedure of original method [54]. The SOD Unit was defined as the sample amount in which V=0.025 absorbency units/min decreases to V=0.0125 absorbency units/min under the circumstance of A2-A1=0.21 absorbency units [24]. Final SOD activity was expressed as m Unit / μg wet wt.

Total SOD activities included cyanide-insensitive Mn-SOD and cyanide-sensitive Cu,Zn-SOD. After coincubation with 1mM cyanide at 37°C for 2 hours, Mn-SOD activity was obtained. Cu,Zn-SOD activity was obtained from total SOD activity minus Mn-SOD activity for each mouse.

Data were statistically examined by ANOVA. If the effects were significant, then the data were further examined by multiple comparison; post-hoc Scheff's test.

Measurement of SOD Isoenzyme Contents

Contents of Mn-SOD and Cu,Zn-SOD were assayed by commercially available ELISA system (Boehlinger) with modifications as follows: All assays were performed within the linear standard regression range, namely, Mn-SOD (0-2.00ng / Assay) and Cu,Zn-SOD (0-1.25ng / Assay). The initial assay volume was minimized and the background was lowered at almost zero level (0.0220ng, 0.0141ng each) so that a very high sensitivity and specificity was obtained.

Data were statistically examined by ANOVA. If the effects were significant, then the data were further examined by post-hoc Scheff's test.

Results

Changes in the SOD Isoenzyme Activities and Contents in the Focus Complex of EL Mice after Acute Administration of ALP

Cu,Zn-SOD activitiy in the parietal cortex (PCx) of EL[s] was increased over 5 times compared with control DDY. After ALP was applied (75 mg/kg body weight, p.o.), Cu,Zn-SOD activity remained at a high level, while Mn-SOD activity was decreased [44].

In the hippocampus (Hipp), on the other hand, Cu, Zn-SOD activity of EL[s] mice was under one-fifth of the control value (DDY mice). Six hours after administration of ALP (75 mg/kg body weight, p.o.), Cu,Zn-SOD activity was markedly enhanced by the drug more than 10 times. Forty eight hours after administration, Cu,Zn-SOD activity was still at high levels in EL[s] mice.

In the case of SOD isoenzyme contents, there was no remarkable change in either Mn-SOD or Cu,Zn-SOD in the PCx of EL[s] after acute administration of ALP, even compared with the control value (DDY) [44]. The discrepancy between activity and content of Mn-SOD isoenzyme after administration of ALP was remarkable, in such a way that the activity was decreasing while the content increasing.

In the hippocampus (Hipp), Mn-SOD content showed no remarkable change [44]. Although Cu,Zn-SOD activity was increased remarkably after ALP administration, the content showed a tendency of decreasing

Change in the SOD Activities in the Focus Complex of EL Mice after Chronic Administration of ALP

To investigate the chronic antiepileptic effects of ALP, the drug (75mg/kg body weight, p.o.) was applied to EL mice during the course of acquiring their susceptibility by seizure provoking stimulations. From the aspects of seizure susceptibility, allopurinol(+) group of EL mice exhibited no induced seizures throughout all the ages from 10- to 30-week old. In contrast, allopurinol(-) group exhibited induced seizures after 10 weeks of age, and the seizure threshold become lowered gradually with development and repetitive seizure history. After 20 weeks of age, all mice in the allopurinol(-) group exhibited full seizures. In respect of the seizure susceptibility, there was no statistical difference between allopurinol(-) group and EL[s] mice that had experienced the toss-up stimulation since 5 weeks of age without pharmacological treatment.

In the parietal cortex (PCx), there was no significant difference in the SOD activities between allopurinol(+) and allopurinol(-) groups [44]. Both groups, however, showed a similar tendency to increase SOD activities by about 30% during development from 10 to 30 weeks of age. SOD activities in the hippocampus were also measured (as shown in Fig. 3), in which SOD activities of allopurinol(-) were markedly decreased to about one tenth during development with repetitive seizure history. In contrast, SOD activities of allopurinol(+) were gradually decreased at most by 30%. After 20 weeks of age, the SOD activity level was remained at a plateau level.

Developmental Changes in the SOD Isoenzyme Activities and Contents in the PCx in DDY, EL[ns] and EL[s] Mice

In the parietal cortex (PCx) of the control DDY mice, Mn-SOD activity gradually decreased during development, while Cu,Zn-SOD activity showed almost no change [44]. In EL[ns] mice which had not experienced seizures, the Mn-SOD level was decreased at 10 weeks of age and then remained at a plateau level. Contrary to this, the Cu,Zn-SOD level was gradually increased up to the age of 40 weeks. As in the case of EL[ns], the Mn-SOD level in EL[s] mice was decreased at 10 weeks of age, but increased at 20 weeks, and then, decreased again to a plateau level up to the age of 40 weeks. The Cu,Zn-SOD level was decreased to almost zero at 20 weeks of age, and then, increased to a high level up to the age of 40 weeks, the level being much higher compared with those in EL[ns] and DDY mice.

Thus, only in PCx of EL[s], there was a remarkable and significant increase in Cu,Zn-SOD activity at 30 to 40 weeks of age.

The activities and the contents of the two isoenzyme types showed parallel changes in the control DDY mice [44]. In EL[ns] mice, the contents of the two types changed in parallel with their enzyme activities, as observed similarly in DDY. In EL[s] mice, at 30 to 40 week of age, the increase was reproduced in respect of the Cu,Zn-SOD activity.

No discrepancy between isoenzyme activities and contents was found in PCx during development.

Free radicals

and the superoxide radicals scavenging enzyme Cu, Zn-SOD

Recently, several lines of evidence indicate that free radicals and their scavenger SOD might be involved in the establishment of long term potentiation (LTP) in the hippocampal CA 1 and further the formation of epileptogenesis.

EL[s] mice which experienced frequent seizures and showed epileptogenecity have abnormal superoxide dismutase (SOD) isoenzyme activities pattern characterized by a marked decrease in the hippocampus. And once epileptogenecity was obtained, SOD activities were maintained at low levels, especially those of mitochondrial Cu,Zn-SOD.

SOD scavenge O_2^- radicals. Free radicals may increase during the formation of abnormal plasticity in the hippocampus

Fig. 8. Role of free radicals

Developmental Changes in the SOD Isoenzyme Activities and Contents in the Hippocampus of DDY, EL[ns] and EL[s] Mice

In the hippocampus (Hipp) of the control DDY mice, both Mn-SOD and Cu,Zn-SOD activities were maintained at plateau levels from 5 to 40 weeks of age [44]. In EL[ns] mice at 10 weeks of age, both Mn-SOD and Cu,Zn-SOD isoenzyme activities were decreased by half, and then, maintained at a plateau level until 40 weeks of age. In EL[s] mice, the total SOD was decreased by half, and then, Mn-SOD was maintained at a plateau level, as in the case of EL[ns] at 10-40 weeks of age. However, the Cu,Zn-SOD level was gradually decreased to almost zero at 30 weeks of age. In the hippocampus, EL[s] and EL[ns] showed activity dips in both Mn-SOD and Cu,Zn-SOD isoenzymes at 10 weeks of age. Only EL[s] showed a remarkable decrease in the Cu,Zn-SOD activity to almost zero during development **(Fig. 9).**In the control DDY mice, Mn-SOD content was maintained at a plateau level during development while Cu,Zn-SOD content showed a tendency to decrease up to the age of 30 weeks. In EL[ns] mice, Mn-SOD content was decreased at 10 weeks of age and kept at a plateau level [44]. Cu,Zn-SOD content was decreased at 10 weeks of age, but after 30 weeks, the content was recovered, apparently reflecting the enzyme activity. In EL[s] mice, Mn-SOD content stayed almost at a plateau level during development. In contrast, Cu,Zn-SOD content was decreased at 10 weeks of age, and then, increased up to the age of 30-40 weeks. The tendency did not reflect the activity of Cu,Zn-SOD in which at 30 weeks of age the activity was decreased to zero level, but the content increased. In the hippocampus, only EL[s] showed a significant discrepancy between activity and content of Cu,Zn-SOD isoenzyme [44].

Discussion

In EL mice, the parietal cortex plays an important role in the initiation of induced seizure and the hippocampus relates to the generalization of seizure discharges [55]. In the parietal cortex, Cu,Zn-SOD activity was relatively small, but this isoenzyme component was inducible quickly by application of ALP. Contrary, Mn-SOD activity was decreased after application of ALP. The discrepancy between activity and content of Mn-SOD after ALP administration suggests that Mn-SOD activity might be inactivated by ALP.

On the other hand, in the hippocampus of EL mice, SOD activities were maintained at low levels once epileptogenesis was established. When ALP was applied, Cu,Zn-SOD activity was markedly increased. Even after 48 hours when the seizure threshold had already been lowered, the Cu,Zn-SOD activity was maintained at a relatively high level once epileptogenesis was established. These phenomena suggest that the induction of region-specific Cu,Zn-SOD activities by ALP might control the seizure susceptibility.

The discrepancy between activity and content of the hippocampal Cu,Zn-SOD [43] after acute administration of ALP suggests that activators of Cu,Zn-SOD might be induced by ALP.

ALP administered chronically might prevent the hippocampus-specific SOD activities from reduction in EL mice, thereby exerting antiepileptic effects on the secondarily generalized seizures observed in untreated EL mice **(Table 9).**

Decreased Cu, Zn SOD Activities in the Hippocampus of EL[s]

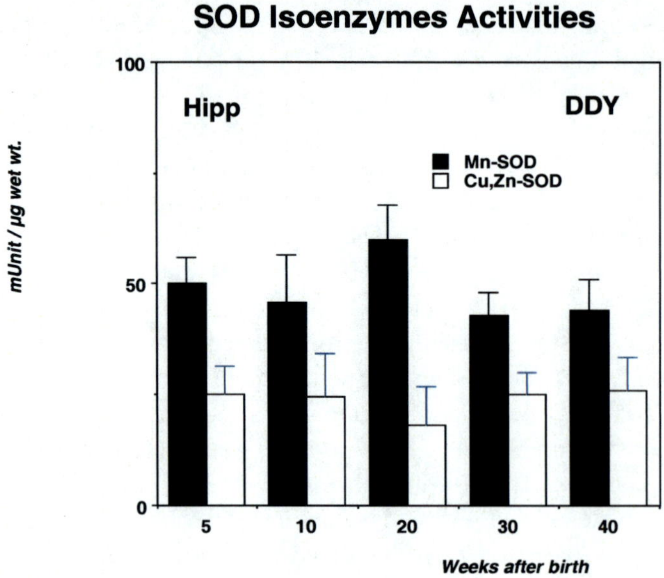

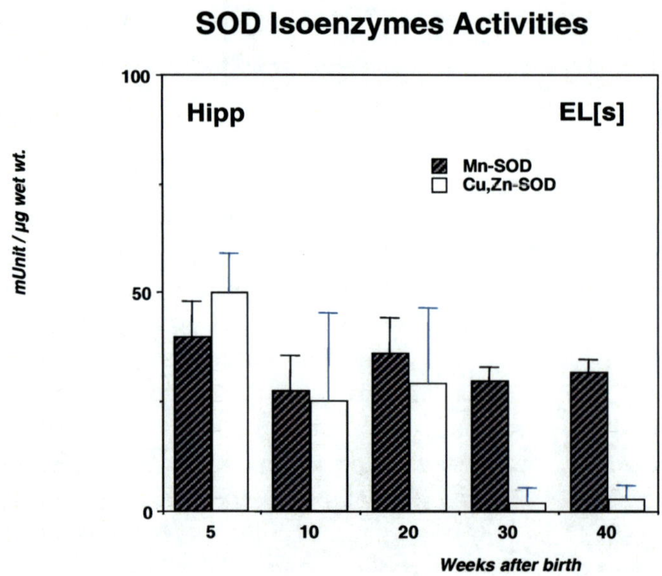

Fig. 9 Developmental changes in SOD isoenzyme activities in the hippocampus (Hipp) of DDY and EL[s] mice. Twelve mice were used for each age. Cu,Zn-SOD activity was obtained from total SOD activity minus Mn-SOD activity for each mouse. Activities are represented by mean ± SEM mUnit / µg wet wt. Statistical examination: by two-way ANOVA (weeks after birth and mouse strain). Mn-SOD: Weeks after birth and Mn-SOD activities, $F(4,165)=5.55$, $P<0.0003$ Mouse strains and Mn-SOD activities, $F(2,165)=14.35$, $P<0.0001$ Post-hoc Scheff's test between EL[ns](5W) and EL[ns](30,40W); $P<0.02$ Cu,Zn-SOD: Weeks after birth and Cu,Zn-SOD activities, $F(4,165)=8.739$, $P<0.0001$ Mouse strains and Cu,Zn-SOD activities, $F(2,165)=17.30$, $P<0.0001$ Weeks after birth, mouse strain and Cu,Zn-SOD activities, $F(8,165)=4.200$, $P<0.0001$ Post-hoc Scheff's test between EL[ns](5W) and EL[ns] (10,20,30,40W); $P<0.01$ DDY,EL[ns](30,40W) and EL[s](30,40W); $P<0.001$

Table 9. Role of Cu, Zn-SOD and ALP in the abnormal plasticity in EL

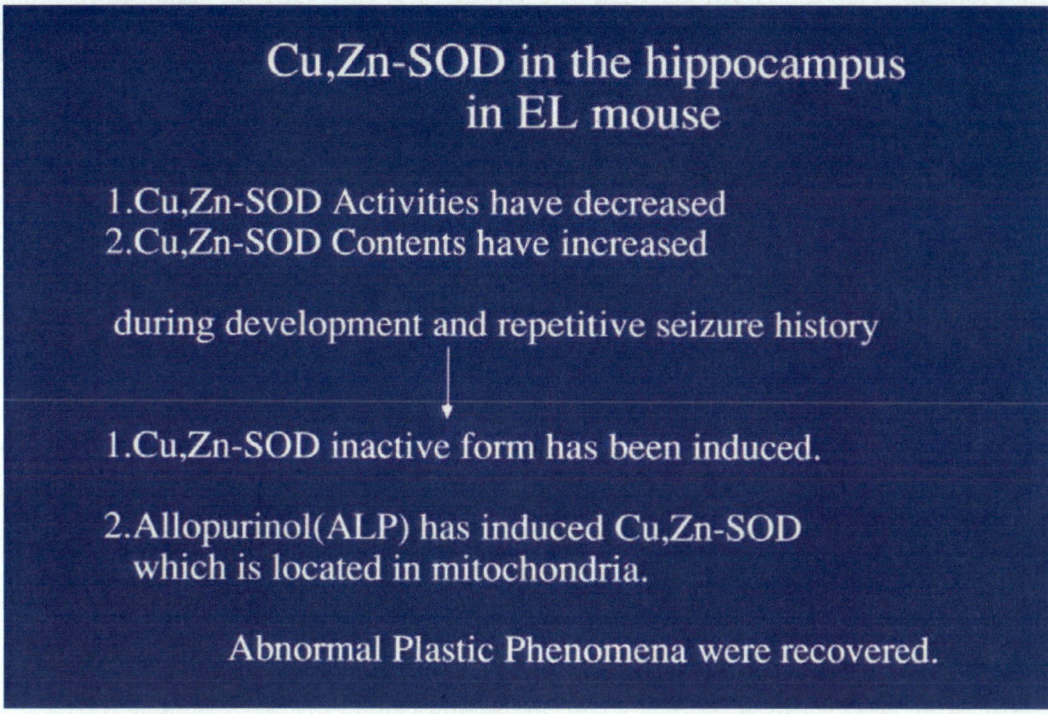

ALP is an inhibitor of xanthine oxidase which is a key enzyme for the synthesis of uric acid and O_2^- radical from xanthine. To exclude the possibility of direct effects of ALP on the uric acid synthesis pathway, serum uric acid concentrations were determined according to the age on both allopurinol(+) and allopurinol(-) [65]. Although the serum uric acid level was decreased during development, there was no statistical difference between allopurinol(+) and allopurinol(-) groups [44]. In the case of EL mice, to which 75mg/kg ALP p.o. was applied every other day since 5-week old, they did not develop seizures, nor show an abnormal decrease of SOD in the hippocampus during development. They never showed an decrease in the level of serum uric acid. Taking a small dosage of ALP (75mg/kg body weight every other day p.o.) into account, the drug might not be enough to inhibit xanthine oxidase, but enough to induce region-specific enzymes such as hippocampus-specific Cu,Zn-SOD. It is therefore conceivable that the antiepileptic effects of ALP might result from the induction of hippocampus-specific Cu,Zn-SOD during development in the mutant EL, rather than the inhibition of systemic xanthine oxidase.

In the case of myoclonus epilepsy of the Unvericht-Lundborg type, myoclonus seizure is partially controlled, and the clinical course of deterioration is prevented by the treatment of antioxidant, N-acetylcysteine [53], which has the potency of activating several antioxidant enzymes, such as SOD.

As a cause of intractable epileptic seizures, systemic selenium deficiency has been described [67]. Seleno-dependent peroxidase is speculated to play a key role in the defense of neural cells against oxygen radical formation and per oxidative processes. The increase of free radicals by triggering selenium depletion against cell defense in the brain will constitute an important factor for the origin of intractable seizures and subsequent neural damage.

Recent evidence would seem to support the relationship between free radicals and scavenger enzymes. Anticonvulsants play a role, as they influence free radical generating systems [52, 58, 59, 60, 77]. Many of patients who are on polytherapeutic regimens of most of the common anticonvulsants have shown excessive free radical production and induces a worsening the disease process. Drugs which can surpress free radical generation and protect brain such as ALP may be promising as new anti epileptic agents.

5. Ictogenesis and Epileptogenesis in EL Mice Brain Related to DNA Fragmentation

Introduction

An attempt was made to identify the region of EL brain targeted by free radicals as measured by DNA fragmentation [48, 50, 76] (**Fig. 8**).

In EL[s], DNA fragmentation was detected in the hippocampal CA1 and the parietal cortex by using in situ terminal transferase-mediated dUTP Nick labeling with the aid of alkaliphosphatase (AP) and peroxidase (PO). DNA fragmentation was also detected in EL[ns], which was, however, localized in the parietal cortex and less clear compared with EL[s]. These findings suggest that abnormalities in the region specific Cu,Zn-SOD isoenzyme activity might produce spatially specific free radicals, leading to DNA fragmentations. The process might be responsible, at least in part, for the formation of epileptogenesis.

Materials and Methods

Detection of Cellular DNA Fragmentation of EL Mice

DNA fragmentation was detected by in situ terminal transferase-mediated dUTP Nick End labeling kit (Boehlinger) whose labeling was photomicrographically observed by alkaliphosphatase (AP) and peroxidase (PO) with modifications as follows:

Twelve EL[s], 12 EL[ns] and 6 DDY mice were used. In a cryostat, 10 μm thick serial coronal samples were obtained from the ethanol-dry ice frozen brain in the tissuetek. Three serial samples were used for each Hematoxylin (HE), AP and PO staining. Samples were fixed on gelatin-coated slide glasses and invades with 0.1% sodium citrate and 0.1% Triton X-100 for 10 minutes at 4°C. Fluoroscein-labeled nucleotides were bound with 3'OH terminals of fragmented DNA by using terminal transferase (TdT). Peroxidase- and alkaliphosphatase-binding antifluoroscein antibodies were reacted with fragmented DNA-binding fluoroscein-labeled nucleotides to detect DNA fragmentation by photomicrography. DNAase1-treated samples were used as a positive control and samples without TdT reaction were used as a negative control.

Table 10. DNA fragmentation without cell loss

DNA fragmentation dependent on the seizure history ***In Situ*** Terminal Transferase (TdT) -mediated dUTP Nick end labelling detected by peroxidase (POD) or alkaliphosphatase (AP). In the EL[s] mice which experienced frequent seizures and showed epileptogenecity, DNA fragmentation was detected in the parietal cortex and the hippocampal CA1.

To quantify DNA fragmentation histologically, all of the AP positive cells were counted in the area indicated by a square in **Fig. 8**, left bottom. The region was located from No.298 to 303 (rostro-caudal 120 μm in length) according to Sidman mouse atlas [70], which has been identified as a focus of EL mouse seizures by the deep EEG recording [55]. Three serial sections were used for HE, AP and PO stainings, respectively. Four samples were obtained from one animal. Data were represented by mean ± SEM and statistically examined by t-test.

Preparation of Hematoxylin Eosin Staining (HE)

The results, which utilizes histological sections stained with HE to count the intact neurons in higher magification field were statistically analyzed.

Results

Detection of DNA Fragmentation in the EL[s] and Control DDY Mice

No DNA fragmentation was detected either by using alkaliphosphatase (AP) or peroxidase (PO) in DDY mice. The criteria of DNA fragmentation positive cells are cells which take AP converted grains. In EL[s] mice, DNA fragmentation was found as measured by AP in the parietal cortex (306± 28) and the hippocampal CA1 (106± 9). At a higher magnification, every positive cell was clearly seen. In EL[s] mice, DNA fragmentation was observed by PO in the parietal cortex and in the hippocampal CA1. In EL[ns], DNA fragmentation was detected in the parietal cortex (163 ±15), which was significantly weaker than that of EL[s] ($p<0.01$), and was not found in the hippocampal CA1 (24 ±12) (not significant compared with the control DDY level) **(Fig. 10)**.

No Cell Loss in the Parietal Cortex and Hippocampus

No cell loss were found in the parietal cortex of EL[s].

Both in the rostral and caudal side of hippocampus pyramidal cells, there were no statistically significant difference ($p<0.01$ by t-test) in cell counts between EL and control DDY **(Fig., 12, 13)**.

DNA Fragmentation in the Parietal Cortex and Hippocampus (25 weeks old)

DDY

EL[s]

Fig. 10. DNA fragmentation in DDY and EL[s] mice. DDY which have experienced seizure provoking stimulations like EL[s], stained by alkaliphosphatase (AP), EL[s] stained by AP. For the sample preparations 6 DDY and 12 EL[s] mice (30-week old) were sacrificed for detecting DNA fragmentation by AP.

Rapid Nissle Staining of the Parietal Cortex of EL

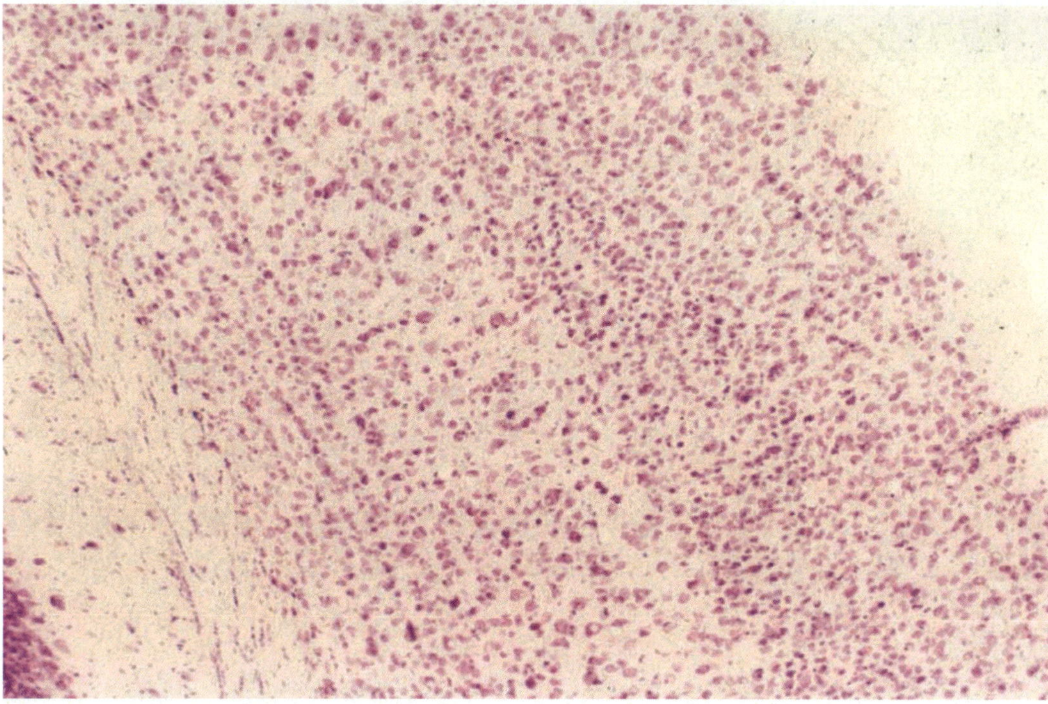

Fig. 11. No cell loss in the parietal cortex of EL

No Cell Loss

DDY/TIP (inbred mother strain of EL)

EL[s]

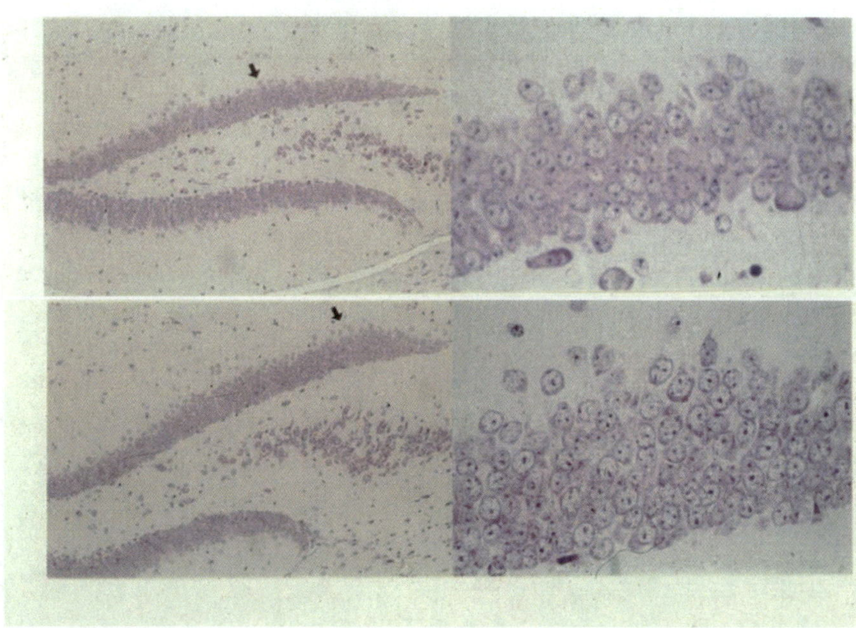

Fig. 12. No cell loss in the rostral side of the hippocampus of EL

No Cell Loss

DDY/TIP (inbred mother strain of EL)

EL[s]

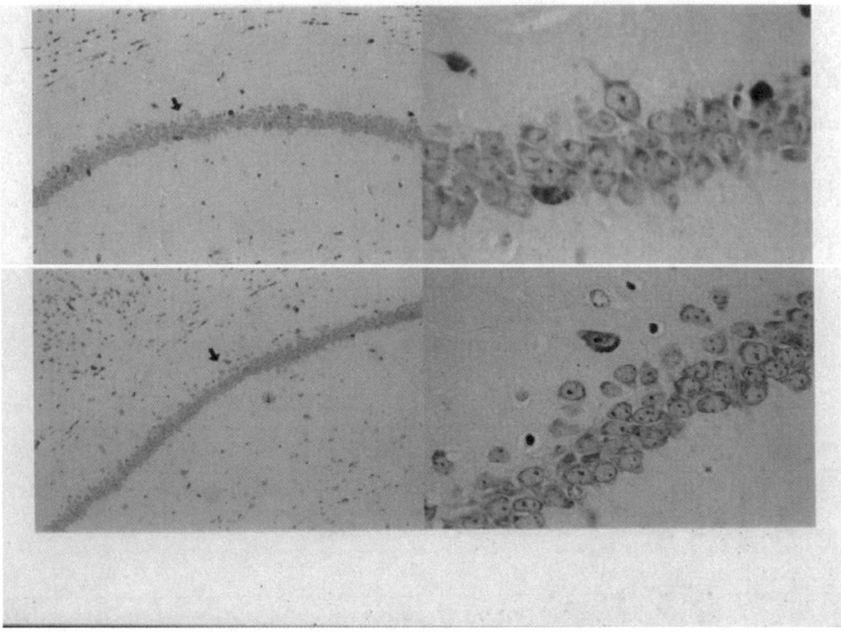

Fig. 13. No cell loss in the caudal side of the hippocampus of EL

Discussion

Under pathologic conditions [78, 56, 61, 62], superoxide free radicals can be generated in excess of a cell antioxidant (free radical scavenger) capacity resulting in severe damage to cellular constituents including proteins, DNA and lipids. The inherent biochemical and physiological characteristics of the brain, including high lipid concentrations and energy requirements, make it particularly susceptible to free radicals [46]. The target of excess free radicals may be DNA primarily resulting in DNA fragmentations. We found DNA fragmentation without cell loss [64] in the hippocampal CA1 of EL[s], but no DNA fragmentation in EL[ns]. Like DNA fragmentation, immediate early gene (IEG) expression showed a similar tendency in such a way that the events were localized to CA1 region of hippocampus of EL[s] mice [20].

6. Ictogenesis and Epileptogenesis in EL Mice Brain Related to Proapoptotic and Antiapoptotic Factors

Introduction

The EL mouse is an inbred mutant strain which has been used as an animal model of secondarily generalized seizures [79, 80]. Several lines of evidence indicate that seizure discharges are initiated in the parietal cortex, and then generalized through the hippocampus [81]. These findings have been substantiated by the histochemical and biochemical analyses of glucose utilization [82] and inhibitory neurotransmissions by gamma-aminobutyric acid (GABA) [83]. The developmental formation of the focus complex, which mainly consists of the parietal cortex and the hippocampus, has been hypothesized to be key to epileptogenesis in EL mice.

In our recent studies, excess free radicals might produce DNA fragmentation [84]. The possible candidates as free radicals are superoxide and superoxynitrite caused by decreased Cu,Zn-Superoxide dismutase (SOD) and increased inducible Nitric oxide synthetase (iNOS) in the brain of EL mice. Ordinarily DNA fragmentation leads to apoptosis in the tissue. To investigate the effects of DNA fragmentation in the tissue of EL mouse brain, we have analyzed cell loss histologically by cell counting.

Immediate early gene expression is nonspecific. However, the expression of localized and continuous IEG expression means that some protein cascades occur *in situ*. To investigate the candidate proteins, so that, pro and antiapoptotic and neurotrophic factors which is closely related to cell loss and cell survival and further to epileptogenesis, we have developmentally analyzed the expression in the parietal cortex (seizure initiation site) and in the hippocampus (seizure generalization site) of EL mice brain **(Table 11).**

Table 11 Possible mechanisms of DNA fragmentation without cell loss

Regional free radical concentrations caused by the dercraesed
Cu, Zn SOD and increased levels of i-NOS might be involved in the DNA fragmentation.

- Then, why neurons can survive?
- **IEG expression** means **Protein cascades.**

Pro- and anti-apoptotic factors and **Neurotrophic factors** may be the candidates.

Cell death regulatory genes of the Bcl-2 and caspase families may play a role in ongoing neuropathologic processes in human epilepsy, and offer novel targets as an adjunct to anticonvulsant therapy [93].

Excessive activation of glutamate receptors accompanied by Ca^{2+} overloading is thought to be responsible for the death of neurons in various conditions including stroke and epilepsy. Neurons also die if deprived of important growth factors and trophic influences, conditions sensitive to certain oncogene products such as the protein Bax [90]. Bcl-2 family gene products are critical to the integration of cell death stimuli that target the mitochondrion. Proapoptotic (Bcl-2-associated death protein) has been shown to dissociate from its sequestered site with the molecular chaperone protein 14-3-3 and displace proapoptotic BAX, Bcl-2-associated X protein (BAD) from antiapoptotic Bcl-XL. BAX subsequently translocates to the mitochondrion and induces cytochrome c release and caspase activation [94]. And seizures elicit divergent cell death and survival responses within neuronal populations and that the BAD cell death pathway may perform an instigator or reinforcement role in seizure-induced neuronal death [94].

Seizure-induced neuronal damage may involve both excitotoxic and apoptotic (programmed cell death) mechanisms. The expression of Bax and Bcl-2, two genes associated with apoptotic cell death, the ratio of Bax/Bcl-2 expression is increased in the hippocampus by seizures, suggest that apoptosis of hippocampal interneurons may lead to dysinhibition in the hippocampus and increased seizure susceptibility [91]. Bcl-2, Bcl-XL and Bax are regulatory proteins which are variably expressed in brain tissue and are known to be involved in the regulation of apoptosis. Bcl-2 and Bc-XL inhibit apoptosis and Bax generally promotes apoptosis [92]. Western blot analysis demonstrated significant increases in levels of Bcl-2 and Bcl-XL protein in seizure brain compared to control [93]. To study whether the Bax/Bcl expression ratio influence the DNA fragmentation without cell loss in the hippocampus of EL mice, we have studied the developmental changes of Bcl family expression in El mouse brain **(Table 12, Fig. 14)**.

Table 12. Proapototic and anti-apoptotic genes

Anti- and Pro-apoptotic Factors
Bcl-2 The Bcl-2 family of proteins play a crucial role in the regulation of cell death in many eukaryotic systems. The Bcl-2 gene was initially isolated from the t(14,18) chromosomal translocation found in human B-cell follicular lymphomas and was subsequently shown to repress cell death triggered by a diverse array of stimuli. However, the biochemical process by which Bcl-2 regulates cell death is poorly understood. Immunogen: A synthetic peptide correspondeing to amino acids 61-76 of mouse Bcl-2 sequence.
Bcl-X_L Bcl-X_L has been shown to promote cell survival through the regulation of mitochondrial homeostasis
Bax Bax has been shown to redistribute from the cytosol to the mitochondoria During apoptosis, and over-expression of Bax canaccellate cell death. Coregulation of Bax dimer form actin and intracellular localization are Associated with Bax conformational changes. Immunogen: A synthetic peptide corresponding to amino acids3-16 of the mouse Bax sequence

Materials

Preparation of Tissues for Immunoblotting Analysis

For immunoblotting analysis of the Bcl family EL mice of 5, 8, 10, 12, 15, 19, 24 weeks of age were used (number of the animals used was six for each group). Six DDY/TIP mice (mother strain of EL) of 10, 20, 30 were used as control. After decapitation, brains were removed and then the parietal cortex (PCx) and the hippocampus (Hipp) were dissected out. About 10% homogenates were prepared with 20 mM Tris-HCl buffer (pH 8.0). Just before use, homogenates with dye were boiled for 3 min and the were centrifuged for 5 min at 2000 x g.

Pro-apoptotic and Anti-apoptotic Factors

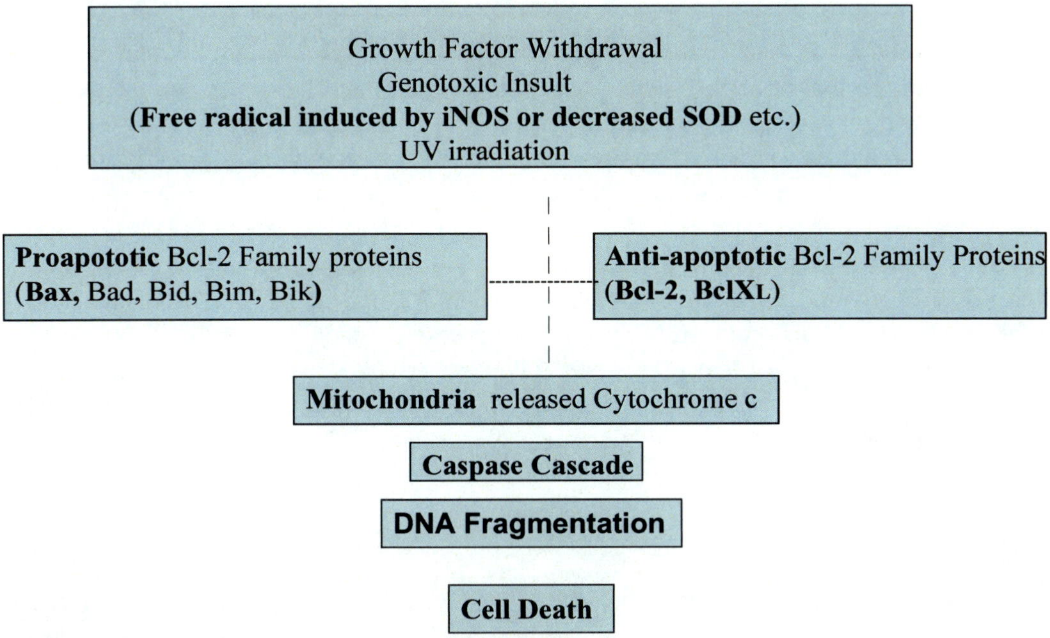

Fig. 14. Apoptotic process and modulating factors

Primary Antibodies and their Specificities

mouse anti-mouse Bax monoclonal antibody, mouse anti-mouse Bcl-2 monoclonal antibody and mouse anti-human Bcl-XL monoclonal antibody were purchased from Trevigen (Gaitherburg, MD, USA). Rabbit anti-mouse brain derived neurotrophic factor (BDNF) polyclonal antibody was purchased from Chemicon (Temecula.CA, USA). Rabbit anti-human NT-3 and rabbit anti-human FGF-2 were purchased from Santa Cruz Biotechnology (USA) **(Table 12)**.

Immunoblotting Procedures

Immunoblotting studies were carried out according to the partially modified procedures by Arima and Ueda [93, 94] For the immunoblot analysis, 10% mouse brain homogenates (total protein of applied samples: 8.33 - 8.43 μg for NOS isoenzymes and 20.0 μg for Bcl family and neorotrophic factors) were separated through 7.5 - 10% SDS-PAGE and transfered to a PVDF membrane (Millipore, Bedford, MA, USA), blocked and then incubated with either of anti-Bax (1:6000), or anti-Bcl-2 (1:7000), or Bcl-XL (1:3000). After washing, the membrane was incubated with goat anti-rabbit or Goat anti-mouse conjugated with horseradish peroxidase (1:20,000 for anti-NOS and 1:10000 for anti-Bcl family and anti-neurotrophic factors; SIGMA), followed by the Western blot-chemiluminescence reagent

(DuPont NEN, Boston, MA, USA). The immunoreactivities on the membrane were detected using Hyperfilm-ECL (Amersham, Little Chalfont, UK).

Results

Developmental Changes of Anti and Proapoptotic Factors (Bcl-2, BclXL, Bax)

In the parietal cortex (Seizure initiation site) **(Fig. 15, 16, 17),** pro-apoptotic Bax has shown over expression from 8-19 weeks old during development which covers the periods of ictogenesis and epileptogenesis. Anti-apoptotic Bcl-2 has also shown over expression corresponding to that of Bax. Anti-apoptotic Bcl-XL has shown the linearly increasing expression and reached maximum level around 24weeks of age (periods of late epileptogenesis).

In the hippocampus (Seizure generalization site) **(Fig. 18, 19, 20)**, pro-apoptotic Bax has shown over-expression from 8 to 19 weeks old which covers the periods of ictogenesis and epileptogenesis. Anti-apoptotic Bcl-2 has shown over-expression from 8 to 19 weeks of age which covers the periods of ictogenesis and epileptogenesis, respectively. Anti-apoptotic Bcl-XL has shown maximum expression at 5 and 24 weeks of age which covered the early periods of ictogenesis and the late periods of epileptogenesis, respectively.

Discussion

Recently the molecular mechanisms of the relation ship between abnormal plasticity and, Bcl family and neurotrophic factor genes has been partially analyzed. the Seizures evoked by micro injection of Cain acid into the amygdala of the rat induced unilateral CA3 pyramidal neuron death with features of apoptosis. In control hippocampus and cortex, BAD was found constitutively bound to 14-3-3, whereas BCL-XL bound Bax. Within damaged hippocampus, seizures induced the dissociation of BAD from 14-3-3 and the subsequent dimerization of BAD with BCL-XL as determined by immunoprecipitation and immunohistochemical colocalization. 14-3-3 was found to translocate to the nucleus of degenerating neurons, whereas Bax accumulated at mitochondrial membranes. In contrast, the primarily uninjured cortex exhibited increased phosphorylation of protein kinase B (Akt), which may phosphorylate and inhibit BAD, and no altered binding of BAD to BCL-XL. And further, administration of an inhibitor of phosphatidylinositol 3-kinase (LY294002), thought to be an upstream activator of Akt, exacerbated cortical apoptosis after seizures. Seizures might elicit divergent cell death and survival responses within neuronal populations and that the BAD cell death pathway may perform an instigator or reinforcement role in seizure-induced neuronal death [94].

During limbic epileptogenesis *in vivo* the dentate granule cells (DGCs) exhibit increased expression of BDNF, followed by striking morphologic plasticities, namely the formation of basal dendrites and the sprouting of mossy fibers. Increased expression of BDNF intrinsic to DGCs may be sufficient to induce morphological plasticities [83].

Developmental Changes of Bcl-2 Expression in the Parietal Cortex

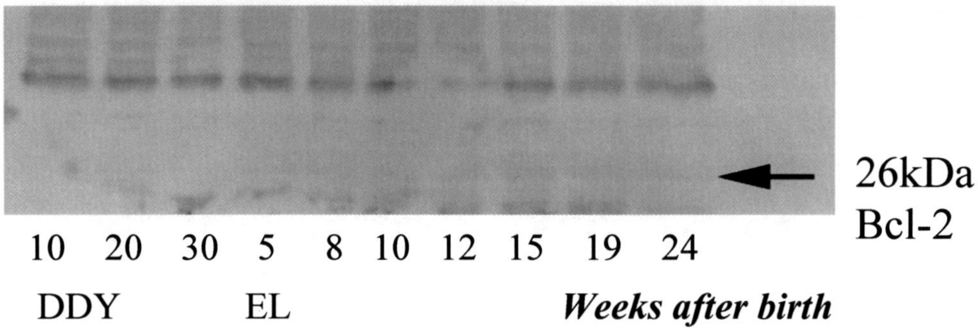

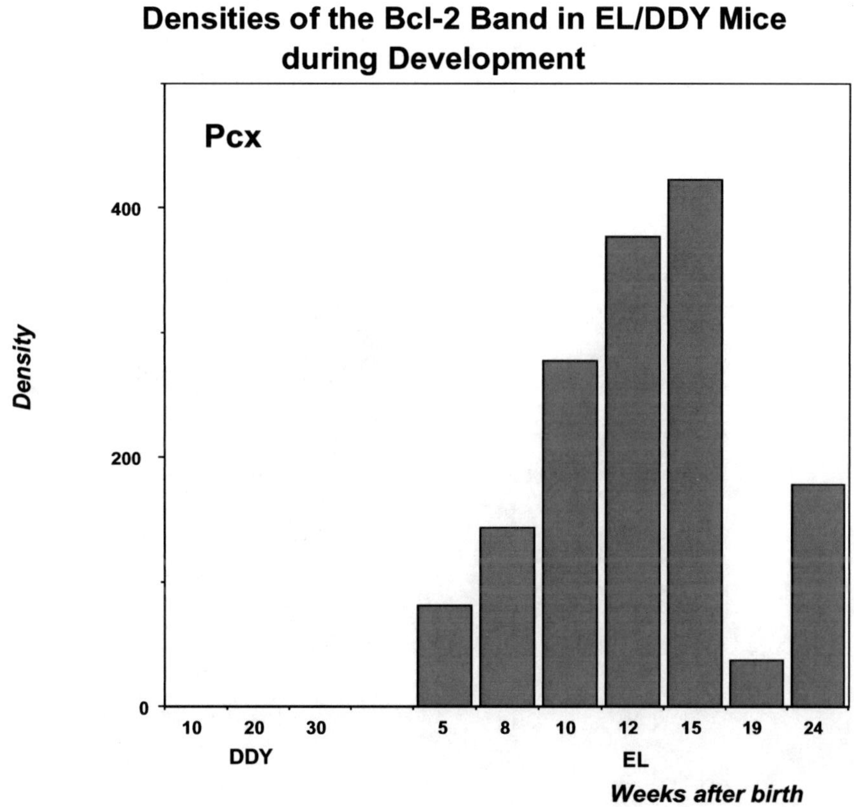

Fig. 15. Developmental changes of Bcl-2 gene expression during epileptogenesis in the parietal cortex of EL mouse brain.

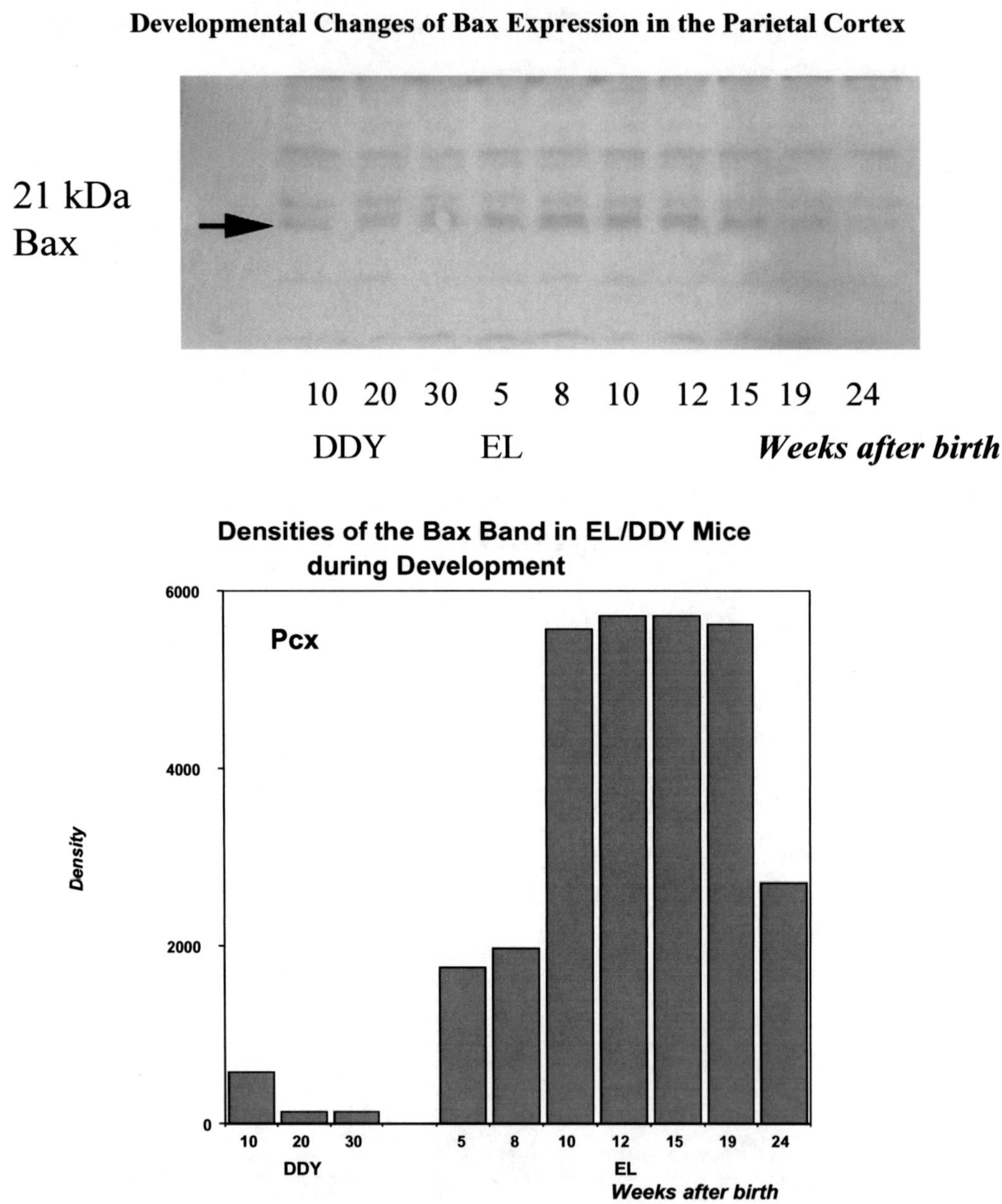

Fig. 16. Developmental changes of Bax gene expression during epileptogenesis in the parietal cortex of EL mouse brain.

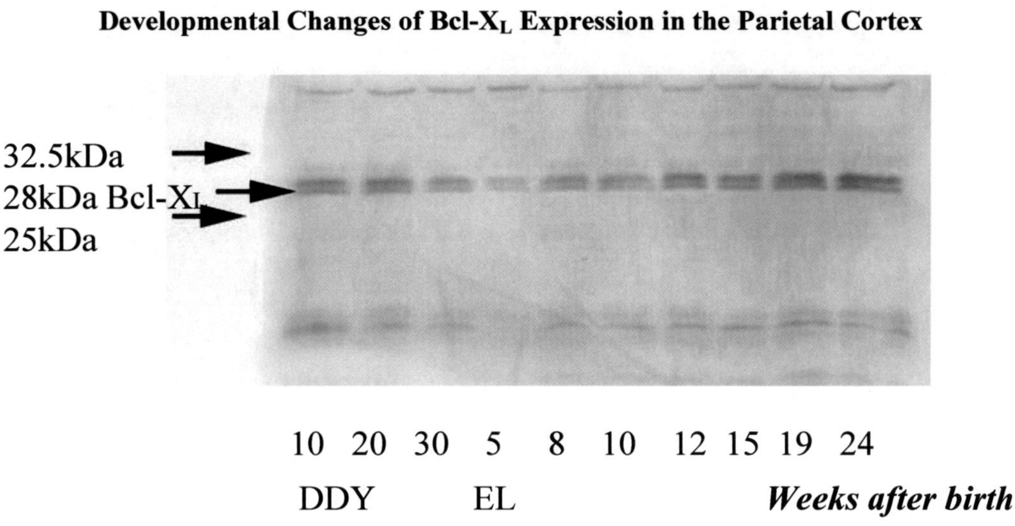

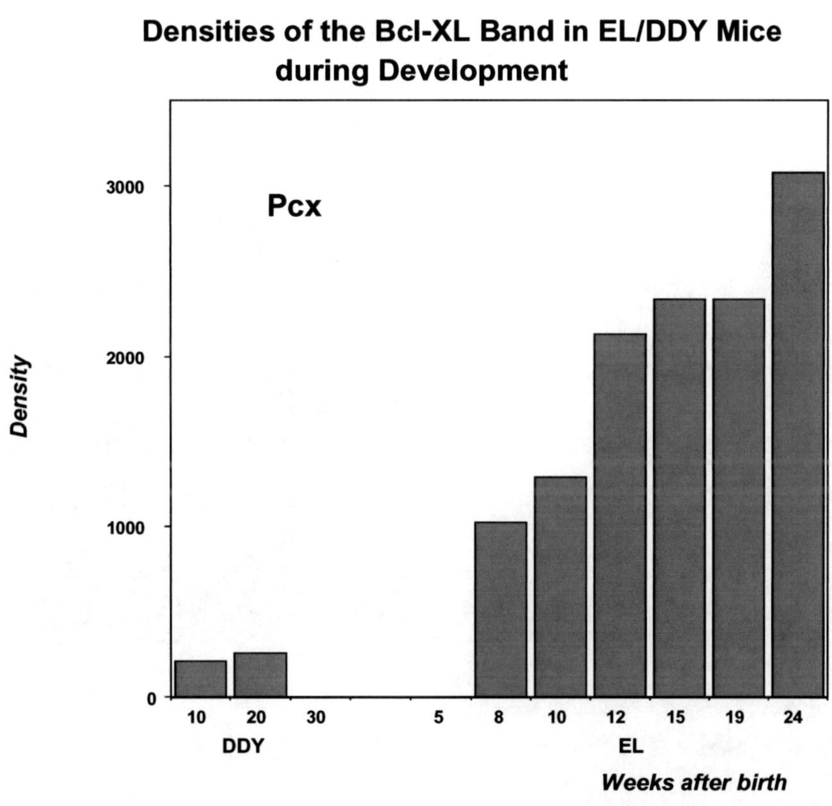

Fig. 17. Developmental changes of Bcl-XL gene expression during epileptogenesis in the parietal cortex of EL mouse brain.

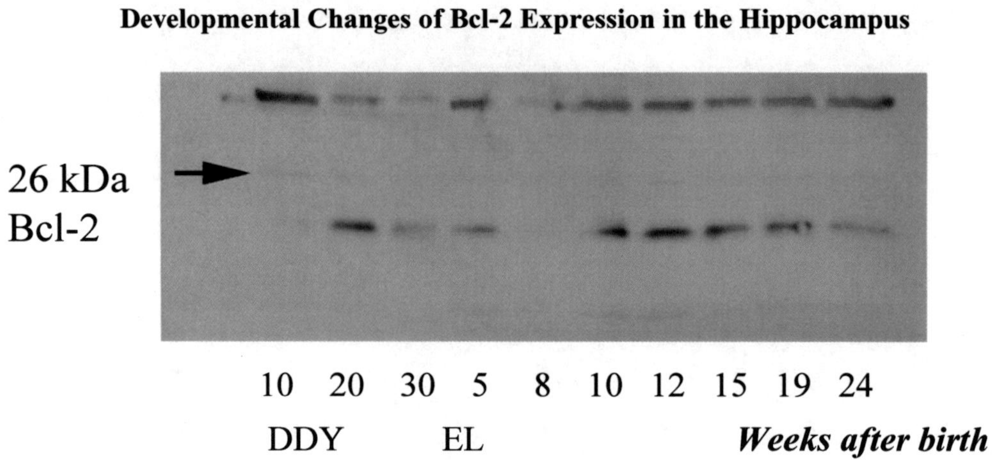

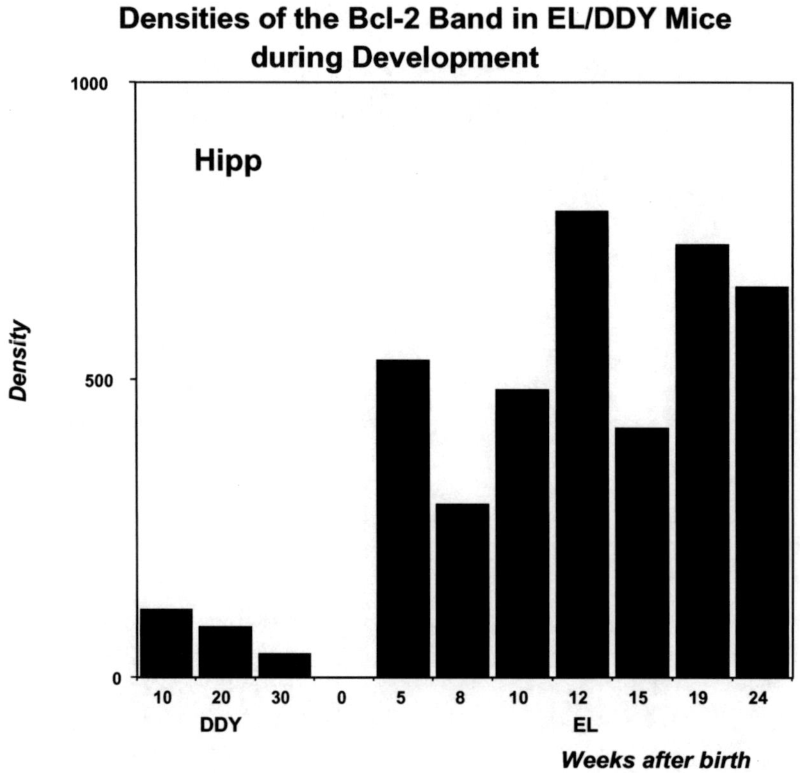

Fig. 18. Developmental changes of Bcl-2 gene expression during epileptogenesis in the hippocampus of EL mouse brain.

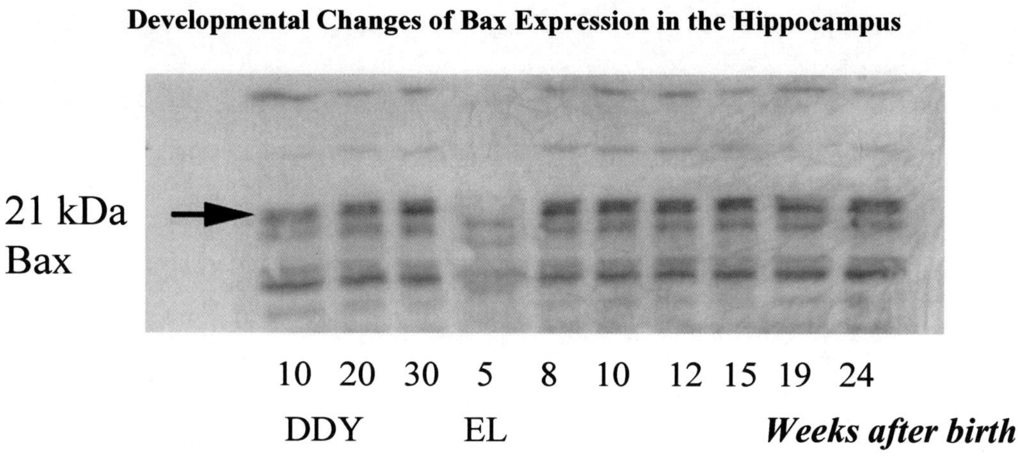

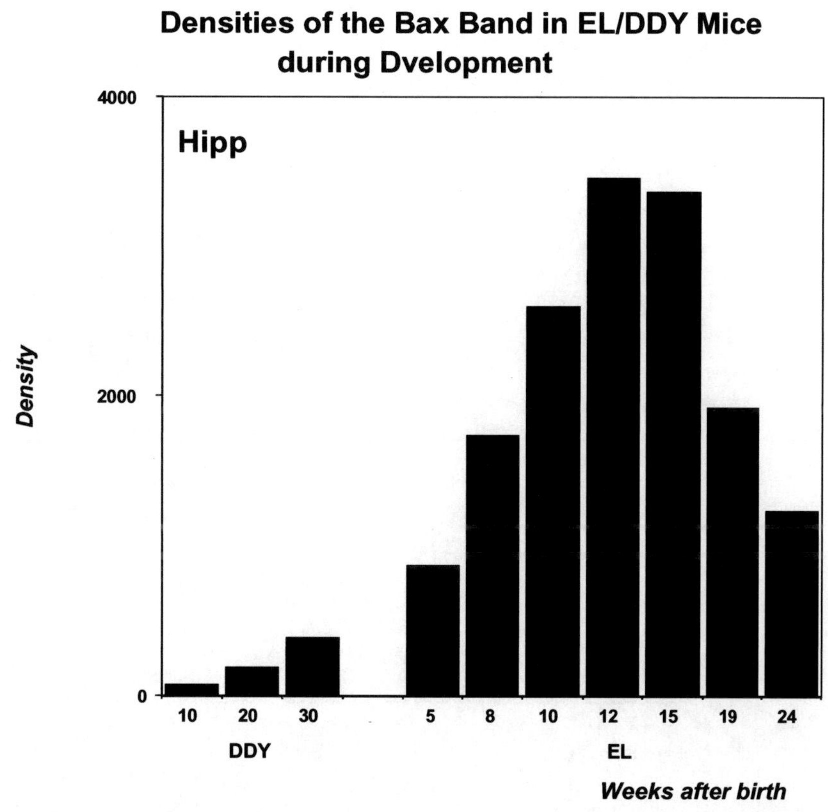

Fig. 19. Developmental changes of Bax gene expression during epileptogenesis in the hippocampus of EL mouse brain.

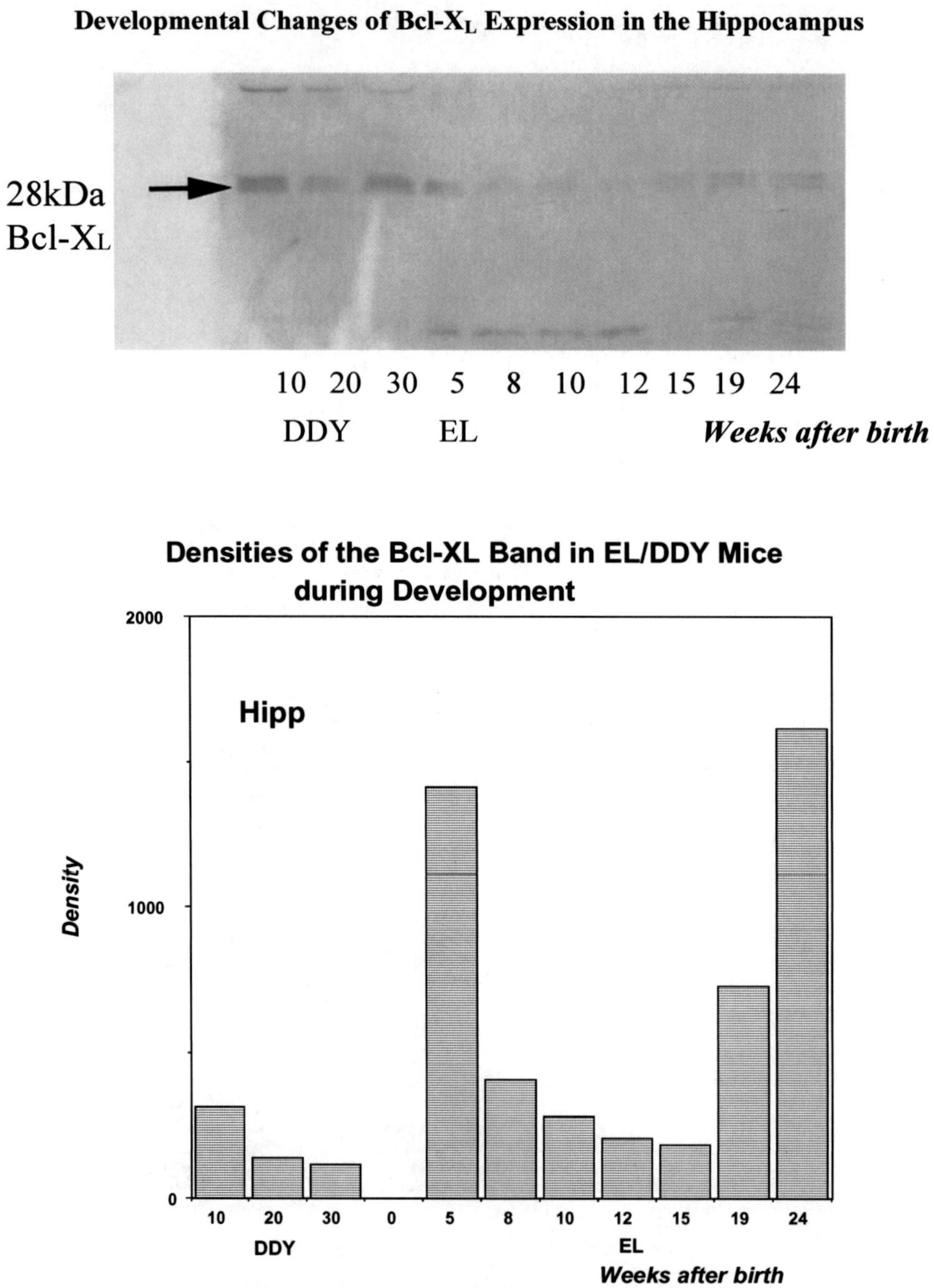

Fig. 20. Developmental changes of Bcl-XL gene expression during epileptogenesis in the hippocampus of EL mouse brain.

In human samples obtained from temporal lobectomy, Bcl-2, Bax and caspase-3 immunoreactivity was increased predominantly in cells with the morphologic appearance of neurons, whereas Bcl-XL immunoreactivity was increased in cells with the appearance of glia. DNA fragmentation was detected in some but not all sections from epileptic brain samples [93].

Bcl-2, Bcl-XL and Bax are regulatory proteins which are variably expressed in brain tissue and are known to be involved in the regulation of apoptosis; Bcl-2 and Bcl-XL inhibit apoptosis and Bax generally promotes apoptosis. Western blot analysis demonstrated significant increases in levels of Bcl-2 and Bcl-XL protein in human seizure brain compared to control [92].

In EL both proapoptotic Bax and antiapoptotic Bcl-2 has shown the bell shape over expression pattern during development which is corresponding to the periods of ictogenesis and epilptogenesis in the parietal cortex and the hippocampus. These results suggest that the expression of Bax and Bcl-2 do not reflect the effects of seizures, because there was almost no signals after 24 weeks of age when the seizure threshold was very low and EL has experienced frequent seizures. And further the relative ratio of Bax/Bcl-2 has once upregulated and then decreased to to control level in the parietal cortex. In the hippocampus Bcl-2 was relatively dominant compared to that of Bax at the age of 24 weeks, suggesting that the findings of DNA fragmentation without cell loss might be caused by the inbalance of Bcl-2 and Bax, so that, antiapoptotic activation and proapoptotic inactibation.

7. Ictogenesis and Epileptogenesis in EL Mice Brain Related to Neurotrophic Factors

Introduction

Fibroblast growth factor-2 (FGF-2), also refereed to as basic FGF, is a member of a family of growth factors that stimulate proliferation of cells of mesenchymal, epitherial and neuroectodermal origin. These members share 30-55% amino acid sequence identity, similar gene structure, and are capable of transforming cultured cells when overexpressed in transfected cells. Cellular receptors for FGF's are members of a second multigene family including four tyrosine kinases, designated Flg, Berk, TKF and FGFR-3 [92].

Neurotrophin-3 (NT-3), a member of the neurotrophin family of neurotrophic factors, is important for cell survival, axonal growth and neuronal plasticity. Epileptiform activation can regulate the expression of neurotrophins, and increases or decreases in neurotrophins can affect both epileptogenesis and seizure-related axonal growth [82].

Epileptic seizures increase the expression of BDNF in the hippocampus. Since this neurotrophin exerts modulatory effects on neuronal excitability in this structure, it may play an important role in hippocampal epileptogenesis [88].

Several studies suggest that brain-derived neurotrophic factor (BDNF) can exacerbate seizure development during status epilepticus (S.E.) and subsequent epileptogenesis in the adult brain [79]. On the other hand, evidence exists for the protective effect of BDNF. To study this controversy, we have studied the developmental changes of neurotrophic factors expression in EL mouse brain.

Materials

Preparation of Tissues for Immunoblotting Analysis

For immunoblotting analysis of the neurotrophic factors, EL mice of 5, 8, 10, 12, 15, 19, 24 weeks of age were used (number of the animals used was six for each group). Six DDY/TIP mice (mother strain of EL) of 10, 20, 30 were used as control. After decapitation, brains were removed and then the parietal cortex (PCx) and the hippocampus (Hipp) were dissected out. About 10% homogenates were prepared with 20 mM Tris-HCl buffer (pH 8.0). Just before use, homogenates with dye were boiled for 3 min and the were centrifuged for 5 min at 2000 x g.

Primary Antibodies and their Specificities

Rabbit anti-mouse brain derived neurotrophic factor (BDNF) polyclonal antibody was purchased from Chemicon (Temecula.CA, USA). Rabbit anti-human NT-3 and rabbit anti-human FGF-2 were purchased from Santa Cruz Biotechnology (USA) **(Table 13).**

Table 13. Neurotrophic factors

Neurotrophic Factors
Brain Derived Neurotrophic Factor (BDNF)
The Neurotrophiin family of proteins play a crucial role in the regulation of cell survival. The molecular weight of BDNF is 13.6kD. BDNF of human origin is identical to corresponding mouse or pig sequence. **BDNF has been shown to promote cell survival.** High levels of m-RNA BDNF expression have been found in the hippocampus and some localized neocortex. Rabbit anti-brain derived neurotrophic factor (BDNF) *Immunogen*: A 10 amino acid peptide corresponding to the amino-terminal of mouse brain. Derived BDNF is coupled to ovalubmin. The sequence is H2N-HSDPARRGEL- The neutrophin have provide difficult to localize which may be due to masking by, for example, their association with the trk receptors or very low concentrations
NT-3
Neurotrophins function to **regulate naturally occurring cell death of neurons during development.**The prototype neutrophin is nerve growth factor (NGF), originally discovered in the 1950s as a soluble peptide promoting the survival of, and neuritic outgrowth from, sympathetic ganglia. Three additional structurally homologous neurotrophic factors have been identified. These include BDNF, neurotrophin-3 (NT-3) and NT-4. The Trk B receptor binds equally well both BDNF and NT-4, and to a lesser extent NT-3, while the Trk C receptor only binds NT-3. *Immunogen*: Rabbit polyclonal antibody against a peptide mapping at the carboxy terminus of the mature form from NT-3 of human origin (identical to corresponding mouse sequence).
FGF-2
Fibroblast growth factor-2 (FGF-2), also refereed to as basic FGF, is a member of **a family of growth factors that stimulate proliferation of cells of** mesenchymal, epitherial and **neuroectodermal origin.** These members share 30-55% amino acid sequence identity, similar gene structure, and are capable of transforming cultured cells when overexpressed in transfected cells. Cellular receptors for FGF's are members of a second multigene family including four tyrosine kinases, designated Flg, Berk, TKF and FGFR-3. *Immunogen*: A peptide mapping within the amino terminal domain of FGF-2 of human origin (differs from corresponding mouse and chicken sequences by a single amino acid)

Immunoblotting Procedures

Immunoblotting studies were carried out according to the partially modified procedures by Arima and Ueda [93, 94]. 20.0 μg for neorotrophic factors were separated through 7.5 - 10% SDS-PAGE and transfered to a PVDF membrane (Millipore, Bedford, MA, USA), blocked and then incubated with either of anti-BDNF (1:1000), or Anti-NT-3 (1:1000), or anti-FGF-2 (1:1000). After washing, the membrane was incubated with goat anti-rabbit or Goat anti-mouse conjugated with horseradish peroxidase (1:10000 for anti-neurotrophic factors; SIGMA), followed by the Western blot-chemiluminescence reagent (DuPont NEN, Boston, MA, USA). The immunoreactivities on the membrane were detected using Hyperfilm-ECL (Amersham, Little Chalfont, UK).

Results

Developmental Changes of Neurotrophic Factors (BDNF, NT-3, FGF-2)

In the parietal cortex **(Fig. 21, 22, 23)**, BDNF has shown over expression during the early developmental period which covered the periods of ictogenesis. NT-3 has shown over expression after 15 weeks of age which covered the periods of late epileptogenesis. FGF-2 has been over expressed from 5 to 10 weeks of age which covered the early periods of ictogenesis)

In the hippocampus **(Fig. 24, 25, 26),** BDNF has shown the double phasic over-expression, from 8 to 12 and around 19week old which covered the periods of ictogenesis and late epileptogenesis, respectively. NT-3 has shown peak expression from 8 to 12 week old which covered the periods of icttogenesis. FGF-2 has shown linearly increasing expression and reached maximum level at 24 weeks of age which covered the late periods of epileptogenesis.

Discussion

After febrile seizures (FSs) the induction of BDNF mRNA was observed in the dentate gyrus peaked at 3 h and also the induction of *c-fos* mRNA was observed in the dentate gyrus at 30 min and 1 h. BDNF and *c-fos* are the genes whose expression can be altered by FSs and might be related to pathologic alterations after FSs [95].

BDNF are hypothesized that the expression is related to pathological alteration after seizures, We reported that the expression of BDNF reached maximum during the period of epileptogenesis, not after the frequent seizures, because aster 20 weeks of age, the signal decreased and returned to basal level at the age of 24 weeks of age, when EL mice have experienced most frequent seizures.

Application of BDNF increased the amplitude and frequency of spontaneous excitatory postsynaptic currents and increased the amplitude of evoked excitatory postsynaptic currents. BDNF had no effect on spontaneous inhibitory postsynaptic currents but produced a decrease in amplitude of evoked inhibitory postsynaptic currents. BDNF's effects were abolished by coapplication of the tyrosine kinase inhibitor K252a. Therefore, BDNF enhances fast excitatory transmission in the epileptic human dentate gyrus and may play an important role in epileptogenesis in temporal lobe epilepsy [96]. And BDNF may play an important role in ictogenesis a d epileptogenesis, This raises the possibility of designing therapies for this disorder that may be both anticonvulsant and antiepileptogenic agent [84].

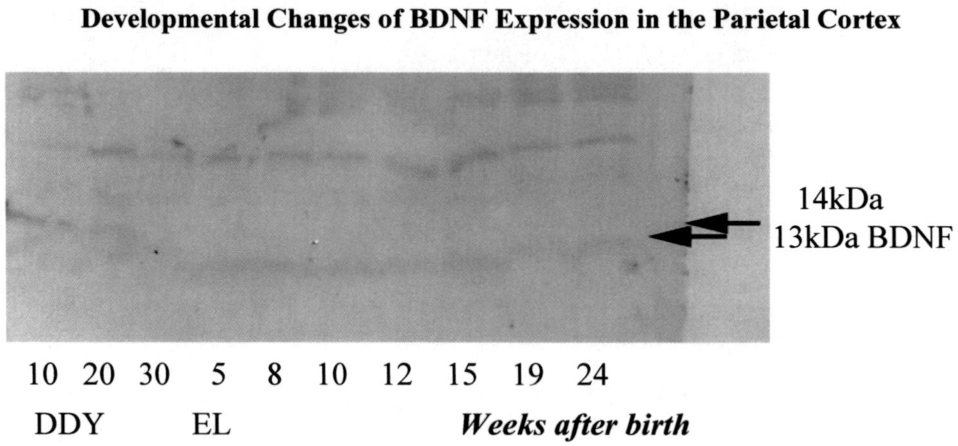

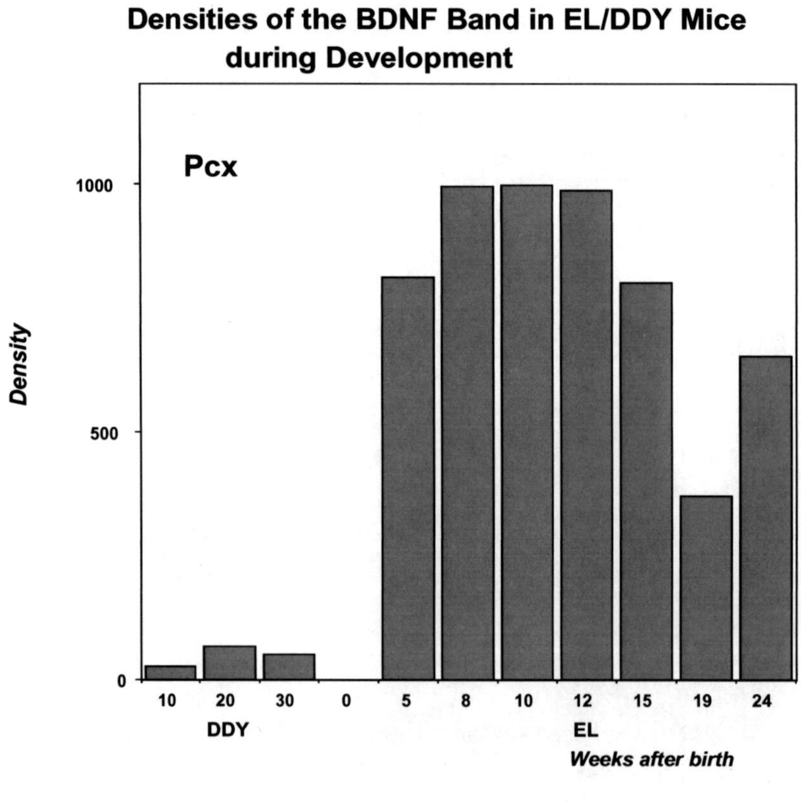

Fig. 21. Developmental changes of BDNF gene expression during epileptogenesis in the parietal cortex of EL mouse brain.

Developmental Changes of NT-3 Expression in the Parietal Cortex

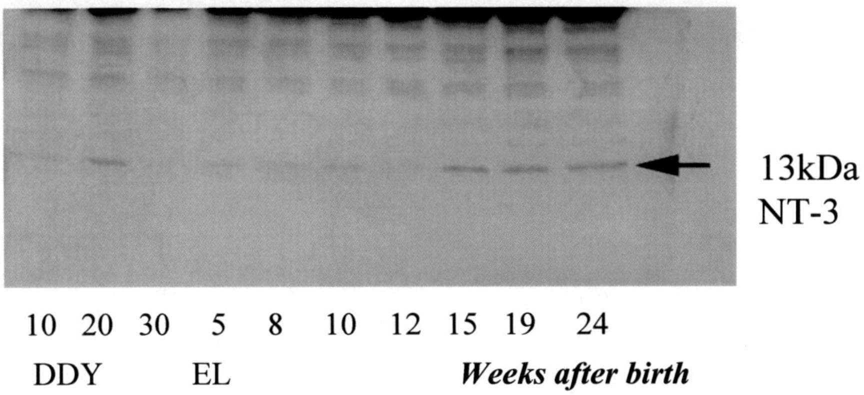

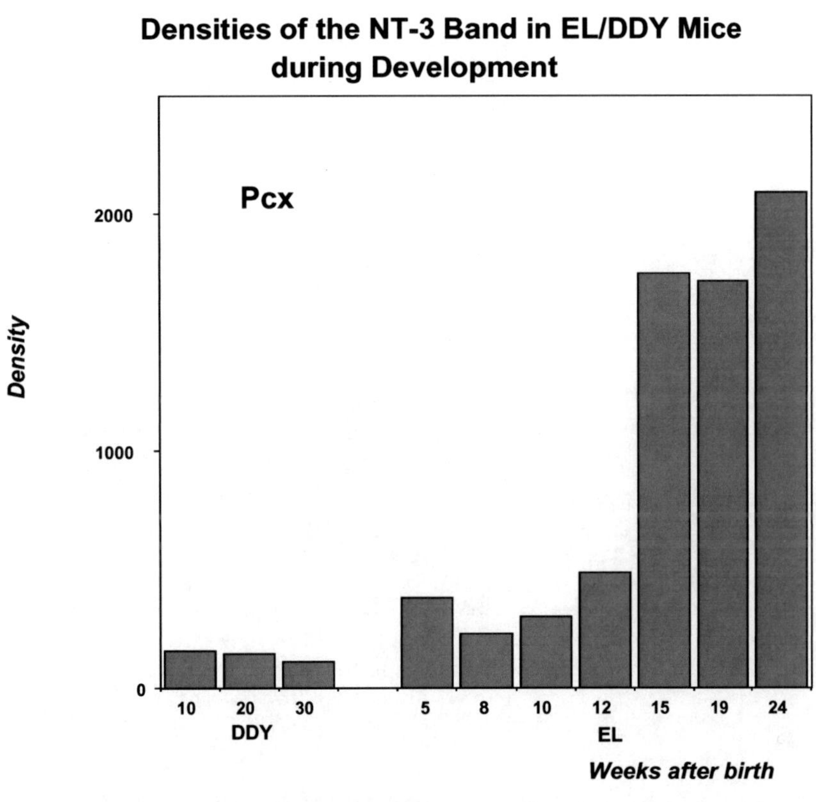

Fig. 22. Developmental changes of NT-3 gene expression during epileptogenesis in the parietal cortex of EL mouse brain.

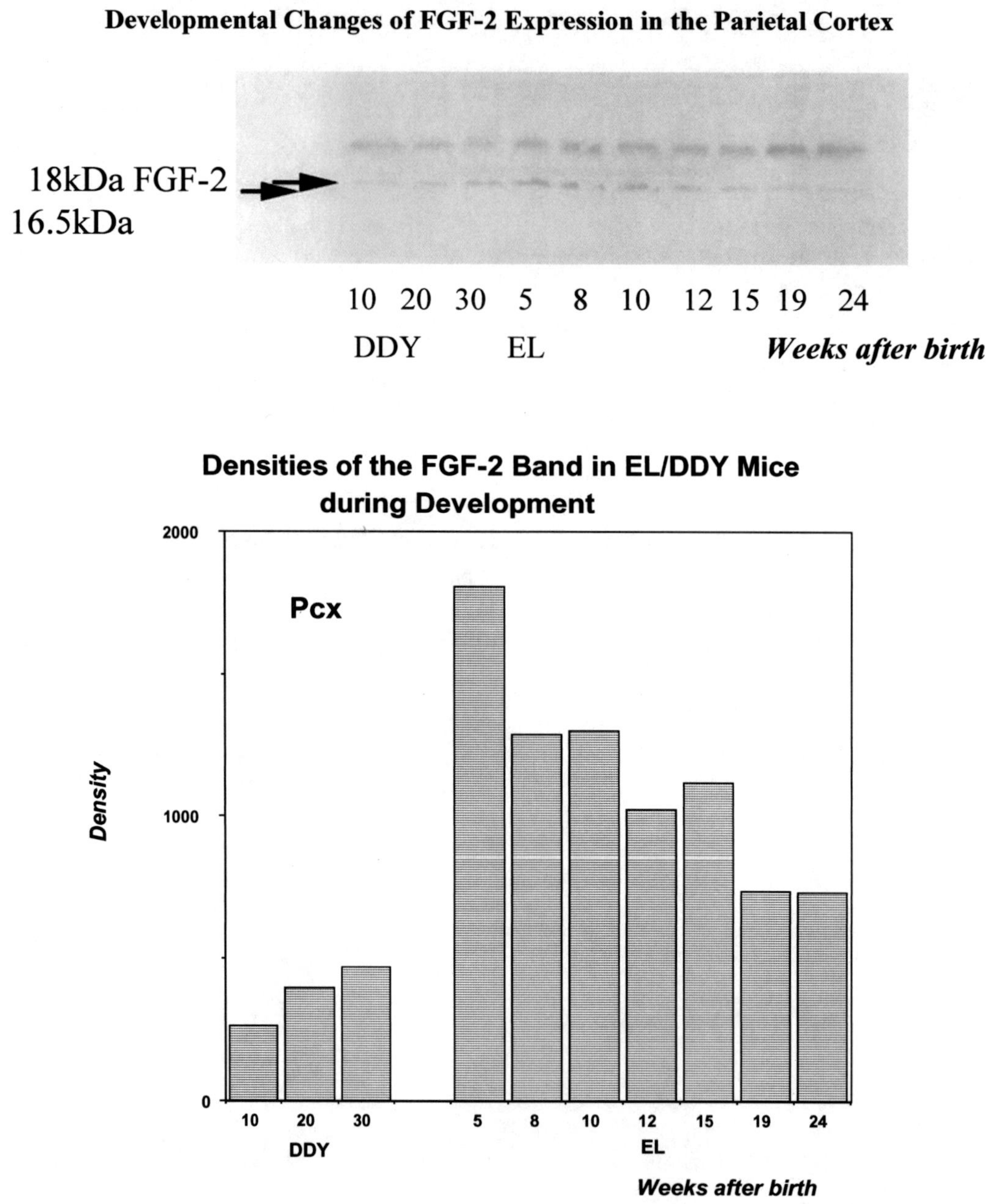

Fig. 23. Developmental changes of FGF-2 gene expression during epileptogenesis in the parietal cortex of EL mouse brain.

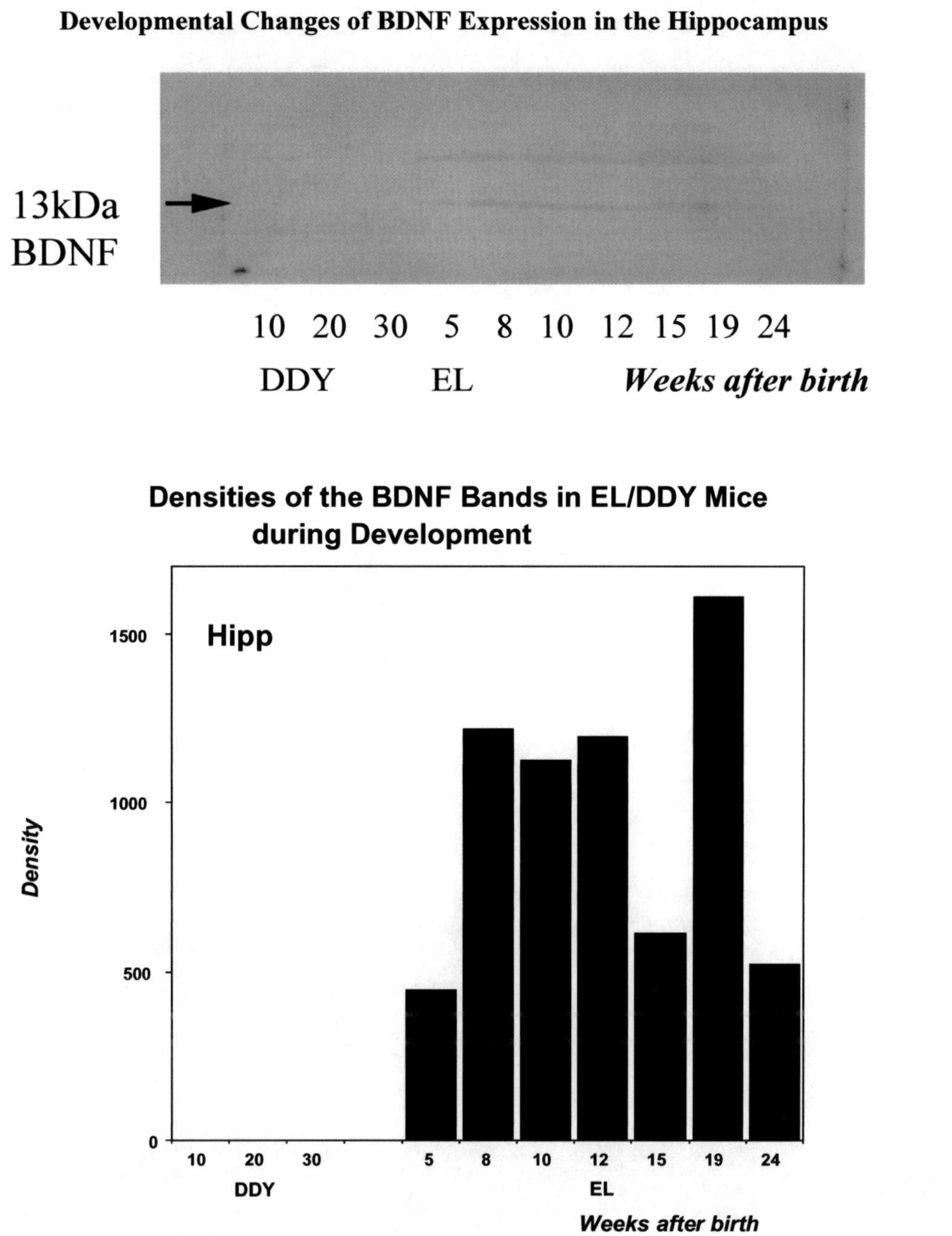

Fig. 24. Developmental changes of BDNF gene expression during epileptogenesis in the hippocampus of EL mouse brain.

Developmental Changes of NT-3 Expression in the Hippocampus

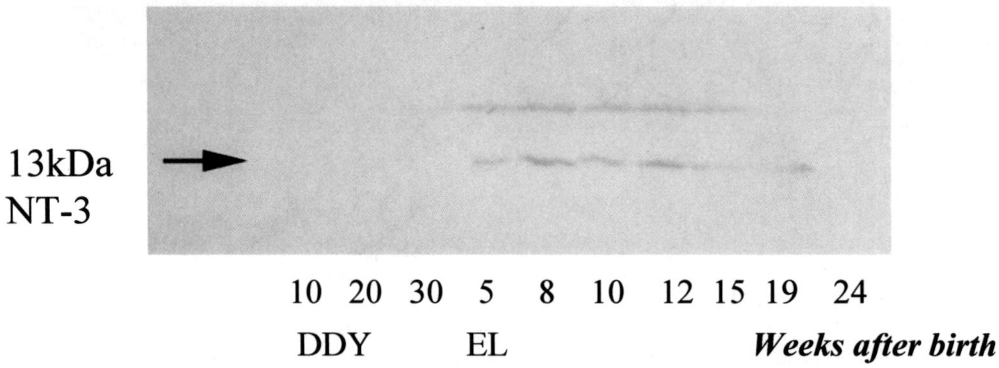

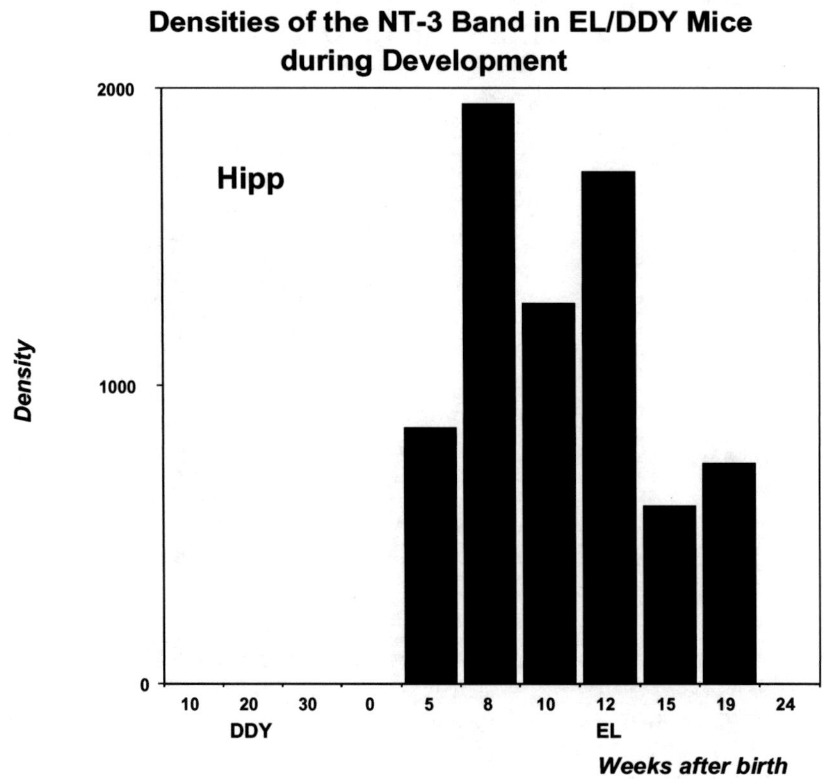

Fig. 25. Developmental changes of NT-3 gene expression during epileptogenesis in the hippocampus of EL mouse brain.

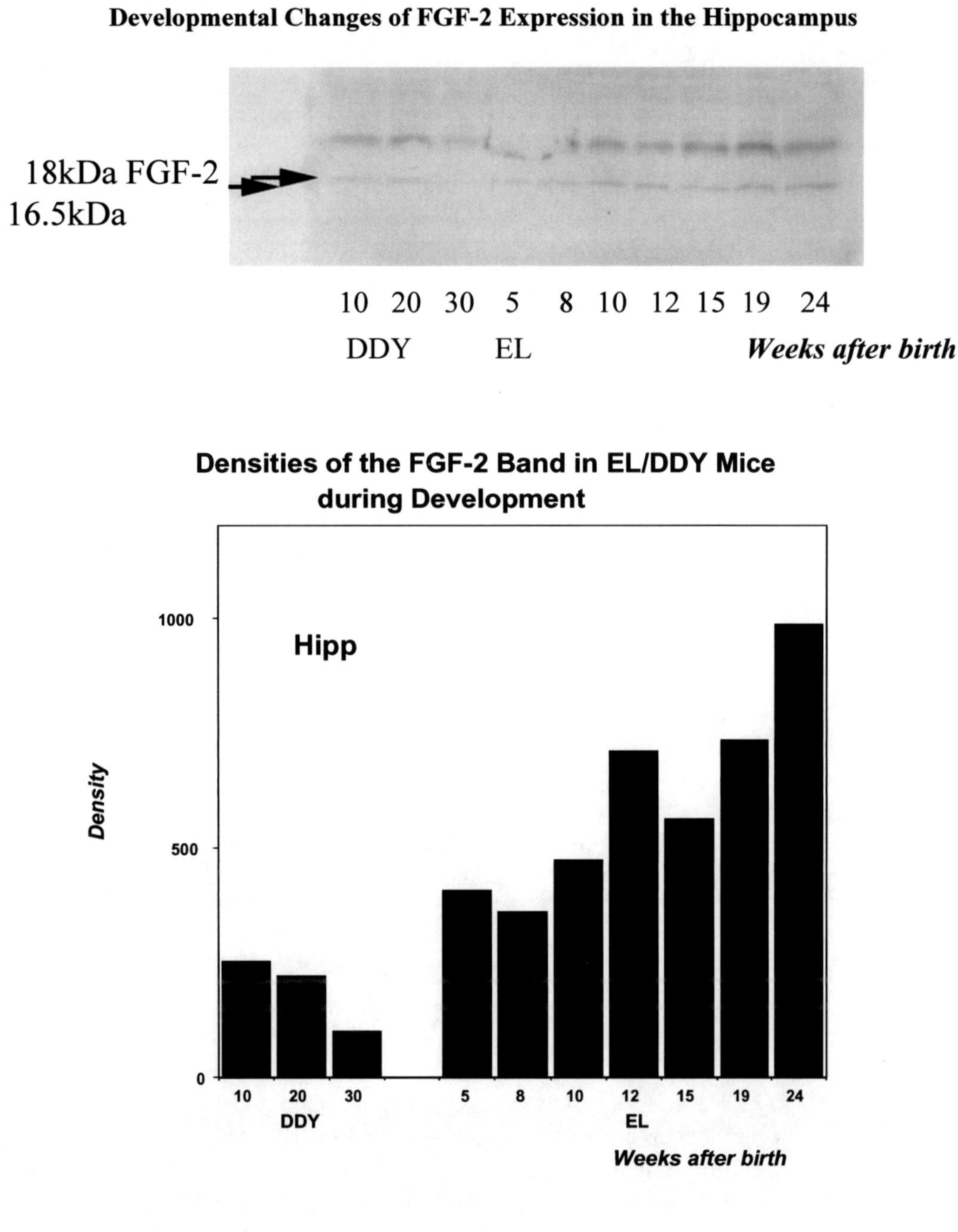

Fig. 26. Developmental changes of FGF-2 gene expression during epileptogenesis in the hippocampus of EL mouse brain.

It is reported that the expression of nerve growth factor and BDNF is rapidly up-regulated following seizures, while NT-3 mRNA remains unchanged or undergoes a delayed down-regulation, suggesting that NT-3 might have a different function in epileptogenesis [82].

In EL mice NT-3 was upregulated following the seizures in the parietal cortex, but was dwonregulated in the hippocampus, which might explain the different role of NT-3 in the focus complex, because seizures were initiated in the parietal cortex and were propagated and generalized in the hippocampus.

Chronic, but not acute, exposure to minimal electroconvulsive shock (ECS) has been shown to decrease vulnerability to neuronal cell death, without itself causing neuronal damage. One potential mechanism for the neuroprotective effect of ECS is the increase in fibroblast growth factor-2 (FGF-2) which occurs after chronic, but not acute, minimal electroconvulsive shock (ECS) exposure. This raises the possibility that repeated seizures over a period of several days may alter the transcriptional regulation of FGF-2. Chronic ECS treatment may lead to an enhanced rate of transcription of message for FGF-2 but not for NGF, in selected brain regions. At the same time, the results indicate that chronic ECS treatment induces FGF-2 and NGF mRNA expression in a tissue-specific manner and that this induction is maintained over the 7-day treatment period. The sustained increases in mRNAs for these trophic factors may contribute to the neuroprotective actions of chronic ECS treatment [85].

In EL, FGF-2 expression increased linearly with the development. The sustained increased expression of FGF-2 will be protective to the seizures of EL. And it is compatible that although hippocampus and parietal cortex constitute the focus complex, no cell loss was found in the brain.

BDNF and FGF-2 in the kindling model, A single kindling stimulation did not modify BDNF gene expression, whereas it increased FGF-2 messenger RNA (mRNA) levels in the hippocampus and the cortex. In contrast, kindled seizures produced a great increase in hippocampal and cortical BDNF mRNA levels, but FGF-2 mRNA was increased only in the ipsilateral cortex. [87]. BDNF and FGF-2 are recruited at different stages of kindling and, accordingly, may play different roles in the adaptive changes taking place during epileptogenesis [87].

It is interesting that each neurotrophic factors (BDNF, NT-3 and FGF-2) showed the specific patterns in the hippocampus and parietal cortex, respectively in EL mice brain

References

[1] Berridge M. Second messenger dualism in neuromodulation and memory. *Nature* 1986; 323: 294-295.

[2] Murashima YL, Kasamo K, Suzuki J. Developmental and seizure-related regional differences in immediate early gene expression and GABAergic abnormalities in the brain of EL mice. *Epilepsy Res.* 1996; 26:3-14.

[3] Murashima YL, Kasamo K, Suzuki J. Developmental abnormalities of GABAergic system are involved in the formation of Epileptogenesis in the EL. *Neurosciences* 1992; 18: 63-73

[4] Murashima YL, Suzuki J. Role of immediate early gene expression during establishment of epileptogenesis in the brain of EL mice. *Psychiatry and Clinical Neurosciences* 1995; 49: 201-206

[5] Agranoff, B.W. Learning and memory: Biochemical approaches. In *Basic neurochemistry*, 3rd. edition (ed.G.J. Siegel et al.), (1981) pp801.

[6] Berridge, M.:Second messenger dualism in neuromodulation and memory. *Nature* 323 (1986) 294-295.

[7] Christy, B.A., Lau, L.F. and Nathans, D.:A gene activated in mouse 3T3 cells by serum growth factors encoded a protein with "zinc finger" sequences. *Proc.Natl.Acad.Sci.* 85 (1988) 7857-7861.

[8] De Deyn, P.P., Marescau, B. and MacDonald, R.L., Epilepsy and the GABA hypothesis a brief review and some examples. *Acta Neurol Belg.,* 90 (1990) 65-81

[9] Murashima, Y.L., Kasamo, K. and Suzuki, J. Regional differences of immediate early gene expressions in the brain of El mice as examined with development and seizure history. *Jpn.J.Psy.Neurol.* 48 (1994) 275-279.

[10] Murashima, Y.L., Suzuki, J. Role of immediate early gene expression duringestablishment of epileptogenesis in the brain of El mice. Psychiatr. Clin. Neurosci., 49 (1995).201-206

[11] Suzuki, J., Murashima, Y.L., Kasamo, K., Ishida, N. and Takazawa, A., Etiology of psychiatric and neurological disorders and abnormal plasticity, In *Neurotransmitters in neural plasticity, in neurotransmitters in neural plasticity and psychiatric disorders.* (Ed. Torn, M.) (1993) pp64-80, Exceptra Medica.

[12] Suzuki, J. and Nakamoto, Y.: Abnormal plastic phenomena in the mutant El mouse of sensory precipitating epilepsy. *Exper Neurol.* 75 (1976) 440-452.

[13] Saffen, D.W., Cole, A.J., Worley, P.F., Christy, B.A., Byder, K. and Baraban, J.M.: Convulsion-induced increase in transcription factor messenger RNAs in rat brain. *Proc. Natl. Acad. Sci.* 85 (1988) 7795-7799.

[14] Largent, B.L., Jones, D.T., Reed, R.R., Peason, R.C.A. and Snyder, S.H.: G protein mRNA mapped in rat brain by in situ hybridization. *Proc Natl. Acad. Sci.* 85,(1988) 2864-2868.

[15] Segal, D. and Shilo, B.-Z.: Tissue localization of Drosophila melanogaster ras transcripts during development *Mol. Cell Biol. 6*, (1986) 2241-2248.

[16] Hafen, E., Levine, M., Garber, R.L.and Gehring, V.J., An improved in situ hybridization method for the detection of cellular RNAs in Dorosophila tissue sections and its application for localizing transcripts of the homeotic antennapedia gene complex. *EMBO J* 2 (1983) 617-623

[17] Murashima, Y.L. and Kato, T. An improved microassay method for glutamate decarboxylase. *Biomed. Res.* 5 (1984) 527-532

[18] Lowry, O.H. and Passoneau, J.V. *A flexible system of enzymatic analysis.* Academic Pess, New York/ London.(1972)

[19] Sidman, R.L., Angevine, J.P.Jr. and Pierce, E.T. *Atlas of the mouse brain and spinal cord.* Harvard University Press, Cambridge.(1971)

[20] Murashima, YL., Kasamo, K., Suzuki, Z., 1996. Developmental and seizure-related regional differences in immediately early gene expression and GABAergic abnormalities in the brain of EL mice. *Epilepsy Res.* 26, 3-14

[21] Berridge, M.:Second messenger dualism in neuromodulation and memory. *Nature* 323 (1986) 294-295.

[22] Christy, B.A., Lau, L.F. and Nathans, D.:A gene activated in mouse 3T3 cells by serum growth factors encoded a protein with "zinc finger" sequences. *Proc.Natl.Acad.Sci.* 85 (1988) 7857-7861.

[23] De Deyn, P.P., Marescau, B. and MacDonald, R.L., Epilepsy and the GABA hypothesis a brief review and some examples. *Acta Neurol Belg.,* 90 (1990) 65-81

[24] Greenberg, M.E. and Greene, L.A. and Ziff, E.B.:Stimulation of 3T3 cells induces transcription of the *c-fos* proto-oncogene. *Nature* 311 (1984) 433-438.

[25] Hafen, E., Levine, M., Garber, R.L.and Gehring, V.J., An improved in situ hybridization method for the detection of cellular RNAs in Dorosophila tissue sections and its application for localizing transcripts of the homeotic antennapedia gene complex. *EMBO J* 2 (1983) 617-623

[26] Halazonetis, T.D., Georgopoulos, K., Greenberg, M.E. and Leder, P.: c-Jun dimerizes with itself and with c-Fos, forming complexes of different DNA binding affinities. *Cell* 55 (1988) 917-924.

[27] King, JTJr, LaMoOtte, CC. El mouse sa a model of focal epilepsy: a review. *Epilpsia* 1989;30:257-65

[28] Murashima YL, Suzuki J. Abnormalities of superoxide dismutase isoenzyme pattern during development and formation of abnormal plasticity in epileptic mutant EL mice brain. In: A Mori, ed. *Free Radicals in Brain Physiology and Disorders*, New York: Academic Press, 1996:157-72.

[29] Murashima YL, Kasamo K, Suzuki J. Antiepileptic effects of allopurinol on EL mice are associated with changes in SOD isoenzyme activities. *Epilepsy Res.* 1998; 32:254-65.

[30] Fang FC. Mechanisms of nitric oxide-related antimicrobial activity. *J. Clin. Invest.* 1997; 99:2818-25.

[31] Palmer RM, Ferrige AG, Moncada S. Nitric oxide release accounts for the biological activity of endothelium-derived relaxing factor. *Nature* 1987; 327:524-6.

[32] Pereira de Vasconcelos A, Baldwin RA, Wasterlain CG. Nitric oxide mediates the increase in local cerebral blood flow during focal seizures. *Proc. Natl. Acad. Sci. U.S.A.* 1995; 92:3175-9.

[33] Snyder SH. Nitric oxide: first in a new class of neurotransmitters. *Science* 1992; 257:494-6.

[34] Schuman EM, Madison DV. Nitric oxide and synaptic function. *Ann. Rev. Neurosci.* 1994; 17:153-83.

[35] Garthwaite J, Boulton CL. Nitric oxide signaling in the central nervous system. *Ann. Rev. Physiol.* 1995; 57:683-706. 5.5

[36] Mayer B, Hemmens B. Biosynthesis and action of nitric oxide in mammalian cells. *TIBS* 1997; 22:477-81.

[37] Arima K, Uéda K, Sunohara N, Arakawa K, Hirai S, Nakamura M, Tonozuka-Uehara H, Kawai M. NACP/a-synuclein immunoreactivity in fibrillary components of neuronal and oligodendroglial cytoplasmic inclusions in the pontine nuclei in multiple system atrophy. *Acta Neuropathol.* 1998; 96:439-44.

[38] Arima K, Uéda K, Sunohara N, Hirai S, Izumiyama Y, Tonozuka-Uehara H, Kawai M. Immunoelectron-microscopic demonstration of NACP/a-synuclein-epitopes on the filamentous component of Lewy bodies in Parkinson's disease and in dementia with Lewy bodies. *Brain Res.* 1998; 808:93-100.

[39] Son H, Hawkins RD, Martin K, Kiebler M, Huang PL, Fishman MC, Kandel ER. Long-term potentiation is reduced in mice that are doubly mutant in endothelial and neuronal nitric oxide synthase. *Cell* 1996; 87:1015-23.

[40] Suzuki J, Nakamoto Y. Abnormal plastic phenomena of sensory-precipitated epilepsy in the mutant El mouse. *Exp. Neurol.* 1982; 75:440-52.

[41] Murashima, YL, Yoshii, M, Suzuki, J. Role of nitric oxide in the epileptogenesis of EL mice. *Epilepsia*, 41 (Suppl. 6): S195-S199, 2000.

[42] Borgstahl, G.E., Parge, H.E., Hickey, M.J., Johnson, M.J., Boissinot, M., Hollowly, R.A., Lepock, J.R., Cabelli, D.E. and Tainer, J.A.: Human mitochondrial manganese superoxide dismutase polymorphic variant lle58Thr reductase activity by destabilizing the tetrameric interface. *Biochemistry,* 35 (1996) 4287-4297

[43] Caroline, G.E., Schwarzman, A.L., Rise, M.L. and Seyfried, T.N., Ceruloplasmin gene defect associated with epilepsy in EL mice. *Nature Genetics* 6 (1994) 426-431

[44] Murashima, YL, Kasamo, K, Suzuli, J. Antiepileptic effects of allopurinol on EL mice are associated with changes in SOD isoenzyme activities. *Epilepsy Res.* 32 (1998) 254-265

[45] Chan, P.H., Chu, L. and Fishman, R.A., Reduction of activities of superoxide dismutase but not glutathione peroxidase in rat brain regions following decapitation ischemia. *Brain Res.* 439 (1988) 388-390.

[46] Dawson, V.L. and Dawson, T.M., Nitric oxide neurotoxicity. *J. Chem. Neuroanat* 10 (1996) 179-190

[47] De-Marco, P. and Zagnoni, P., Allopurinol in severe epilepsy. *Neuropsychobiology* 19 (1988) 51-53.

[48] Dragunow, M., Faull, R.L., Lawlor, P., Beiharz, E.J., Singleton, K., Walker, E.B. and Mee, E., In situ evidence for DNA fragmentation in Huntington's disease striatum and Alzheimer's disease temporal lobes.: *Neuroreport.* 6 (1995) 1053-1057

[49] Fernandez, N.L., Alvarez, X.A., Semprere, J.M., Miguel, H.JJ., Diaz, J, Franco, M.A. and Cacabelos, R., Effects of anapsos on the activity of the enzyme Cu,Zn-SOD in an animal model of neuronal degeneration. *Methods.Find, Exp. Clin. Pharmacol.* 19 (1997) 99-106

[50] Fletcher, C.F., Lutz, C.M., O'Sullivan, T.N., Shaughnessy, J.D.Jr., Hawkes, R., Frankel, W.N., Copland, N.G. and Jenkins, N.A. Absence epilepsy in tottering mutant mice is associated with calcium channel defects.: *Cell* 87 (1996) 607-617

[51] Hass, M.A., Iqbal, J. and Clerch, L.B., Rat lung Cu,Zn superoxide dismutase. Isolation and sequence of a full-length cDNA and studies of enzyme induction. *J. Clin. Invest.* 83 (1991)1241-1246.

[52] Hamada, H., Hiramatsu, M., Edamatsu, R. and Mori, A., Free radical scavenging action of baicalein. *Arch. Biochem. Biophys.* 306 (1993) 261-266

[53] Hud, R.W., Wilder, B.J., Helveston, W.R. and Uthman, B.M.: Treatment of four siblings with progressive myoclonus epilepsy of the Unverricht-Lundborg type with N-acetylcysteamine. *Neurology* 47 (1996) 1264-1268

[54] Imlay, J.R. and Fridovich, I., Assay of metabolic superoxide production in E. colli. *J. biol. Chem.* 266 (1991) 6957-6965.

[55] Ishida, N., Kasamo, K. and Suzuki, J., The role in parietal cortex and hippocampus in seizures of the EL mouse. *Jpn. J. Neurol. Psychiat.* 41 (1987) 498-499.

[56] Kraemer, D.L. and Awad, I.A., Vascular malformation and epilepsy: clinical consideration and bawsic mechanisms. *Epilepsia* 35 (1994) 30-43

[57] Kulkarni, N.A., Getchell, T.V. and Getchell, M.L., Differntial expression of manganese and copper-zinc superoxide dismutase in the olfactory and vomeronasal receptor neurons of rats during ontogeny: *J.cop.Newurol* 381 (1997) 31-40

[58] Kurekci, A.E., Alpay, F., Tanidi, S., Gokcay, E., Ozcan, O., Akin, R., Ismimer, A. and Sayal, A.: Plasma trace element, plasma glutathione peroxidase, and superoxide dismutase levels in epileptic children receiving antiepileptic drug therapy. *Epilepsia* 36 (1995) 600-604

[59] Liu, J. and Mori, A., Antioxidant and free radical scavenging activities of Gastrodiaelata Bl. and Uncaria rhynchophyllaJacks.*Neuropharmacology* 31 (1992) 1287-1298

[60] Liu, J., Edamatsu, R., Kabuto, H. and Mori, A., Antioxidant action of guilingji in the brain of rats with FeC13-induced epilepsy. *Free Radic. Biol. Med.* 9 (1990) 451-454

[61] Maertens, P., Dyken, P., Graf, W., Pippenger, C, Chronister, R and Shah, A.: Free radicals, anticonvulsans and the neuronal ceroid-lipofuscinoses. *Am.J.Med.Genet.* 57 (1995) 57 225-228

[62] Mori, A., Hiramatsu, M., Yokoi, I. and Edamatsu, R., Biochemical pathogenesis of posttraumatic epilepsy. Pavlov. *J. Biol. Sci.* 25 (1990-) 54-62

[63] Marrosu, F., Marrosu, G., Rachele, M.G., Masala, C. and Giagheddu, M., Allopurinol ad-on treatment in intractable seizures. *Acta Neurol. Napoli.* 12 (1990) 207-213.

[64] Murashima, Y.L. and Suzuki, J., Developmental and seizure related differences in immediate early gene expression and GABAergic abnormalities in the brain of EL mice. *Epi.Res.* 26 (1996) 3-14

[65] Murashima, Y.L. and Suzuki, J., Abnormalities of superoxide dismutase isoenzyme pattern during development and formation of abnormal plasticity in epileptic mutant EL mice brain. In: Mori, A. et al.(Eds.), *Free radicals in brain physiology and disorders*, (1996) pp157-172. Academic Press, New York.

[66] Pellmar, T.C., Hollinden, G.E. and Sarvey, J.M., Free radicals accellate the decay of long-term potentiation in field CA1 of guinea pig hippocampus. *Neuroscience* 44 (1991) 353-359.

[67] Ramaekers, V.T., Calomme, M, Vanden, B.D. and Makropoulos, W., Selenium deficiency triggering intractable seizures. *Neuropediatrics* 25 (1994) 217-223

[68] Sander, J.W. and Patsalos, P.N., Allopurinol as an add-on drug in the management of intractable epilepsy. *Epi.Res.. 2* (1988) 223-225.

[69] Shull, S, Heinz, N.H. and Persasamy, M., Differential regulation of antioxidant enzymes in response to oxidants. *J.biol. Chem.* 266 (1988) 24398-24403.

[70] Sidman, R.L.: *Atlas of the mouse brain and spinal cord.* Harvard University Press, Caimbridge, MA (1971)

[71] Suzuki, J. and Nakamoto, Y., Seizure patterns and electroencephalograms of EL mouse. *Electroenceph. Clin. Neurophysiol.*43 (1977) 299-311

[72] Suzuki, J. and Nakamoto, Y., EL mouse: a model of sensory precipitating epilepsy. *Excepta Medica 427* (1997) 81-82

[73] Suzuki, J., Abnormal plastic phenomena in the mutant EL mouse of sensory precipitating epilepsy. *Exp. Neurol.* 75 (1976) 440-452.

[74] Suzuki, J., Genetic and physiological mechanisms of epileptic seizures. In Suzuki, J. et al. (Eds), *Art and science of epilepsy* (1989) pp27-33. Elsevier Science Publisher, Amsterdam.

[75] Tada, H., Morooka, K., Arimoto, K. and Matso, T., Clinical effects of allopurinol on intractable epilepsy. *Epilepsia* 32 (1991) 279-283.

[76] Uz, T., Giusti, P., Franceschini, D., Kharlamov, A. and Manev, H., Protective effect of melatonin against hippocampal DNA damage induced by intraperitoneal administration of kainate to rats. *Neuroscience* 73 (1996) 631-636

[77] Yokoi, I, Toma, J. Liu, J., Kabuto, H. and Mori, A.: Adenosines scavenged hydroxyl radicals and prevented posttraumatic epilepsy., *Free Radic. Biol.Med* 19 (1995) 473-479

[78] Bonfoco, E., Krainc, D., Ankarcrona, M., Nicotera, P. and Lipson, S.A., Apoptosis and necrosis: two distinct events induced, respectively, by mild and intence insults with NMDA or nitric oxide / superoxide in cortical cell cultures.:*Proc.Natl.Acad.Sci.USA.* 92 (1995) 7162-7166.

[79] Suzuki J. Paroxysmal discharges in the electroencephalogram of the El mouse. *Experientia* 1976; 32:336-7.

[80] King JTJr, LaMotte CC. El mouse as a model of focal epilepsy: a review. *Epilepsia 1989; 30*:257-65.

[81] Ishida N, Kasamo K, Nakamoto Y, Suzuki J. Epileptic seizure of El mouse initiates at the parietal cortex: depth EEG observation in freely moving condition using buffer amplifier. *Brain Res.* 1993; 608:52-7.

[82] Suzuki J, Nakamoto Y, Shinkawa Y. Local cerebral glucose utilization in epileptic seizure of mutant El mouse. *Brain Res.* 1983; 266:359-63.

[83] Murashima YL, Kasamo K, Suzuki J. Developmental and seizure-related regional differences in immediate early gene expression and GABAergic abnormalities in the brain of EL mice. *Epilepsy Res.* 1996; 26:3-14.

[84] Murashima YL, Suzuki J. Abnormalities of superoxide dismutase isoenzyme pattern during development and formation of abnormal plasticity in epileptic mutant EL mice brain. In: A Mori, ed. *Free Radicals in Brain Physiology and Disorders*, New York: Academic Press, 1996:157-72.

[85] Prehn JH, Bindokas VP, Marcuccilli CJ, Krajewski S, Reed JC, Miller RJ. Related Articles, Links Free in PMC Regulation of neuronal Bcl2 protein expression and calcium homeostasis by transforming growth factor type beta confers wide-ranging protection on rat hippocampal neurons. *Proc Natl Acad Sci U S A.* 1994 Dec 20;91 (26):12599-603.

[86] Zhang LX, Smith MA, Li XL, Weiss SR, Post RM. Related Articles, Links t Apoptosis of hippocampal neurons after amygdala kindled seizures. *Brain Res Mol Brain Res.* 1998 Apr; 55 (2):198-208.

[87] Prayson RA. Related Articles, Links Abstract Bcl-2, bcl-x, and bax expression in dysembryoplastic neuroepithelial tumors. Clin Neuropathol. 2000 Mar-Apr;19 (2):57-62.

[88] Henshall DC, Clark RS, Adelson PD, Chen M, Watkins SC, Simon RP. Related Articles, Links Alterations in bcl-2 and caspase gene family protein expression in human temporal lobe epilepsy. *Neurology.* 2000 Jul 25; 55 (2):250-7.

[89] Xu B, Michalski B, Racine RJ, Fahnestock M. Related Articles, Abstract Continuous infusion of neurotrophin-3 triggers sprouting, decreases the levels of TrkA and TrkC, and inhibits epileptogenesis and activity-dependent axonal growth in adult rats. *Neuroscience.* 2002;115 (4):1295-308.

[90] 1Reibel S, Larmet Y, Le BT, Carnahan J, Marescaux C, Depaulis A. Brain-derived neurotrophic factor delays hippocampal kindling in the rat. *Neuroscience.* 2000;100 (4):777-88.

[91] Lahteinen S, Pitkanen A, Koponen E, Saarelainen T, Castren E. Exacerbated status epilepticus and acute cell loss, but no changes in epileptogenesis, in mice with increased brain-derived neurotrophic factor signaling. *Neuroscience.* 2003;122(4):1081-92.

[92] Bregola G, Frigati L, Zucchini S, Simonato M. Different patterns of induction of fibroblast growth factor-2 and brain-derived neurotrophic factor messenger RNAs during kindling epileptogenesis, and development of a herpes simplex vector for fibroblast growth factor-2 gene transfer in vivo. *Epilepsia.* 2000;41 Suppl 6:S122-6.a

[93] Largent, B.L., Jones, D.T., Reed, R.R., Peason, R.C.A. and Snyder, S.H.: G protein mRNA mapped in rat brain by in situ hybridization. *Proc Natl. Acad. Sci.* 85,(1988) 2864-2868.

[94] Suzuki, J., Murashima, Y.L., Kasamo, K., Ishida, N. and Takazawa, A., Etiology of psychiatric and neurological disorders and abnormal plasticity, In *Neurotransmitters in neural plasticity, in neurotransmitters in neural plasticity and psychiatric disorders.*(Ed. Torn, M.) (1993) pp64-80, Exceptra Medica.

[95] Hafen, E., Levine, M., Garber, R.L.and Gehring, V.J., An improved in situ hybridization method for the detection of cellular RNAs in Dorosophila tissue sections and its application for complex. *EMBO J* 2 (1983) 617-62

[96] Arima K, Uéda K, Sunohara N, Arakawa K, Hirai S, Nakamura M, Tonozuka-Uehara H, Kawai M. NACP/a-synuclein immunoreactivity in fibrillary components of neuronal and oligodendroglial cytoplasmic inclusions in the pontine nuclei in multiple system atrophy. Acta Neuropathol. 1998; 96:439-44. Tiekoter KL, Taki W, Simon RP. Related Articles, Links Activation of Bcl-2-associated death protein and counter-response of Akt within cell populations during seizure-induced neuronal death. *J Neurosci.* 2002 Oct 1;22(19):8458-65.

[97] Arima K, Uéda K, Sunohara N, Hirai S, Izumiyama Y, Tonozuka-Uehara H, Kawai M. Immunoelectron-microscopic demonstration of NACP/a-synuclein-epitopes on the filamentous component of Lewy bodies in Parkinson's disease and in dementia with Lewy bodies. *Brain Res.* 1998; 808:93-100.

[98] Son H, Hawkins RD, Martin K, Kiebler M, Huang PL, Fishman MC, Kandel ER. Long-term potentiation is reduced in mice that are doubly mutant in endothelial and neuronal nitric oxide synthase. *Cell* 1996; 87:1015-23.

[99] Zhu WJ, Roper SN. Related Articles, Brain-derived neurotrophic factor enhances fast excitatory synaptic transmission in human epileptic dentate gyrus. *Ann Neurol.* 2001 Aug;50(2):188-94.

[100] Danzer SC, Crooks KR, Lo DC, McNamara JO. Related Articles, Increased expression of brain-derived neurotrophic factor induces formation of basal dendrites and axonal branching in dentate granule cells in hippocampal explant cultures. *J Neurosci.* 2002 Nov 15;22(22):9754-63.

[101] Kondratyev A, Ved R, Gale K. *The effects of repeated minimal electroconvulsive shock exposure on levels of mRNA encoding fibroblast growth factor-2 and nerve growth factor in limbic regions.* Kondratyev A, Ved R, Gale K.

In: Focus on Epilepsy Research
Editor: Shawn M. Benjamin, pp. 199-220

ISBN 1-59454-087-X

Chapter VIII

The Role of the Efflux Transporter P-glycoprotein (P-gp) on the Disposition of Antiepileptic Drugs: Implications for Drug Interactions

M. Strolin Benedetti*, R. Whomsley**, P. Espié** and E. Baltes*

* UCB Pharma, 21 rue de Neuilly - 92003 Nanterre Cedex, France

** UCB Pharma, Chemin du Foriest - 1420 Braine-l'Alleud, Belgium

Abstract

There is now an increasing appreciation of transport processes as determinants of drug disposition. The main purpose of this paper is to review the role of the efflux transporter P-glycoprotein (P-gp) on the disposition of antiepileptic drugs (AEDs), including brain penetration, as well as the impact of the 1st (e.g. carbamazepine, phenobarbital, phenytoin and valproate) and 2nd generation (e.g. felbamate, gabapentin, lamotrigine, levetiracetam, oxcarbazepine, tiagabine, topiramate, vigabatrin and zonisamide) AEDs which are substrates, inhibitors and/or inducers of P-gp on the pharmacokinetics of concomitantly administered drugs. In addition, the possible impact of AEDs on the over-expression of P-gp in pharmacoresistant epilepsy has also been examined.

Overall, it can be concluded from in vitro and in vivo animal models as well as from human interaction studies that, among the 1st generation AEDs, phenytoin definitively appears to be a substrate of P-gp, whereas it is still not clear whether it has some P-gp inducing properties; it is still debatable whether carbamazepine is a P-gp substrate, whereas valproate does not appear to interfere with P-gp; contradictory and non conclusive results have been obtained for phenobarbital as a substrate and/or an inducer of P-gp. Concerning the 2nd generation AEDs, particularly relevant are the data obtained in human studies where some (levetiracetam, tiagabine and topiramate) were administered with digoxin, as they confirm that levetiracetam and tiagabine in clinical practice should not interact with P-gp.

In view of the key role of P-gp in absorption, distribution and excretion of compounds which are P-gp substrates, a lack of interaction with P-gp appears to be an additional positive aspect for a 2ndgeneration AED for avoiding drug-drug interactions. For levetiracetam, both in vitro and in vivo information in humans are presently available confirming that no clinically relevant interaction should occur with P-gp. The information on the involvement of P-gp in gabapentin transport is poor, as the limited in vitro data give the impression of a lack of interaction, whereas the data obtained in an animal model are contradictory and in vivo data in humans are not available. Information on the interference between P-gp and vigabatrin is also very poor: the results obtained in in vitro and animal models suggest a lack of interaction of this compound with P-gp, but information in humans is necessary. None or inconclusive information appears to exist in the literature concerning zonisamide or oxcarbazepine and P-gp, whereas the limited in vitro and/or in vivo animal and human information on felbamate, lamotrigine and topiramate suggests that they might be P-gp substrates or interact with P-gp.

In conclusion, the major AEDs of both generations deserve to be more deeply investigated concerning their interactions with P-gp. Indeed, even when the available data indicate that an AED is only a relatively weak substrate for P-gp under normal conditions, over-expression of such transporter could significantly reduce brain levels of the drug and thereby critically contribute to pharmacoresistance in epilepsy.

INTRODUCTION

Therapy with traditional antiepileptic drugs (AEDs) is associated with a wide range of pharmacokinetic drug-drug interactions; in particular enzyme induction and enzyme inhibition can result in considerable changes in plasma concentrations of concomitantly administered drugs. In the design and development of new AEDs, emphasis has been put on the importance that these agents be poorly metabolized and that they be as much as possible devoid of the enzyme inducing and/or inhibitory properties of the older drugs. In contrast, the role of the uptake and efflux transporters on the disposition of the AEDs and the consequences of these compounds being substrates, inhibitors and/or inducers of such transporters as far as drug interactions are concerned have been poorly taken into account. Even in very recent review papers [1, 2], the involvement of transporters in drug interactions in epilepsy therapy is not discussed. Indeed some antiepileptic drug interactions at the level of absorption, distribution and/or excretion that are currently ascribed to other mechanisms could be due, at least partially, to interactions with transporters.

There is now an increasing appreciation of transport processes as determinants of drug disposition. The main purpose of this paper is to review the role of the efflux transporter P-glycoprotein (P-gp) on the disposition of the AEDs (including brain penetration) as well as the impact of the AEDs which are substrates, inhibitors or inducers of this transport protein on the pharmacokinetics of concomitantly administered drugs. Moreover, the possible impact of AEDs on the overexpression of this efflux protein in pharmacoresistant epilepsy will also be examined.

Both traditional (1st generation, e.g. carbamazepine, phenobarbital, phenytoin and valproate) and new AEDs [2nd generation, e.g. felbamate, gabapentin, lamotrigine, levetiracetam (KEPPRA ®), oxcarbazepine, tiagabine, topiramate, vigabatrin and zonisamide] will be reviewed as substrates, inhibitors and/or inducers of P-gp. The pharmacokinetic drug-drug interactions (or the lack of pharmacokinetic interactions) observed with these compounds will be tentatively discussed taking into account this more novel aspect together with the usual aspects related to their interactions with the drug metabolizing enzymes.

P-GP IN HUMANS AND IN RODENTS

In humans, there are two P-gp transporters encoded by *MDR1* and *MDR3*. The encoded gene products have apparent molecular weights of approximately 170 kDa. Only the *MDR1* gene product is thought to significantly participate in drug disposition, as the *MDR3* gene encodes for a phospholipid transport protein or phospholipid flippase, expressed exclusively on the canalicular domain of hepatocytes [3-5].The *MDR1* gene product P-gp is an efflux pump, i.e. it translocates its substrates from the intracellular to the extracellular compartment. P-gp is a member of the so-called ATP-Binding Cassette (ABC) transporter superfamily, one of the largest superfamilies of proteins. There are at least 48 human ABC transporters belonging to 7 subfamilies. P-gp is one of the eleven members of the subfamily ABCB [6]. A total of 48 variants were identified in the *MDR1* gene, including 13 that result in an amino acid change in P-gp (non-synonymous variants). There is a polymorphism in the human *MDR1* gene, C3435T, which is associated with lower intestinal P-gp expression, reduced protein function in peripheral blood cells and higher plasma concentrations of the classical P-gp substrate digoxin [7-10]. The functional significance of *MDR1* variation on pharmacokinetics and pharmacodynamics is still controversial. For example increased digoxin absorption [11, 12], as well as decreased digoxin absorption [13, 14] and no effect on digoxin absorption [15-17] were associated with the C3435T *MDR1* variant.

In rodents three *mdr* genes are present, *mdr1a, mdr1b* and *mdr2*. The *mdr1a/1b* gene products function as drug efflux transporters whereas the *mdr2* gene product has an essential role in the secretion of phosphatidylcholine into bile and may be a phospholipid transport protein or phospholipid flippase [4]. Identification of a mouse strain naturally deficient in *mdr1a* as well as the generation of mice with a target disruption of *mdr1a/1b* have greatly enhanced the understanding of the in vivo relevance of P-gp to drug disposition. Such mice appear to be completely healthy and fertile, indicating that the encoded transporter has no essential physiological function. In principle, this is reassuring for the development of P-gp inhibitors in humans, although it is possible that humans may respond differently than mice to the absence of mdr1-type P-gp activity. However, when challenged by exposure to xenobiotics that are P-gp substrates, *mdr-1a* –deficient mice appear to be particularly susceptible to the toxic effects of such compounds [18-23].

Although the single MDR1 protein (P-gp) in humans is generally thought to perform the same function as the two *mdr1* subtypes (*mdr1a* and *mdr1b*) found in rodents [20, 24], there are species differences in P-gp transport activity between humans and animals, and the species differences appear to be substrate-dependent [25]. However, available data so far support the notion that species-related differences are modest [26]. This review will deal mainly with human P-gp, but reference to animal work will be done when necessary.

P-gp and Cytochrome P-450 3A4/5

Many classical and new AEDs (carbamazepine, phenobarbital, primidone, phenytoin, felbamate, oxcarbazepine, tiagabine, topiramate, zonisamide) appear to interact either extensively or to some extent with the cytochrome P450 (CYP) 3A subfamily, in particular CYP3A4, for which they are either substrates or inhibitors and/or inducers [for review, see 27].

There is an overlap in substrate and inhibitor/inducer specificity for P-gp and for CYP3A4/5, although the overlap is not absolute [28, 29]. Therefore, it is difficult to differentiate between P-gp and CYP3A4-mediated drug interactions. Some CYP3A substrates (e.g. terfenadine, erythromycin and lovastatin), but not all (e.g. nifedipine and midazolam), were found to be P-gp substrates. Studies in *mdr1a* disrupted mice confirmed that erythromycin was a P-gp substrate but the CYP3A-inhibitor ketoconazole was not. Moreover, there are selective and potent P-gp inhibitors under development [e.g. the cyclopropyldibenzosuberane derivative LY335979, VX710 (biricodar) or the diarylimidazole derivative OC 144-093] able to inhibit P-gp without significantly affecting drug metabolism, including the metabolic pathways carried out by the CYP3A subfamily [30]. Overall, these results indicate that the overlap in substrate and inhibitor specificities of CYP3A and P-gp appears to be fortuitous rather than indicative of a more fundamental relationship. Nevertheless, in terms of drug disposition, the phenomenon of substrate overlap is of importance because P-gp and CYP3A4/5 are frequently expressed in the same cells such as the enterocyte and the hepatocyte. Thus, for drugs that are substrates of both P-gp and CYP3A, the complementary functions of these proteins likely result in greater than expected reduction in systemic exposure.

In terms of induction of P-gp expression, available data support a coordinate expression of CYP3A4 and P-gp in the presence of known inducers of CYP3A such as rifampicin [31]. Digoxin oral absorption is impaired during concomitant rifampicin therapy and this effect was associated with increased intestinal P-gp expression [32]. A decrease in C_{max} and AUC of fexofenadine, a known P-gp substrate which is not metabolized, has also been observed in humans during concomitant rifampicin therapy [33]. In human colon carcinoma cells, phenobarbital was found to strongly up-regulate both P-gp and CYP3A4, whereas phenytoin caused only a modest change in the expression of P-gp and was without effect on the expression of CYP3A4/5 [31]. More recent studies in a human colon carcinoma cell line have demonstrated that induction of P-gp expression may be transcriptionally regulated through activation of the pregnane X receptor (PXR), a nuclear receptor which is also involved in the regulation of CYP3A4 [34, 35]. Indeed, many of the compounds shown to induce P-gp are ligands for PXR. Very recently, it has been shown that ligand-activated PXR also regulates P-gp activity at the blood-brain barrier [36].

P-gp and Pharmacoresistant Epilepsy

P-gp was originally detected in cancer cells and identified by its capacity to confer multidrug resistance (MDR) to tumor cells against anticancer drugs. P-gp is localized in the plasma membrane of the cell, where it can actively extrude a variety of drugs from the cell, thus making it resistant to the cytotoxic activity of these drugs [20, 37].

The other member of the ABC transporter protein family identified to date that confers MDR is MRP (MDR-associated protein) [37, 38]. Probenecid is an inhibitor of MRP and valproate [39-41], phenytoin [42] and carbamazepine [43] interact with this transporter. However, MRP will not be specifically discussed in the present paper.

It is now known that P-gp is highly expressed not only in cancer cells but also in a variety of normal tissues and cells [18, 19, 44], including brain [20, 45], gut, liver [46], adrenal gland, kidneys, lymphocytes [7, 26, 47], placenta, uterus and testis **(see Table 1),** and it has recently been suggested that it could confer MDR in normal tissues including the brain [48].

Table 1: Expression and function of P-gp in some tissues.

Tissue	*Function*
Brain (capillary endothelial cells, blood-brain barrier)	Limits uptake of drugs from blood circulation into brain
Liver (bile canalicular membrane of the liver)	Excretion into bile (excretion of drugs out of hepatocytes into the adjacent luminal space)
Kidney (renal tubular epithelial cells)	Excretion into urine (excretion of drugs out of renal tubules into the adjacent luminal space)
Lymphocytes (T cells)	P-gp expression in T cells inhibits HIV-1 infectivity (reduction of HIV-1 infectivity in P-gp expressing cells occurs both during the fusion of viral and plasma membranes and at subsequent step(s) in the HIV-1 life cycle)
Placenta	Control of fetal exposure to xenobiotics
Gut (intestinal epithelial cells)	Limits absorption of drugs from intestinal lumen into epithelial cells
Testis (blood-testis barrier)	Limits uptake in testis (protection of sensitive tissues)

There is accumulating evidence demonstrating that multidrug transporters such as P-gp are over-expressed in capillary endothelial cells and astrocytes in epileptogenic brain tissue surgically resected from patients with medically intractable epilepsy [41]. P-gp and members of the MDR-associated protein family in the blood-brain barrier are thought to act as an active defence mechanism restricting the penetration of lipophilic substances into the brain. Several AEDs, which have been made lipophilic to penetrate into the brain, seem to be substrates for multidrug transporters in the blood-brain barrier. Over-expression of multidrug transporters (e.g. of P-gp) in epileptogenic tissue is thus likely to reduce the amount of drug reaching the epileptic neurons, which would be a likely explanation for pharmacoresistance. However, although over-expression of multidrug transporters in general and of P-gp in particular is a novel and reasonable hypothesis to explain MDR in epilepsy, further studies are needed to establish this concept. Resistance to therapy with antiseizure drugs is almost certainly due to multiple factors. One of these is likely to be genetic [49, 50]. Moreover, it is still debatable whether chronic treatment with AEDs contributes to the over-expression of P-gp in brain regions of patients with intractable epilepsy. In a recent work by Seegers et al [51] the possibility that chronic treatment with two AEDs, phenobarbital and phenytoin, in the healthy rat may enhance P-gp expression in the blood-brain barrier has been addressed. Prolonged treatment with phenobarbital or phenytoin did not induce any robust increases in P-gp expression in the rat brain. According to the authors, data favour the hypothesis that the P-gp over-expression in epileptogenic brain tissue of patients with drug-resistant epilepsy is not a consequence of chronic treatment with AEDs such as phenytoin or phenobarbital, although they recognize that it cannot be ruled out that epileptic animals or humans can exhibit different responses to AED treatment. Moreover, their study was only limited to the investigation of two AEDs.

Interaction of Antiepileptic Drugs with P-gp

Overall, thirteen models/strategies listed from 1 to 13 (seven in vitro models, four in vivo animal models and two in vivo human approaches) have been essentially used so far to evaluate whether AEDs interact with P-gp.

In Vitro Models

Model No. 1: two neuroectodermal cell lines, DAOY, known not to express *MDR1*, and the derivative cell line DAOYADR2, known to express *MDR1* after exposure to sublethal concentrations of actinomycin D [52]. Using this model, Tishler et al. [52] found that intracellular phenytoin concentrations in the *MDR1*-expressing DAOYADR2 line were only 25% as compared with those in the parental DAOY line. The concentration of phenytoin in DAOYADR2 cells increased to levels equivalent to those in the parental cell line when verapamil, an inhibitor of the efflux function of P-gp, was added, suggesting that P-gp significantly contributes to cell export of phenytoin.

Model No. 2: a LLC-PK1 pig kidney epithelial cell line transfected with expression vectors containing *mdr1a* or *MDR1* cDNA. The clones LLC-PK1, L-MDR1 and L-*mdr1a* were used to measure the transepithelial transport of radiolabelled compounds [18, 53]. Some authors [54] measured intracellular accumulation of P-gp fluorescent-labelled substrates in these cells by confocal laser-scanning microscopy. In the kidney epithelial cell line transfected with *mdr1a* cDNA, phenytoin was transported, which could be blocked by the P-gp inhibitor PSC833 (valspodar) [18, 53]. With the kidney epithelial cell line transfected with *MDR1* cDNA, Weiss et al. [54] found that carbamazepine inhibited P-gp and also phenytoin, lamotrigine, and valproate revealed P-gp inhibitory potency, whereas topiramate, vigabatrin, phenobarbital and gabapentin did not inhibit.

Model No. 3: flow cytometry in lymphocytes using rhodamine 123, a fluorescent substrate for P-gp [55]. Using this model, Owen et al. [55] found that carbamazepine had no effect on rhodamine 123 efflux from lymphocytes, in contrast to verapamil, which increased fluorescence intensity fivefold.

Model No. 4: Caco-2 cells, an in vitro model of the intestinal epithelium known to express high P-gp levels, although a number of other transporters are expressed in these cells [56]. Using this model, Owen et al. [55] found that the transport of carbamazepine in Caco-2 cells was P-gp-independent, and was not affected by PSC833. The authors' conclusion was that carbamazepine is not a substrate for P-gp. The same model was used to study levetiracetam. The apical to basolateral transport of levetiracetam through Caco-2 cell monolayers was not modified by verapamil, a known P-gp inhibitor, suggesting the absence of a P-gp active transport mechanism for this compound. In the same conditions an increased transport of digoxin in the presence of verapamil was observed (Leroux, unpublished results). Although the transport of both carbamazepine and levetiracetam across Caco-2 cell monolayers was unaffected in the presence of P-gp inhibitors, it is not possible to affirm conclusively that neither is a substrate for P-gp as the high passive diffusion rates observed for these drugs may mask any active transport component.

Model No. 5: a cell line derived from a human colon adenocarcinoma, LS180/WT, and its adriamycin-resistant subline, LS180/AD50 [31]. The same cell line LS 180 (cells selected for elevated P-gp levels with increasing concentrations of vinblastine) and the use of rhodamine 123 to get information on inhibition and induction of P-gp [29]. Using this model, phenobarbital and, to a much lesser extent, phenytoin were found to up-regulate P-gp.

Model No. 6: cultured human hepatocytes [57] to study changes in expression of P-gp. With this model, in contrast to the data obtained with model No. 5, phenobarbital induced CYP3A4 but not P-gp [57].

Model No. 7: porcine brain capillary endothelial cells and calcein uptake [54]. Calcein-acetoxymethylester (calcein-AM) is a fluorogenic, highly lipid-soluble dye that rapidly penetrates the plasma membrane. Inside the cell, endogenous esterases cleave the ester bonds, producing the hydrophilic and fluorescent dye calcein, which cannot leave the cell via the plasma membrane. Whereas calcein-AM is a substrate of P-gp, calcein is not. Cells expressing high levels of P-gp rapidly extrude nonfluorescent calcein-AM from the plasma membrane, thus preventing accumulation of fluorescent calcein in the cytosol. With this model, Weiss et al. [54] found that only carbamazepine inhibited P-gp, whereas all the other AEDs tested had no effect.

The AEDs investigated and the in vitro models used are summarized in **Table 2.**

In Vivo Animal Models

Model No. 8: in vivo brain microdialysis in freely moving rats to study drug transport across the blood-brain barrier (BBB). Using this model, Potschka and Löscher [43, 58] found that brain extracellular levels of intraperitoneally administered carbamazepine and phenytoin can be significantly increased by the P-gp inhibitors verapamil and PSC833 applied locally via a microdialysis probe. With the same model, the same authors found that local perfusion of verapamil via the microdialysis probe increased the concentration of intraperitoneally administered phenobarbital, felbamate, and lamotrigine in the extracellular fluid of the cerebral cortex in a significant manner [59].

Model No. 9: drug penetration into the brain of *mdr1a/1b (-/-)* [55, 60] or of *mdr1a (-/-)* knockout mice compared with wild-type controls [53, 61, 62]. The knockout mice are devoid of P-gp at the BBB. With this model, Owen et al. [55] found that brain penetration of carbamazepine was comparable in wild-type and *mdr1a/1b (-/-)* mice). Brain levels of phenytoin in *mdr1a(-/-)* knockout mice were also reported to be not different from wild-type mice [53]. In contrast, from preliminary results by Sills et al. [61] obtained in *mdr1a(-/-)* knockout mice after subcutaneous administration of eight AEDs, the brain/plasma concentration ratio for carbamazepine was found to be significantly higher in knockout mice than in wild-type controls. Moreover, this ratio was found to be significantly higher for topiramate, lamotrigine, and gabapentin, whereas no significant differences in brain/plasma concentration ratios were found for the other AEDs investigated (phenobarbital, phenytoin, valproate and vigabatrin).The same authors however reported later on [62] more extensive information on their results. Their conclusion was that only the brain/serum concentration ratio of topiramate was higher in *mdr1a(-/-)* mice compared with the wild-type controls and that no consistent effects were observed with any other AED investigated. They suggested that topiramate may be a substrate for P-gp-mediated transport. However, the use of knockout mice has some limitations, as another transport protein may take over the function of one that has been knocked out [20]. Thus, the failure of the knockout to affect AED kinetics cannot be taken as definitive proof that the silenced protein does not transport AEDs.

Model No. 10: prolonged treatment of rats with the AED and analysis of P-gp expression in different brain regions [51]. As previously mentioned, this model was used by Seegers et al. [51]. As P-gp is strongly up-regulated by AEDs such as phenobarbital and, to a lesser extent, phenytoin, in certain cell lines such as LS180/AD50, Seegers et al. examined whether prolonged treatment (11 days) of rats with i.p. administered phenobarbital or phenytoin increases the expression of P-gp in the brain. The authors did not investigate possible increases in the expression of P-gp in other tissues. In phenobarbital-treated rats, a small but statistically significant percent increase (6-7%) of endothelial P-gp expression was determined in the piriform cortex and cerebellum. Furthermore, the intensity of parenchymal P-gp expression was significantly increased by about 30% in the piriform cortex and parietal cortex. Nevertheless, the authors' conclusion was that it is not very likely that these differences to control have any functional meaning.

Model No. 11: measurement of the plasma concentrations of the AED in laboratory animals when administered concomitantly with a well established P-gp substrate, such as digoxin, or with a highly selective P-gp inhibitor, and/or to measure the plasma concentrations of the concomitantly administered drug. With this model, Breznock [63] found in the dog that repeated oral administration of phenobarbital significantly decreased the serum half-life of a single intravenous dose of digoxin, but not of a single intravenous dose of digitoxin. Ravis et al. [64] got similar results with a similar design, whereas the same authors with a different design found different results, i.e. after several days of concomitant oral administration of digoxin and phenobarbital, serum digoxin concentration increased or did not change [64, 65]. The effect of verapamil on the pharmacokinetics of phenytoin was investigated in the rat and verapamil was found to increase significantly the area under the curve (AUC), the maximum plasma concentration (C_{max}) and the elimination half-life (t½) of phenytoin [66].

The AEDs investigated and the animal models used are summarized in **Table 3.**

In Vivo Human Approaches

Approach No. 12: measurement of the plasma concentrations of the AED in humans when administered concomitantly with a P-gp substrate or with a P-gp inhibitor, and/or to measure the plasma concentrations of the concomitantly administered drug.

Approach No. 13: evaluation of whether the plasma levels of an AED correlate with a polymorphism in the *MDR1* gene, C3435T.

Table 2: In vitro models used to evaluate the interaction of antiepileptic drugs (AEDs) with P-gp

(*S* for AED = P-gp substrate; *Inh* for AED = P-gp inhibitor; *Ind* for AED = P-gp inducer).

In vitro model No / *AED*	*Carbamazepine*	*Felbamate*	*Gabapentin*	*Lamotrigine*	*Levetiracetam*	*Oxcarbazepine*	*Phenobarbital*	*Phenytoin*	*Tiagabine*	*Topiramate*	*Vigabatrin*	*Valproate*	*Zonisamide*
1								S					
2	Inh		Not Inh	Inh			Not Inh	S, Inh		Not Inh	Not Inh	Inh	
3	Not Inh												
4	Not S				Not S								
5							Ind	Weak Ind					
6							Not Ind						
7	Inh		Not Inh	Not Inh			Not Inh	Not Inh		Not Inh	Not Inh	Not Inh	

Table 3: In vivo animal models used to evaluate the interaction of antiepileptic drugs (AEDs) with P-gp

(*S* for AED = P-gp substrate; *Inh* for AED = P-gp inhibitor; *Ind* for AED = P-gp inducer).

Animal model No	*AED*	*Carbamazepine*	*Felbamate*	*Gabapentin*	*Lamotrigine*	*Levetiracetam*	*Oxcarbazepine*	*Phenobarbital*	*Phenytoin*	*Tiagabine*	*Topiramate*	*Vigabatrin*	*Valproate*	*Zonisamide*
8		S	S		S			S	S					
9	*[mdr1a]*	S?		S?	S?			Not S	Not S		S	Not S	Not S	
	[mdr1a/1b]	Not S												
10								Weak Ind	Not Ind					
11	*Digoxin*							Ind, not Ind						
	Digitoxin							Not Ind						
	Verapamil								S ?					

Table 4: In vivo human approaches used to evaluate the interaction of antiepileptic drugs (AEDs) with P-gp

(*S* for AED = P-gp substrate; *Inh* for AED = P-gp inhibitor; *Ind* for AED = P-gp inducer).

Human Approach No	*AED*	*Carbama-zepine*	*Felba-mate*	*Gaba-pentin*	*Lamo-trigine*	*Leveti-racetam*	*Oxcarba-zepine*	*Pheno-barbital*	*Phenytoin*	*Tiaga-bine*	*Topira-mate*	*Viga-batrin*	*Val-proate*	*Zonisa-mide*
12	*Digoxin*					Not S Not Inh			Ind	Not S Not Inh	Weak Ind ?			
	Digitoxin	Ind ?						Not Ind	Ind ?					
	Cyclosporin	Ind ?					Not Ind		Ind ?					
	Piperine								S ?					
	Quinidine							Ind ?	Ind ?					
	Verapamil	S ?					Not S	Ind ?	S ?				S ?	
	St John's wort	Not S												
13									S					

Approaches no. 12 and 13 are clearly a priori the most significant but the information collected up to now with these two approaches is very poor, in particular because the P-gp substrates and inhibitors used were not selective enough or were extensively metabolized, so that further investigation for a correct interpretation of most of the results available is necessary.

The AEDs investigated and the approaches used in vivo in humans to try to establish whether they interact with P-gp are summarized in **Table 4.**

Concerning the AEDs investigated in humans concomitantly with an established P-gp substrate (digoxin), levetiracetam and tiagabine do not modify the pharmacokinetics of digoxin and digoxin does not influence the pharmacokinetics of levetiracetam and tiagabine [27, 67, 68], whereas topiramate caused a small decrease in the AUC of digoxin, which is however probably of no clinical relevance [69]. It has been reported that concomitant administration of digoxin with phenytoin may result in reduced plasma concentrations of digoxin and an unfavourable effect on the management of cardiac failure [1, 70]. Moreover, phenytoin shortens the half lives and /or decreases the plasma levels of digitoxin [70, 71]. Recent data in Caco-2 cells have provided evidence that digitoxin behaves in this model as digoxin, i.e. that digitoxin is a P-gp substrate [72]. The CYP inducing properties of phenytoin might contribute to explain the results obtained with digitoxin but not with digoxin, as digoxin is not metabolised by CYP isozymes. To explain the effect of phenytoin on the pharmacokinetics of digoxin, it should be important to know whether phenytoin, an inducer of CYP isozymes, induces P-gp as well. It is possible that phenytoin is also an inducer of P-gp, at least in some tissues [31] if not in all [51]. Further investigation is necessary to know if phenytoin, at the therapeutic doses administered, induces P-gp in the human gastrointestinal tract to produce a decrease of digoxin absorption. Freeman et al. [73] studied the influence of oral phenytoin on the pharmacokinetics of oral cyclosporin. Phenytoin significantly reduced the serum C_{max} and AUC and the investigators thought this was possibly due to enhanced metabolism of cyclosporin related to induction of CYP enzymes by phenytoin, but Rowland and Gupta [74] reassessed the cyclosporin and phenytoin interaction observed by Freeman et al. [73] and suggested that phenytoin reduces cyclosporin absorption. Induction of cyclosporine metabolism by phenytoin has also been demonstrated in human hepatocytes [75]. Therefore, in vivo phenytoin probably produces both reduction of absorption and induction of metabolism of cyclosporin. Carbamazepine is also known to reduce cyclosporin serum concentrations [76, 77] whereas oxcarbazepine has a less pronounced effect [76, 78].

Concerning the AEDs studied in humans concomitantly with a P-gp inhibitor (or a P-gp substrate/inhibitor), the plasma concentrations of phenytoin were increased in healthy volunteers by piperine, a major constituent of black pepper which inhibits both the drug transporter P-gp and the major drug-metabolizing enzyme CYP3A4 [79, 80]. Elevation of plasma carbamazepine to potentially toxic concentrations can be caused by verapamil, a P-gp inhibitor which is also a substrate [3, 77, 81]. The increase in concentrations of carbamazepine was accompanied by a simultaneous fall in the ratio of the principal metabolite, carbamazepine -10,11-epoxide, to carbamazepine [82], whereas no change occurred in carbamazapine-10,11-epoxide levels. It is impossible, without a more specific investigation, to fully interpret this type of data. In the study performed by Macphee [82], verapamil also increased the phenytoin plasma concentrations in one patient and the sodium valproate plasma concentrations in another patient. Moreover, verapamil appears to moderately decrease the concentrations of the active metabolite of oxcarbazepine, the 10,11-

dihydro-10-hydroxy-carbazepine, without changing the concentrations of the parent drug [78, 83]. The effect of AEDs which are classical enzyme inducers (mainly of CYP3A4) such as phenobarbital on the decrease in plasma concentrations of verapamil [84] or the effect of phenobarbital, phenytoin and carbamazepine on the decrease of plasma concentrations of quinidine [85, 86], an inhibitor of CYP2D6 metabolized by CYP3A4 and which is also an inhibitor/substrate of P-gp [3, 87], cannot be correctly interpreted at the moment but draw attention to the possible contribution of P-gp on the interactions observed. St John's wort, which seems to be efficacious for mild to moderate depression, is a P-gp inhibitor following a single dose and probably a weak inducer after repeated administration [88, 89]. This agent has also CYP3A4-inducing properties [89, 90]. The effect of repeated administration of St John's wort on carbamazepine pharmacokinetics at steady state in healthy volunteers has been investigated. It appears that St John's wort does not significantly affect carbamazepine pharmacokinetics [91]. According to the authors, these findings were somewhat unexpected and should indicate that carbamazepine is not a P-gp substrate although the interpretation of these findings is very complex.

Finally, in a study in healthy volunteers (approach No. 13), phenytoin plasma levels correlated with a polymorphism in the *MDR1* gene C3435T, which is associated with a decreased intestinal P-gp activity. The MDR1*CC genotype was more common in volunteers with low phenytoin levels [92].

DISCUSSION

There are some inconsistencies in the results obtained when the interaction of an AED with P-gp has been studied in different in vitro models (e.g. carbamazepine, phenobarbital). A range of models is required for each AED to substantiate the results observed in only one model. Models should also be validated, which is not presently frequently the case. In approaches using the Caco-2 cell line and bi-directional transport studies, attention should be paid for example on the effect of passive permeability on apparent P-gp kinetics [93, 94]. Compounds with high transmembrane permeability overcame MDR efflux compared to those with slower transmembrane movement. Using a mechanistic permeation model, Doppenschmitt et al. [95] also demonstrated that compounds with lower passive permeability are more likely to be affected by P-gp, even with lower affinity to P-gp. In addition, it has also been shown that low passive permeability might mask a P-gp effect as well [94]. Moreover the concentrations used in the in vitro models should be comparable to the therapeutic plasma concentrations present after usual therapeutic doses, whereas frequently they are much higher.

When using in vivo animal models, attention should be paid to the fact that there are significant species differences in P-gp transport activity between humans and animals and the species differences appear to be substrate–dependent. Moreover, when interaction studies between an AED and a P-gp substrate and/or inhibitor are done in vivo in animals, the species differences can be also metabolic, e.g. a drug which is a P-gp substrate both in animals and humans might be metabolized differently in animals and humans, with evident complications in the interpretation of the data and their extrapolation to humans.

In vitro and in vivo animal models have some potential to predict possible interactions of an AED with P-gp. However, only data obtained in vivo in well-designed human studies where AEDs are administered at therapeutic doses, both after single and multiple dosing, with poorly metabolized drugs known to be selective substrates and/or inhibitors of P-gp, administered at therapeutic doses, allow definitive conclusions to be drawn on the type of interaction of an AED with P-gp and its clinical significance. Nevertheless, while P-gp plays an important role in drug absorption, many structurally unrelated P-gp substrates have reasonably good oral bioavailability e.g. digoxin (40-80%), indinavir (60-70%), ritonavir (60-70%), furosemide (70%). This may be due in part to saturation of the efflux process during absorption [96]. Similarly, intestinal first pass metabolism can also be saturated when a high oral dose is given. Therefore, attention should be paid when designing in vivo studies, specifically when selecting drug doses.

Digoxin should be preferred to other P-gp substrates (e.g.cyclosporine or digitoxin) to investigate the interaction of AEDs with P-gp in humans because CYPs in general and CYP3A4/5 in particular are not involved in digoxin metabolism [25, 97], although according to a recent article, digoxin appears to be also a substrate of other transporters both in animals and in humans [24]. Alternatively P-gp substrates that are barely metabolized should be used, e.g. fexofenadine, although this compound is also a substrate of other transporters [98].

Among the inhibitors, although quinidine is sometimes preferred to verapamil in in vitro models, it is difficult to state which one should be preferred to investigate the interaction of AEDs with P-gp in humans. Limited information appears to be available on their selectivity as P-gp inhibitors and their possible inhibition of other transporters in humans. Moreover, they are also P-gp substrates. Both compounds are extensively metabolized. Quinidine is known to be a potent inhibitor of CYP2D6 [99, 100] and a substrate for CYP3A4 and verapamil is a substrate/inhibitor of CYP3A4 [101-105].

Overall, taking into account the in vitro and in vivo animal models as well as the human interaction studies, the following conclusions can be drawn. Among the 1st generation AEDs, phenytoin definitively appears to be a substrate of P-gp, whereas it is still not clear whether it has some P-gp inducing properties. It is still debatable whether carbamazepine is a P-gp substrate, whereas valproate does not appear to interfere with P-gp. As a substrate and/or an inducer of P-gp, contradictory and non conclusive results have been obtained for phenobarbital.

Concerning the 2nd generation AEDs, particularly relevant are the data obtained in human studies where some (levetiracetam, tiagabine and topiramate) were administered with digoxin, as they confirm that levetiracetam and tiagabine in clinical practice should not interact with P-gp. Moreover, for levetiracetam, a drug not bound to plasma proteins and poorly metabolized [106], the ratios of brain/blood concentrations of radioactivity in the mouse, rat, rabbit and dog are very close to 1, although this value is attained relatively slowly after oral administration of the labelled compound (UCB, data on file) [107]. Similar data [108] have been obtained in the rat by measuring the ratio of cerebrospinal fluid/serum levetiracetam concentrations after intraperitoneal administration of the cold compound, this further indicating that levetiracetam should not interact with P-gp. It is also interesting to observe that the phenytoin-resistant kindled rat, a new screening model, displays a unique sensitivity to the anticonvulsant action of levetiracetam [109, 110]. Indeed, in a number of studies where patients with refractory epilepsy were treated with levetiracetam, the compound proved to be effective [111-114]. A clearance which is not too dependent on metabolism, particularly by CYP3A4, is generally considered as a positive aspect as far as susceptibility to drug-drug interactions [see 27]. In view of the key role of P-gp in absorption, distribution and excretion of compounds which are P-gp substrates, a lack of interaction of a 2ndgeneration AED with P-gp appears to be an additional positive aspect for avoiding drug-drug interactions. For levetiracetam, both in vitro and in vivo information in humans are presently available confirming that no clinically relevant interaction should occur with P-gp. For gabapentin, it would appear that this compound concentrates in brain tissue via an active transport process believed to be the L-amino acid transport system (system -L) [115]. However, regarding the involvement of P-gp in gabapentin transport, the information is poor, as the limited in vitro data give the impression of a lack of interaction, whereas the data obtained in an animal model are contradictory and no data in vivo in humans are available. This information is necessary as the lack of metabolism of gabapentin is not sufficient to predict that drug-drug interactions should not occur with this compound. Finally, information on interference between P-gp and vigabatrin is also very poor; according to in vitro and animal models, the results obtained suggest a lack of interaction of this compound with P-gp, but information in humans is necessary and might be useful to try to explain interactions reported with vigabatrin, e.g. the vigabatrin-induced decrease in serum phenytoin concentrations, the mechanism of which remains unknown [1, 27]. None or inconclusive information appears to exist in the literature concerning zonisamide or oxcarbazepine and P-gp, whereas the limited in vitro and/or in vivo animal and human information on felbamate, lamotrigine and topiramate suggests that they might be P-gp substrates or that they may interact with P-gp.

In conclusion, the major AEDs, both of the 1st and 2nd generation, deserve to be more deeply investigated concerning their interactions with P-gp. Indeed, even when the available data indicate that an AED is only a relatively weak substrate for P-gp under normal conditions, over-expression of such transporter could significantly reduce brain levels of the drug and thereby critically contribute to pharmacoresistance in epilepsy.

For a compound used in epilepsy therapy, being a substrate or an inducer of P-gp is in principle a negative aspect both for the efficacy and for the possibility of drug–drug interactions On the other hand, inhibition of this efflux protein could be of some benefit. Specific inhibitors of P-gp [e.g. the cyclopropyldibenzosuberane derivative LY335979, VX710 (biricodar) or the diarylimidazole derivative OC 144-093)] are currently under clinical evaluation for reversal or prevention of intrinsic and acquired multidrug resistance in human cancer [30, 116] and may soon become available for clinical trials on adjunctive treatment in refractory epilepsy, although possible adverse effects of P-gp inhibition need careful consideration.

ACKNOWLEDGEMENTS

The authors thank Mrs. C. Doumergue for her invaluable help in providing the documentation and Mrs. M. Rovei for the preparation of the manuscript.

REFERENCES

[1] P.N. Patsalos, W. Fröscher, F. Pisani, C.M. van Rijn. The importance of drug interactions in epilepsy therapy. *Epilepsia*, 2002, 43(3), 365-385

[2] P.N. Patsalos and E. Perucca. Clinical important drug interactions in epilepsy: general features and interactions between antiepileptic drugs. *The Lancet Neurology*, 2003, 2, 347-356.

[3] R.B. Kim. Drugs as P-glycoprotein substrates, inhibitors, and inducers. *Drug Metab. Rev.*, 2002, 34 (1&2), 47-54.

[4] J.J.M. Smit, A.H. Shinkel, R.P.J. Oude Elferink, A.K. Groen, E. Wagenaar, L. van Deemter, C.A.A.M. Mol, R. Ottenhoff, N.M.T. van der Lugt, M.A. van Roon, M.A. van der Valk, G.J.A. Offerhaus, A.J.M. Berns, P. Borst. Homozygous disruption of the murine *mdr2* P-glycoprotein gene leads to a complete absence of phospholipids from bile and to liver disease. *Cell*, 1993, 75, 451-462.

[5] Y. Romsicki and F.J. Sharom. Phospholipid flippase activity of the reconstituted P-glycoprotein multidrug transporter. *Biochemistry*, 2001, 40(23), 6937-6947.

[6] 48 human ABC-transporters, [http://nutrigene.4t.com/humanabc.htm], update January 2003.

[7] M. Hitzl, S. Drescher, H. van der Kuip, E. Schäffeler, J. Fischer, M. Schwab, M. Eichelbaum, M.F. Fromm. The C3435T mutation in the human *MDR1* gene is associated with altered efflux of the P-glycoprotein substrate rhodamine 123 from $CD56^+$ natural killer cells. *Pharmacogenetics*, 2001, 11, 293-298.

[8] R.B. Kim, B.F. Leake, E.F. Choo, G.K. Dresser, S.V. Kubba, U.I. Schwarz, A. Taylor, H.G. Xie, J. McKinsey, S. Zhou, L.B. Lan, J.D. Schuetz, E.G. Schuetz, G.R. Wilkinson. Identification of functionally variant MDR1 allelles among European Americans and African Americans. *Clin. Pharmacol. Ther.*, 2001, 70(2), 189-199.

[9] S. Drescher, E. Schaeffeler, M. Hitzl, U. Hofmann, M. Schwab, U. Brinkmann, M. Eichelbaum, M.F. Fromm. *MDR1* gene polymorphisms and disposition of the P-glycoprotein substrate fexofenadine. *Br. J. Clin. Pharmacol.*, 2002, 53, 526-534.

[10] C. Verstuyft, M. Schwab, E. Schaeffeler, R. Kerb, U. Brinkmann, P. Jaillon, C. Funk-Brentano, L. Becquemont. Digoxin pharmacokinetics and *MDR1* genetic polymorphisms. *Eur. J. Clin. Pharmacol.*, 2003, 58, 809-812.

[11] S. Hoffmeyer, O. Burk, O. von Richter, H.P. Arnold, J. Brockmoller, A. Johne, I. Cascorbi, T. Gerloff, I. Roots, M. Eichelbaum, U. Brinkmann. Functional polymorphisms of the human multidrug-resistance gene: multiple sequence variations and correlation of one allele with P-glycoprotein expression and activity in vivo. *Proc. Natl Acad. Sci. USA*, 2000, 97(7), 3473-3478.

[12] Y. Kurata, I. Ieiri, M. Kimura, T. Morita, S. Irie, A. Urae, S. Ohdo, H. Ohtani, Y. Sawada, S. Higuchi, K. Otsubo. Role of human MDR1 gene polymorphism in bioavailability and interaction of digoxin, a substrate of P-glycoprotein. *Clin. Pharmacol. Ther.*, 2002, 72(2),209-219.

[13] T. Sakaeda, T. Nakamura, M. Horinouchi, M. Kakumoto, N. Ohmoto, T. Sakai, Y. Morita, T. Tamura, N. Aoyama, M. Hirai, M. Kasuga, K. Okumura. MDR1 genotype-related pharmacokinetics of digoxin after single oral administration in healthy Japanese subjects. *Pharm. Res.*, 2001,18(10),1400-1404.

[14] M. Horinouchi, T. Sakaeda, T. Nakamura, Y. Morita, T. Tamura, N. Aoyama, M. Kasuga, K. Okumura. Significant genetic linkage of MDR1 polymorphisms at positions 3435 and 2677: functional relevance to pharmacokinetics of digoxin. *Pharm. Res.*, 2002, 19(10),1581-1585.

[15] L. Becquemont, C. Verstuyft, R. Kerb, U. Brinkmann, M. Lebot, P. Jaillon, C. Funck-Brentano. Effect of grapefruit juice on digoxin pharmacokinetics in humans. *Clin. Pharmacol. Ther.*, 2001, 70(4), 311-316.

[16] T. Gerloff, M. Schaefer, A. Johne, K. Oselin, C. Meisel, I. Cascorbi, I. Roots. MDR1 genotypes do not influence the absorption of a single oral dose of 1 mg digoxin in healthy white males. *Br. J. Clin. Pharmacol.*, 2002, 54(6),610-616.

[17] A. Johne, K. Kopke, T. Gerloff, I. Mai, S. Rietbrock, C. Meisel, S. Hoffmeyer, R. Kerb, M.F. Fromm, U. Brinkmann, M. Eichelbaum, J. Brockmoller, I. Cascorbi, I. Roots. Modulation of steady-state kinetics of digoxin by haplotypes of the P-glycoprotein MDR1 gene. *Clin. Pharmacol. Ther.*, 2002, 72(5), 584-594.

[18] A.H. Schinkel, E. Wagenaar, L. van Deemter, C.A.A.M. Mol, P. Borst. Absence of the mdr1a P-glycoprotein in mice affects tissue distribution and pharmacokinetics of dexamethasone, digoxin and cyclosporin A. *J. Clin. Invest.*, 1995, 96, 1698-1705.

[19] A.H. Schinkel, U. Mayer, E. Wagenaar, C.A.A.M. Mol, L. van Deemter, J.J.M. Smit, M.A. van der Valk. A.C. Voordouw, H. Spits, O. van Tellingen, J.M.J.M. Zijlmans, W.E. Fibbe, P. Borst. Normal viability and altered pharmacokinetics in mice lacking mdr1-type (drug-transporting) P-glycoprotein. *Proc. Natl. Acad. Sci.*, 1997, 94, 4028-4033.

[20] A.H. Schinkel. P-glycoprotein, a gatekeeper in the blood-brain barrier. *Adv. Drug Deliv. Rev.*, 1999, 36, 179-194.

[21] T.R. Pippert and D.R. Umbenhauer. The subpopulation of CF-1 mice deficient in P-glycoprotein contains a murine retroviral insertion in the mdr1a gene. *J. Biochem. Mol. Toxicol.*, 2001, 15, 83-89.

[22] G.Y. Kwei, R.F. Alvaro, Q. Chen, H.J. Jenkins, C.E.A.C. Hop, C.A. Keohane, V.T. Ly, J.R. Strauss, R.W. Wang, Z. Wang, T.R. Pippert, D.R. Umbenhauer. Disposition of ivermectin and cyclosprin A in CF-1 mice deficient in *MDR1A* P-glycoprotein. *Drug Metab. Dispos.*, 1999, 27(5), 581-587.

[23] D.R. Umbenhauer, G.R. Lankas, T.R. Pippert, L.D. Wise, M.E. Cartwright, S.J. Hall, C.M. Beare. Identification of a P-glycoprotein-deficient subpopulation in the CF-1 mouse strain using a restriction fragment length polymorphism. *Toxicol. Appl. Pharmacol.*, 1997, 146, 88-94.

[24] S. Lowes, M.E. Cavet, N.L. Simmons. Evidence for a non-MDR1 component in digoxin secretion by human intestinal Caco-2 epithelial layers. *Eur. J. Pharmacol.*, 2003, 458, 49-56.

[25] H. Lin-Jiunn, M. Yamazaki. Role of p-glycoprotein in pharmacokinetics: clinical implications. *Clin. Pharmacokin.*, 2003, 42(1), 59-98.

[26] C. Chen, X. Liu, B.J. Smith. Utility of Mdr-1 deficient mice in assessing the impact of P-glycoprotein on pharmacokinetics and pharmacodynamics in drug discovery and development. *Curr. Drug Metab.*, 2003, 4, 272-291.

[27] M. Strolin Benedetti. Enzyme induction and inhibition by new antiepileptic drugs: a review of human studies. *Fund. Clin. Pharmacol.*, 2000, 14, 301-319.

[28] R.B. Kim, C. Wandel, B. Leake, M. Cvetkovic, M.F. Fromm, P.J. Dempsey, M.R. Roden, F. Belas, A.K. Chaudhary, D.M. Roden, A.J.J. Wood, G.R. Wilkinson. Interrelationship between substrates and inhibitors of human CYP3A and P-glycoprotein. *Pharmaceut. Res.*, 1999, 16(3), 408-414.

[29] M.D. Perloff, E. Störmer, L.L. von Moltke, D.J. Greenblatt. Rapid assessment of P-glycoprotein inhibition and induction *in vitro*. *Pharmaceut. Res.*, 2003, 20(8), 1177-1183.

[30] A.H. Dantzig, K.L. Law, J. Cao, J.J. Starling. Reversal of multidrug resistance by the P-glycoprotein modulator, LY335979, from the bench to the clinic. *Curr. Med. Chem.*, 2001, 8(1), 39-50.

[31] E.G. Schuetz, W.T. Beck, J.D. Schuetz. Modulators and substrates of P-glycoprotein and cytochrome P4503A co-ordinately up-regulate these proteins in human colon carcinoma cells. *Mol. Pharmacol.*, 1996, 49(2), 311-318.

[32] B. Greiner, M. Eichelbaum, P. Fritz, H.P. Kreichbauer, O. von Richter, J. Zundler, H.K. Kroemer. The role of intestinal P-glycoprotein in the interaction of digoxin and rifampin. *J. Clin. Invest.*, 1999, 104, 147-153.

[33] M.A. Hamman, M.A. Bruce, B.D. Haehner-Daniels, S.D. Hall. The effect of rifampin administration on the disposition of fexofenadine. *Clin. Pharmacol. Ther.*, 2001, 69(3), 114-121.

[34] A. Geick, M. Eichelbaum, O. Burk. Nuclear receptor response elements mediate induction of intestinal MDR1 by rifampin. *J. Biolog. Chem.*, 2001, 276(18), 14581-14587.

[35] G. Luo, M. Cunningham, S. Kim, T. Burn, J. Lin, M. Sinz, G. Hamilton, C. Rizzo, S. Jolley, D. Gilbert, A. Downey, D. Mudra, R. Graham, K. Carroll, J. Xie, A. Madan, A. Parkinson, D. Crist, B. Selling, E. Lecluyse, L-S. Gan. CYP3A4 induction by drugs: correlation between a pregnane X receptor reporter gene assay and CYP3A4 expression in human hepatocytes. *Drug Metab. Dispos.*, 2002, 30(7), 794-804.

[36] B. Bauer, A.M.S. Hartz, G. Fricker, D.S. Miller. *Ligands of the nuclear xenobiotic receptor, PXR, upregulate P-glycoprotein at the blood-brain barrier*. International Conference on Cerebral Vascular Biology, Amarillo (Texas), June 2003, Abstracts book, p. 503.

[37] V. Ling. Multidrug resistance: molecular mechanisms and clinical relevance. *Cancer Chemother. Pharmacol.*, 1997, 40(Suppl), S3-S8.

[38] H. Huai-Yun, D.T. Secrest, K.S. Mark, D. Carney, C. Brandquist, W.F. Elmquist, D.W. Miller. Expression of multidrug resitance-associated protein (MRP) in brain microvessel endothelial cells. *Biochem. Biophys. Res.*, 1998, 243(3), 816-820.

[39] H.-H. Frey and W. Löscher. Distribution of valproate across the interface between blood and cerebrospinal fluid. *Neuropharmacology*, 1978, 17, 637-642.

[40] D.D. Shen. Absorption, distribution, and excretion. In: *Milestones in Drug Therapy*, W. Löscher (Ed.), Birkhäuser Verlag, Basel, Switerland, 1999, pp. 77-90.

[41] W. Löscher and H. Potschka. Role of multidrug transporters in pharmacoresistance to antiepileptic drugs. *J. Pharmacol. Exp. Ther.*, 2002, 301(1), 6-14.

[42] H. Potschka and W. Löscher. Multidrug resistance-associated protein is involved in the regulation of extracellular levels of phenytoin in the brain. *Neuropharmacol. Neurotoxicol, Neuroreport*, 2001, 12(11), 2387-2389.

[43] H. Potschka, M. Fedrowitz, W. Löscher. P-glycoprotein and multidrug resistance-associated protein are involved in the regulation of extracellular levels of major antiepileptic drug carbamazepine in the brain. *Neuropharmacol. Neurotoxicol, Neuroreport*, 2001, 12(16), 3557-3560.

[44] F. Thiebaut, T. Tsuruo, H. Hamada, M.M. Gottesman, I. Pastan, M.C. Willingham. Cellular localization of the multidrug-resistance gene product P-glycoprotein in normal human tissues. *Proc. Natl. Acad. Sci.*, 1987, 84, 7735-7738.

[45] R.B. Kim, M.F. Fromm, C. Wandel, B. Leake, A.J.J. Wood, D.M. Roden, G.R. Wilkinson. The drug transporter P-glycoprotein limital oral absorption and brain entry of HIV-1 protease inhibitors. *J. Clin. Invest.*, 1998, 10, 289-294.

[46] A. Bohan, J.L. Boyer. Mechanisms of hepatic transport of drugs: implications for cholestatic drug reactions. *Seminars in liver disease*, 2002, 22(2), 123-136

[47] C.G. Lee, M. Ramachandra, K.T. Jeang, M.A. Martin, I. Pastan, M.M. Gottesman. Effect of ABC transporters on HIV-1 infection: inhibition of virus production by the *MDR*1 transporter. *FASEB*, 2000, 14, 516-522.

[48] P.L. Golden and W.M. Pardridge. Brain microvascular P-glycoprotein and a revised model of multidrug resistance in the brain. *Cell. Mol. Neurobiol.*, 2000, 20(2), 165-181.

[49] A. Siddiqui, R. Kerb, M.E. Weale, U. Brinkmann, A. Smith, D. Goldstein, N.W. Wood, S.M. Sisodiya. Association of multidrug resistance in epilepsy with a polymorphism in the drug-transporter gen ABCB1. *N. Engl. J. Med.*, 2003, 348(15), 1442-1448.

[50] T.A. Pedley, M. Hirano. Is refractory epilepsy due to genetically determined resistance to antiepileptic drugs? *N. Engl. J. Med.*, 2003, 348(15), 1480-1482

[51] U. Seegers, H. Potschka, W. Löscher. Lack of effect of prolonged treatment with Phenobarbital or phenytoin on the expression of P-glycoprotein in various rat brain regions. *Eur. J. Pharmacol.*, 2002, 451, 149-155.

[52] D.M. Tishler, K.T. Weinberg, D.R. Hinton, N. Barbaro, G.M. Annett, C. Raffel. MDR1 gene expression in brain of patients with medically intractable epilepsy. *Epilepsia*, 1995, 36, 1-6.

[53] A.H. Schinkel, E. Wagenaar, C.A. Mol, L. van Deemter. P-glycoprotein in the blood-brain barrier of mice influences the brain penetration and pharmacological activity of many drugs. *J. Clin. Invest.*, 1996, 97, 2517-2524.

[54] J. Weiss, C. J. Kerpen, H. Lindenmaier, S. M. G. Dormann. Interaction of antiepileptic drugs with human P-glycoprotein in vitro, *J. Pharmacol. Exp. Ther.*, 2003, 307(1), 262-267.

[55] A. Owen, M. Pirmohamed, J.N. Tettey, P. Morgan, D. Chadwick, B.K. Park. Carbamazepine is not a substrate for P-glycoprotein. *Br. J. Clin. Pharmacol.*, 2001, 51(4), 345-349.

[56] J. Taipalensuu, H. Törnblom, G. Lindberg, G. Einarsson, F. Sjöqvist, H. Melhus, P. Garberg, B. Sjöström, B. Lundgren, P. Artursson. Correlation of gene expression of ten drug efflux proteins of the ATP-Binding Cassette transporter family in normal human jejunum and in human intestinal epithelial Caco-2 cell monolayers. *J. PPharmacol. Exp. Ther.*, 2001, 299(1), 164-170.

[57] D. Runge, C. Köhler, V.E. Kostrubsky, D. Jäger, T. Lehmann, D.M. Runge, U. May, D. Beer Stolz, S.C. Strom, W.E. Fleig, G.K. Michalopoulos. Induction of cytochrome P450 (CYP)1A1, CYP1A2, and CYP1A3 but not of CYP2C9, CYP2C19, multidrug resistance (MDR-1) and multidrug resistance associated protein (MRP-1) by prototypical inducers in human hepatocytes. *Biochem. Biophys. Res. Commun.*, 2000, 273(1), 333-341.

[58] H. Potschka and W. Löscher. In vivo evidence for P-glycoprotein-mediated transport of phenytoin at the blood-brain barrier of rats. *Epilepsia*, 2001, 42(10), 1231-1240.

[59] H. Potschka, M. Fedrowitz, W. Löscher. P-glycoprotein-mediated efflux of Phenobarbital, lamotrigine and felbamate at the blood-brain barrier: evidence from microdialysis experiments in rats. *Neurosci. Lett.*, 2002, 327(3), 173-176.

[60] M. Rizzi, G. Guiso, F. Mulé, D. Moneta, G. Sperk, A. Vezzani, S. Caccia. Induction of MDR-1 by limbic seizures in mice: relevance for drug resistance in epilepsy. *Soc. Neurosci.*, 2001, 27, 553.2 (abstract).

[61] G.J. Sills, P. Kwan, E.C.M. de Lange, E. Butler, M.J. Brodie. P-glycoprotein-mediated antiepileptic drug transport: a role in refractory epilepsy. *Epilepsia*, 2001, 42(7), 83 (abstract 1.260).

[62] G.J. Sills, P. Kwan, E. Butler, E.C.M. de Lange, D.J. van der Berg, M.J. Brodie. P-glycoprotein-mediated efflux of antiepileptic drugs: preliminary studies in mdr1a knockout mice. *Epilepsy Behav.*, 2002, 3/5(I), 427-432.

[63] E.M. Breznock. Effects of Phenobarbital on digitoxin and digoxin elimination in the dog. *Am. J. Vet. Res.*, 1975, 36(4), 371-373.

[64] W.R. Ravis, W.M. Pedersoli, J.D. Turco. Pharmacokinetics and interactions of digoxin with Phenobarbital in dogs. *Am. J. Vet. Res.*, 1987, 48(8), 1244-1249.

[65] W.M. Pedersoli, V.K. Ganjam, R.F. Nachreiner. Serum digoxin concentrations in dogs before, during, and after concomitant treatment with Phenobarbital. *Am. J. Vet. Res.*, 1980, 41(10), 1639-1642.

[66] M.S. Al-Humayyd. Diltiazem and verapamil elevate plasma phenytoin concentrations in the rat. *Intern. J. Pharmaceut.*, 1996, 131, 153-158.

[67] P.N. Patsalos. Pharmacokinetic profile of levetiracetam: towards ideal characteristics. *Pharmacol. Ther.*, 2000, 85, 77-85.

[68] H. Mengel, J.A. Jensen, K. Sommerville, J.H.G. Jonkman, K. Vesnes, A. Cohen, G.F. Carlson, R. Marschall, S. Snel, J. Dirach, H. Kastberg. Tiagabine: evaluation of the risk of interaction with theophylline, warfarin, digoxin, cimetidine, oral contraceptives, triazolam, or ethanol. *Epilepsia*, 1995, 36, S160.

[69] B.F.D. Bourgeois. Drug interaction profile of topiramate. Epilepsia, 1996, 37, S14-S17.

[70] R.L. Nation, A.M. Evans, R.W. Milne. Pharmacokinetic drug interactions with phenytoin (Part II). *Clin. Pharmacokin.*, 1990, 18(2), 131-150.

[71] Phenytoin (sodium). In: *Therapeutic Drugs*, C. Dollery (Ed.), 2nd edition, Churchill Livinstone, Edinburgh, 1999, vol. 2, P110-P115.

[72] C. Pauli-Magnus, T. Muerdter, A. Godel, T. Mettang, M. Eichelbaum, U. Klotz, M.F. Fromm. P-glycoprotein-mediated transport of digoxin, alpha-methyldigoxin and beta-acetyldigoxin. *Naunym Schmiedebergs Arch. Pharmacol.*, 2001, 363(3), 337-343.

[73] D.J. Freeman, A. Laupacis, P.A. Keown, C.R. Stiller, S.G. Carruthers. Evaluation of cyclosporine-phenytoin interaction with observations on cyclosporine metabolites. *Br. J. Clin. Pharmacol.*, 1984, 18, 887-893.

[74] M. Rowland, S.K. Gupta. Cyclosporin-phenytoin interaction: reevaluation using metabolite data. *Br. J. Clin. Pharmacol.*, 1987, 24, 329-334.

[75] L. Pichard, I. Fabre, G. Fabre, J. Domergue, B. Saint Aubert, G. Mourad, P. Maurel. Cyclosporin A drug interactions. Screening for inducers and inhibitors of cytochrome P-450 (cyclosporine A oxidase) in primary cultures of human hepatocytes and in liver microsomes. *Drug Metab. Disp.*, 1990, 18(5), 595-606.

[76] J. Roesche, J. Fröscher, D. Abendroth, J. Liebel. Possible oxcarbazepine interaction with cyclosporine serum levels: a single case study. *Clin. Neuropharmacol.*, 2001, 24(2), 113-116.

[77] E. Spina, F. Pisani, E. Perucca. Clinically significant pharmacokinetic drug interactions with carbamazepine. An uptdate. *Clin. Pharmacokin.*, 1996, 31(3), 198-214.

[78] T.W. May, E. Korn-Merker, B. Rambeck. Clinical pharmacokinetics of oxcarbazepine. *Clin. Pharmacokin.*, 2003, 42(12), 1023-1042.

[79] G. Bano, V. Amla, R.K. Raina, U. Zutshi, C.L. Chopra. The effect of piperine on pharmacokinetics of phenytoin in healthy volunteers. *Planta Med.*, 1987, 63, 568-569.

[80] R.K. Bhardwaj, A. Glaeser, L. Becquemont, U. Klotz, S.K. Gupta, M.F. Fromm. Piperine, a major constituent of black pepper, inhibits human P-glycoprotein and CYP3A4. *J. Pharmacol. Exp. Ther.*, 2002, 302(2), 645-650.

[81] B. Beattie, J. Biller, B. Mehlhaus, M. Murray. Verapamil-induced carbamazepine neurotoxicity. *Eur. Neurol.*, 1988, 28, 104-105.

[82] G.J. Macphee, G.T. McInnes, G.G. Thompson, M.J. Brodie. Verapamil potentiates carbamazepine neurotoxicity: a clinically important inhibitory interaction. *Lancet*, 1986, March 29, 700-703.

[83] G. Krämer, B. Tettenborn, G. Flesch. Oxcarbazepine-verapamil drug interaction in healthy volunteers. *Epilepsia*, 1991, 32 (1), 70-71.

[84] D.R. Rutledge, J.A. Pieper, D.M. Mirvis. Effects of chronic phenobarbital on verapamil disposition in humans. *J. Pharmacol. Experiment. Ther.*,1988, 246(1), 7-13.

[85] J.L. Data, G.R. Wilkinson, A.S. Nies. Interaction of quinidine with anticonvulsant drugs. *N. Engl. J. Med.*, 1976,294, 699-702.

[86] C.C. Chafin, T.H. Self. Quinidine-drug interactions: how to avoid risk. *J. critical illn.*, 1999, 14(6), 319-321.

[87] M. Strolin Benedetti, M. Bani. Metabolism-based drug interactions involving oral azole antifungals in humans. *Drug Metab. Rev.*, 1999, 31(3), 665-717.

[88] Z. Wang, M.A. Hamman, S.M. Huang, L.J. Lesko, S.D.Hall, Effect of St John's wort on the pharmacokinetics of fexofenadine. *Clin. Pharmacol. Ther.*, 2002, 71(6), 414-420.

[89] G.K. Dresser, U.I. Schwarz, G.R. Wilkinson, R.B. Kim. Coordinate induction of both cytochrome P4503A and MDR1 by St John's wort in healthy subjects. *Clin. Pharmacol. Ther.*, 2003, 73(1), 41-50.

[90] P.N. Patsalos, E. Perucca. Clinically important drug interactions in epilepsy: interactions between antiepileptic drugs and other drugs. *Lancet*, 2003, 2, 473-481.

[91] A.H. Burstein, R.L. Horton, T. Dunn, R.M. Alfaro, S.C. Piscitelli, W.Theodore. Lack of effect of St John'swort on carbamazepine pharmacokinetics in healthy volunteers. *Clin. Pharmacol. Ther.*, 2000, 68, 605-612.

[92] R. Kerb, A.S. Aynacioglu, J. Brockmöller, R. Schlagenhaufern S. Bauer, T. Szekeres, A. Hamwi, M. Fritzer- Szekeres, C. Baumgarner, H.Z. Öngen, P. Güzelbey, I. Roots, U. Brinkmann. he predictive value of MDR1, CYP2C9, and CYP2C19 polymorphisms for phenytoin plasma levels. *Pharmacogenomics J.*, 2001, 1, 204-210.

[93] G.D. Eytan, R. Regev, G. Ore, Y.G. Assaraf. The role of passive transbilayer drug movement in multidrug resistance and its modulation. *J. Biol. Chem.*, 1996, 271, 12897-12902.

[94] K.A. Lentz, J.W. Polli, S.A. Wring, J.E. Humphreys, J.E. Polli. Influence of Passive Permeability on Apparent P-glycoprotein Kinetics. *Pharm. Res.*, 2000, 17(12), 1456-1460.

[95] S. Doppenschmitt, H. Spahn-Langguth, C.G. Regardh, P. Langguth. Role of P-glycoprotein-mediated secretion in absorptive drug permeability: an approach using passive membrane permeability and affinity to P-glycoprotein. *J. Pharm. Sci.*, 1999, 88, 1067-1072.

[96] J.H. Lin. M. Chiba, I.W. Chen, J.A. Nishime, F.A. Deluna, M. Yamazaki, Y.J. Lin. Effect of dexamethasone on the intestinal first-pass metabolism of indinavir in rats: evidence of P-450 cytochrome and P-glycoprotein induction. *Drug Metab. Dispos.*, 1999, 27(10), 1187-1193.

[97] Digoxin. In: *Therapeutic Drugs*, C. Dollery (Ed.), 2nd edition, Churchill Livinstone, Edinburgh, 1999, vol. 1, D123-D130.

[98] P.D. Hansten and R.H. Levy. Role of P-glycoprotein and organic anion transporting polypeptides in drug absorption and distribution. *Clin. Drug Invest.*, 2001, 21(8), 587-596.

[99] G.R. Strobl, S. von Kruedener, J. Stoeckigt, F.P. Guengerich, T. Wolff. Development of a pharmacophore for inhibition of human liver cytochrome P-450 2D6: molecular modelling and inhibition studies. *J. Med. Chem.*, 1993, 36(9), 1136-1145.

[100] S. Kobayashi, S. Murray, D. Watson, D. Sesardic, D.S. Davies, A.R. Boobis. The specificity of inhibition of debrisoquine 4-hydroxylase activity by quinidine and quinine in the rat is the inverse of that in man. *Biochem. Pharmacol.*, 1989, 38(17), 2795-2799.

[101] G.L. Lemma, M.A. Hamman, S.D. Hall, Z. Wang. The effects of verapamil administration on the pharmacokinetics of fexofenadine. *Clin. Pharmacol. Ther.*, 2003, 73(2), P16 (PI-56).

[102] T. Kantola, K.T. Kivistoe, P.J. Neuvonen. Erythromycin and verapamil considerably increase serum simvastatin and simvastatin acid concentrations. *Clin. Pharmacol. Ther.*, 1999, 65(5), 583-585.

[103] J.S. Wang, X. Wen, J.T. Backman, P. Taatvitsainen, P.J. Neuvonen, K.T. Kivistoe. Midazolam alpha-hydroxylation by human liver microsomes in vitro: inhibition by calcium channel blockers, itraconazole and ketoconazole. *Pharmacol. Toxicol.*, 1999, 85(4), 157-161.

[104] B. Ma, T. Prueksaritanont, J.H. Lin. Drug interactions with calcium channel blockers: possible involvement of metabolite-intermediate complexation with CYP3A. *Drug Metab. Dispos.*, 2000, 28(2), 125-130.

[105] K.R. Yeo, W.W. Yeo. Inhibitory effects of verapamil and diltiazem on simvastatin metabolism in human liver microsomes. *Br. J. Clin. Pharmacol.*, 2001, 51(5), 461-470.

[106] M. Strolin Benedetti, R. Whomsley, J.M. Nicolas, C. Young, E. Baltes. Pharmacokinetics and metabolism of ^{14}C-levetiracetam, a new antiepileptic agent, in healthy volunteers. *Eur. J. Clin. Pharmacol.*, 2003, 59, 621-630.

[107] M. Strolin Benedetti, R. Coupez, R. Whomsley, J.M. Nicolas, P. Collart, E. Baltes. Comparative pharmacokinetics and metabolism of levetiracetam, a new antiepileptic agent, in the mouse, rat, rabbit and dog.*Xenobiotica*, 2004, 34 (3), 281-300.

[108] H.C. Doheny, N. Ratnaraj, M.A. Whittington, J.G.R. Jefferys, P.N. Patsalos. Blood and cerebrospinal fluid pharmacokinetics of the novel anticonvultsant levetiracetam (ucb L059) in the rat. *Epilepsy Res.*, 1999, 34, 161-168.

[109] H.S. White. Preclinical development of antiepileptic drugs: past, present and future directions. *Epilepsia*, 2003, 44(7), 2-8.

[110] W. Löscher, E. Reissmüller, U. Ebert. Anticonvulsant efficacy of gabapentin and levetiracetam in phenytoin-resistant kindled rats. *Epilesy Res.*, 40, 2000, 63-77.

[111] I. Leppik, M. Mrrell, P. Godfroid, C. Arrigo. Seizure free days observed in randomised placebo-controlled add-on trials with levetiracetam in partial epilepsy. *Epilepsia*, 2003, 44(10), 1350-1352.

[112] S.D. Shorvon, A. Löwenthal, D. Janz, E. Bielen, P. Loiseau. Multicenter, double-blind, randomized, placebo-controlled trial of levetiracetam as add-on therapy in patients with refractory partial seizures. *Epilepsia*, 2000, 41(9), 1179-1186.

[113] E. Ben-Menachem and E. Gilland. Efficacy and tolerability of levetiracetam during 1-year follow-up in patients with refractory epilepsy. *Seizure*, 2003, 12, 131-135.

[114] J.J. Cereghino, V. Biton, B. Abou-Khalil, F. Dreifuss, L.J. Gauer, I. Leppik. Levetiracetam for partial seizures. Results of a souble-blind, randomized clinical trial. *Neurology*, 2000, 55, 236-242.

[115] M. S. Luer, C. Hamani, M. Dujovny, B. Gidal, M. Cwik, K. Deyo, J.H. Fischer. Saturable transport of gabapentin at the blood-brain barrier. *Neurol. Res.*, 1999, 21, 559-562.

[116] T. Litman, T.E. Druley, W.D. Stein, S.E. Bates. From MDR to MXR new understanding of multidrug resistance systems, their properties and clinical significance. *Cell Mol. Life Sci.*, 2001, 58, 931-959.

INDEX

A

C

D

E

F

G

H

I

L